SMITHSONIAN TREASURY OF 20TH-CENTURY SCIENCE

Edited by Webster P. True

FORMER CHIEF OF THE
EDITORIAL DIVISION,
SMITHSONIAN INSTITUTION

PUBLISHED BY SIMON AND SCHUSTER, INC.,

IN COOPERATION WITH

THE SMITHSONIAN INSTITUTION, WASHINGTON, D. C.

ACKNOWLEDGMENTS

Grateful acknowledgment is expressed to the original publishers for permission to use the articles listed below.

"Beyond the Milky Way," by Thornton Page. From *Popular Astronomy.*

"Advances in Astronomical Technology," by Aden B. Meinel. From *The Indian and Eastern Engineer.*

"Rocket Propulsion," by Ralph S. Cooper. Reprinted by permission from *Bulletin of the Atomic Scientists,* March 1962. Copyright 1962 by the Educational Foundation of Nuclear Science, Inc., 935 E. 60 St., Chicago, Ill.

"Navigation — From Canoes to Spaceships," by Charles S. Draper. From *Proceedings of the American Philosophical Society.*

"Some Astronomical Aspects of Life in the Universe," by Su-Shu Huang. From *Sky and Telescope.*

"The Electron: Its Intellectual and Social Significance," by Karl T. Compton. From *Nature* (London).

"Ultrasonics," by Arthur R. Laufer. From *Physics Today.*

"The New Uses of the Abstract," by George A. W. Boehm. Reprinted by special permission from the July 1958 issue of *Fortune.* Copyright 1958 Time Inc.

"Organic Chemistry: A View and a Prospect," by Sir Alexander Todd. From *The Times Science Review* (London), Winter 1961.

"The New Age of the Sea," by Philip B. Yeager. Reprinted from *Proceedings of the U.S. Naval Institute* by permission. Copyright 1961 by U.S. Naval Institute.

"Drilling Beneath the Deep Sea," by William E. Benson. From *Sperryscope,* Sperry Rand Corporation.

"The Opening of the Arctic Ocean," by Commander James T. Strong. Reprinted from *Proceedings of the U.S. Naval Institute* by permission. Copyright 1961 by U.S. Naval Institute.

"The Place of Genetics in Modern Biology," by George W. Beadle. Eleventh Arthur Dehon Little Memorial Lecture at the Massachusetts Institute of Technology. Reprinted by permission.

"Does Natural Selection Continue to Operate in Modern Mankind?" by Theodosius Dobzhansky and Gordon Allen. From the *American Anthropologist.*

"Man as a Maker of New Plants and New Plant Communities," by Edgar Anderson. From *Man's Role in Changing the Face of the Earth,* published and copyrighted by the University of Chicago Press for the Wenner-Gren Foundation for Anthropological Research, 1956.

"The Promise of Underwater Archeology," by George F. Bass. From *The American Scholar,* vol. 32, No. 2. Copyright 1963 by the United Chapters of the Phi Beta Kappa. By permission of the publishers.

"The Carbon-14 Method of Age Determination," by Frank H. H. Roberts, Jr. From *Transactions of the American Geophysical Union.*

"Jet Streams," by R. Lee. From *The Roundel,* Royal Canadian Air Force.

"An Appraisal of Cloud Seeding as a Means of Increasing Precipitation," by Henry G. Houghton. From *Bulletin of the American Meteorological Society.*

"The Science of Yesterday, Today, and Tomorrow," by W. F. G. Swann. From *Journal of the Franklin Institute.*

CONTENTS

PREFACE

FOUNDED NEARLY A CENTURY and a quarter ago, the SMITHSONIAN INSTITUTION stands today as one of the great world centers of science and culture. It was established in 1846 through the bequest by James Smithson, an English scientist, of his entire fortune "to the United States of America, to found at Washington, under the name of the Smithsonian Institution, an Establishment for the increase and diffusion of knowledge among men."

In addition to its administrative core, housed in the original Smithsonian building, the Institution at present comprises thirteen bureaus and agencies including two museums, four art galleries, the Zoological Park, the Astrophysical Observatory, the International Exchange Service (of publications), the Science Information Exchange, the Canal Zone Biological Area, the Radiation Biology Laboratory, and the recently established John F. Kennedy Center for the Performing Arts. Most of its buildings are located on the Mall in Washington, midway between the Capitol and the Washington Monument, and few visitors to the nation's capital leave without visiting the Smithsonian Institution's very extensive exhibits in the fields of natural history, science and technology, and art. In the year 1964 the number of recorded visits to its several buildings totaled nearly 16,000,000.

To increase knowledge, the Institution has assembled a large staff of scientists who are constantly engaged in basic research in many disciplines. Prominent among the fields covered by Smithsonian investigations are biology, geology, anthropology, and astrophysics. From these specialized studies comes a stream of publications, mostly technical in character, which are distributed to libraries, scientific organizations, and specialists throughout the civilized world.

One series of Smithsonian publications, however, has been

directed toward the general public — namely, the Smithsonian Annual Reports. Each year these volumes have included a General Appendix composed of a selection of articles to highlight important advances in many branches of science, technology and the arts, presented as far as possible in nontechnical language for the benefit of the layman. Some of the articles are specially written for the Report; others are reprinted from scientific journals not readily available to the nonscientist.

In the interests of furthering the second of the Smithsonian's stated purposes, the diffusion of knowledge, the Institution has joined with Simon and Schuster in assembling this volume which aims at presenting a cross section of some of the remarkable scientific achievements of the twentieth century. My thanks are due to the authors of the articles, and to the publishers of those articles taken from scientific journals, for their permission to include the material in this anthology, which it is hoped will aid in fostering an increased interest in the progress of science, so important in our modern world.

S. DILLON RIPLEY
Secretary, Smithsonian Institution

INTRODUCTION

THERE WOULD SEEM TO BE *but little doubt that in the distant future historians will refer to the twentieth century as the Age of the Flowering of Science. Of course, this appellation would in no way belittle the earlier basic pioneering discoveries of Galileo, Pasteur, Faraday, Henry, and many others, yet as recently as the beginning of this century some textbooks still defined atoms as the smallest indivisible particles of matter. Just before the dawn of the twentieth century, there came a series of epoch-making discoveries — among them radioactivity, X-rays, and finally the electron — which changed the entire picture of matter and opened the way for the tremendous acceleration of scientific research and its application that we are witnessing today. These discoveries and the widened vision they afforded of the structure and attributes of matter affected not only physics, but also chemistry, astronomy, biology, and other fields of knowledge. They have given us such practical applications as radio, television, atomic power, the medical uses of X-rays and radioactive isotopes, computers, and more recently the possibility of exploring outer space.*

Since 1846 the Smithsonian Institution has enriched its printed Annual Reports with a collection of articles intended to outline some of the outstanding results of current scientific research. In 1960 the Institution cooperated with Simon and Schuster of New York in publishing a three-volume Treasury of Science, *which drew upon the rich resources of these Annual Reports, some historically important articles even recording the announcement of such break-throughs as the Curies' discovery and isolation of radium as a radioactive element and Roentgen's epoch-making discovery and naming of X-rays.*

For the present volume the intention is to emphasize the newer branches of investigation and recent advances in established sciences. The first two articles deal with current concepts of our vast universe and some of its constituent parts, emphasizing what advances in astronomical knowledge have resulted from modern techniques and instrumentation. These are followed by a discussion of the purposes and methods of present and proposed space exploration, the outstanding challenge of our time. This segment of modern scientific investigation is concluded with Dr. Huang's penetrating assessment of the probability of intelligent life elsewhere in the universe.

In the field of physics, the late Dr. Karl T. Compton summarizes what the discovery of the electron — the tiniest particle of matter known — has meant to the understanding of matter and energy as well as to the innumerable electronic applications that characterize our modern civilization. Other phases of current physical research treated by specialists in their fields include the strange behavior of ultra-high-frequency sound waves and the operation and use of electronic computers. One article deals with the miracles of modern organic chemistry, including the work on the nature of deoxyribonucleic acid (DNA), the basic genic material of living cells.

In the earth sciences, Dr. K. E. Bullen of Australia discusses the internal structure of our earth as disclosed by modern studies of earthquakes and related phenomena. The oceans, the depths of which have been called the last unexplored frontier on earth, come under examination in articles dealing with various phases of the intensive research now under way to learn more of this vitally important segment of the earth's surface.

Genetics is described by Dr. George W. Beadle, President of the University of Chicago, as the keystone of modern biology. Recent work in this field is discussed in a series of articles that provide an insight into the momentous possibilities of genetic research. These articles are followed by a discussion of the fundamental mysteries of the universe and of life that remain even after the most modern scientific discoveries of our time.

Other lines of twentieth-century scientific investigation covered in this anthology are cybernetics, the carbon-14 method of determining ages up to thousands of years, the mysterious high-atmos-

phere air currents, and the possibility of controlling weather. The panorama of today's science is concluded by a penetrating comparison of the scientific outlook of the past and the present, with some cogent thoughts as to the science of the future.

It will be obvious that in a volume of this size it is not possible to cover any substantial proportion of the ever-increasing range and volume of today's scientific work. All that can be hoped for is to give a broad impression of the extent to which science dominates our modern society. If only the problems of human and national relationships could be attacked with the same objectivity, devotion, and intensity attained by the men of science in their work, this world could be transformed into a planet of peace and prosperity, with wars, hunger, and poverty eventually abolished. Perhaps a way will be found by which the scientific drive can be turned more toward that end.

Through the generous cooperation of the authors, the articles have been kept up to date by means of addenda or changes within the text. It is the editor's hope that readers of this volume will experience some of the satisfaction and even excitement that the scientists themselves derive from "the increase and diffusion of knowledge among men" to which the Smithsonian Institution is dedicated.

— WEBSTER P. TRUE
Editor

SMITHSONIAN TREASURY OF 20th-CENTURY SCIENCE

THORNTON PAGE

Beyond the Milky Way

[FROM THE SMITHSONIAN REPORT FOR 1950[1]]

DR. THORNTON PAGE *in this article presents current ideas as to the shape, size, and motion of the celestial bodies that exist entirely outside our own galaxy of stars. Dr. Page, now professor of astronomy at Wesleyan University, has in turn been Rhodes Scholar, professor of astrophysics at the University of Chicago, and Deputy Director of the Johns Hopkins University's Operations Research Office. Through the use of larger and larger telescopes and faster and faster photographic plates it has been possible, the author tells us, to record other galaxies, or extragalactic nebulae, scattered through the infinite cold and blackness of space out to a distance of more than a billion light-years, 1 light-year being approximately 6 trillion miles. He explains how the estimated hundreds of millions of such galaxies appear to be rushing away from us at tremendous speeds, and how they seem to thin out in numbers at the very largest distances where the effects of curved space become significant. In a supplementary note Dr. Page outlines astronomical progress over the last 15 years, including the finding of evidence of enormous explosions in galaxies.*

[1] Revised as of January 1965 by the addition of a supplementary note at end of article.

Before we can appreciate this topic it is necessary to understand precisely what is meant by the term "Milky Way" and how we can know when we are "beyond" it. Initially it is simple to define the Milky Way as the faint band of light which can be seen on clear nights to extend completely around the whole sphere of the sky and which telescopes have resolved into myriads of faint stars. As we shall see, the term has come to mean more than just what we can see; to some extent it is synonymous with the term "galaxy," which describes our concept of an organized system of stars, diffuse clouds of gas, and other material, inside of which we are located, and the study of which has occupied astronomers for several decades and will probably occupy them for several decades to come.

Why should these faint stars be distributed so peculiarly, as if in a doughnutlike ring around us? A simple interpretation comes to mind if we assume, for the moment, that all stars are intrinsically of about the same brightness. Then these faint stars of the Milky Way would be farther away than the brighter stars, their apparent brightness being less the more distant they are. (The apparent brightness of a luminous source is known from other considerations to be inversely proportional to the square of the distance.) Although refinements are necessary, this simple deduction from an unproved assumption is one of the basic methods for measuring astronomical distances. We must investigate further these distances and their measurement before the term "beyond" can have any meaning.

Astronomical distances are well recognized to be considerably larger than the distances we are familiar with; it is quite impossible to comprehend them in an absolute sense. But since we are concerned here only with one thing being "beyond" another, an appreciation of the *relative* sizes of various distances is sufficient. To avoid large numbers, it is convenient to use large units of distance: the "astronomical unit," which is about 100 million miles (accurately, the distance to the sun), and the "light-year" (some 63,000 astronomical units — or the distance light travels in 1 year).

The most basic method of measuring distances between astronomical bodies (where it is impossible to pace out, or scale off, a distance, as we can do on the earth) is triangulation, a method used by surveyors, and familiar to most of you. It depends only on the validity of the axioms of Euclidean geometry, from which the lengths of the sides of a triangle can be deduced if one side and two angles are given (or measured), and the applicability of those axioms to rays of light. Observations from the two ends of a "base line" on the earth itself can thus be used to measure the distances to the nearby members of the solar system — to the moon, sun, planets, and comets — to anything, in fact, within about 50 astronomical units, beyond which the angles involved are too small to measure. Now since the earth goes around the sun in an orbit of known dimensions, this "parallax method" can be vastly extended, by using the diameter of the earth's orbit as base line, to determine distances to stars as far as 500 light-years away. Still, the parallax method is too limited; almost all the faint stars of the Milky Way seem to be considerably farther away than 500 light-years.

Returning to the "brightness method" of measuring distance, we are disappointed to discover (after a few hundred star distances are measured by the parallax method) that our assumption of the stars being all of the same intrinsic luminosity was a poor one; some stars are only one ten-thousandth the candlepower of the sun, others 10,000 times as bright, when the effect of distance is taken into account. However, we might expect to find some subclasses of stars whose members are all of about the same brightness; in other words, we might hope to discover some earmark by which we can recognize the stars of very large candlepower — a thousand times that of the sun, say — and, after checking such a "luminosity criterion" among the closer stars whose distances are measured by the parallax method, use it to determine the distances of other stars much farther away by the brightness method. This is precisely the nature of one of the important research projects being undertaken at the Warner and Swasey Observatory by Dr. Nassau, the director, and Dr. Morgan of the Yerkes Observatory. They are using the B stars — stars of bluish hue that can also be recognized from their spectra — to determine distances to the far reaches of the Milky Way system. Previously, much the same method was applied by Dr. Shapley, first at Mount Wilson, then

ILLUS. 1—*Messier 13 in the constellation Hercules, a nearby example of the class of globular clusters, each of which has a total candlepower some 30,000 times that of the sun. A more distant globular cluster appears fainter, and from this change in apparent brightness with distance, the distances of the globular clusters can be determined. (Photograph Yerkes Observatory.)*

ILLUS. 2—*A photograph of part of the Milky Way, showing that it is formed of myriads of faint stars. (Photograph Yerkes Observatory.)*

at the Harvard Observatory, to the now famous "Cepheid variables" whose period of fluctuation was found to be the earmark
of their intrinsic luminosity. Shapley also found that certain types
of clusters of stars have a total combined candlepower in each case
some 30,000 times that of the sun. These "globular clusters," easily
recognized by their form, are so powerful that they can be used
to measure distances up to a million light-years. Using the distances and directions of the globular clusters, Shapley plotted the
positions of about 100 of them and found that they are distributed
in a large spherical volume of space, the center of this array being
at a point in the brightest part of the Milky Way, in the direction
of the constellation Sagittarius. It was reasonable to assume, as
Shapley did, that this point is the center of the Milky Way system.

At this juncture it is necessary to examine one of those refinements of method with which astronomers continually busy themselves. In using the brightness method of measuring distance,
Shapley assumed that interstellar space is transparent; that the
only reason one globular cluster appears fainter than another is
because of its greater distance. For reasons too lengthy to indicate
here, astronomers now know that dust and gas between the stars
also dim the light of distant stars, and this smokiness of interstellar
space, neglected by Shapley, made his distances somewhat too
large. Correcting for interstellar absorption, we find the distance
to the center of the Milky Way system to be about 30,000 light-
years, a figure corroborated, incidentally, by studies of the dynamics of the galaxy — how it is held together without collapsing, and
how it moves.

Our present picture of the Milky Way, then, is that of a flat
pancake of stars, gas, and dust, some hundred thousand light-years
across, in which the sun and planets are located about two-thirds
of the way from the center to the edge, and which is partly embedded in a spherical array of globular clusters extending out
some 30,000 light-years from the center. Now we can discuss what
is beyond it.

Because they are extended surfaces, in contrast to the stars
which appear as mere points of light in a telescope, the nebulae
are some of the most interesting objects in the sky. From their
form, their spectra, their positions, and, when established, their

distances, two classes of nebulae can be distinguished: the galactic nebulae and the extragalactic nebulae. The former are, by and large, irregular in shape; they show the spectra (colors of light) emitted by low-density gases, and, as their name implies, they are found mostly near the Milky Way in the sky, at distances which place them well within that system. The extragalactic nebulae, on the other hand, have circular, elliptical, and spiral shapes, their spectra are like a mixture of star spectra, they are found predominantly in parts of the sky other than the Milky Way, and their distances have been found to be enormously larger than anything in the galaxy. This last point is the crux of the matter; how can we prove that these spiral and elliptical nebulae are beyond the confines of the Milky Way system?

The answer is simple if you have a large enough telescope. With the large telescopes in existence today, it is possible to photograph the separate stars and clusters in the largest (and closest) of the spirals, the great Andromeda nebula. Using the brightness method, and taking account of the nearby smokiness of our own Milky Way system, but assuming that space outside is transparent, Hubble has shown that the Cepheid variables and clusters in the Andromeda nebula must be about a million light-years away. Once the distances of another half dozen extragalactic nebulae were found by these methods, Hubble determined their average intrinsic luminosity (about 85 million times the sun's), and can now determine the distances to much more distant nebulae with the aid of this information. Using longer and longer exposures on faster and faster photographic plates with larger and larger telescopes, Hubble has pushed the confines of observable space out to over a billion light-years. In this vast volume he estimates there are some hundreds of millions of extragalactic nebulae, basing this estimate, of course, on a limited number of "sample" plates. Surveys now under way with the 20-inch refractor at the Lick Observatory and the 48-inch Schmidt camera at Palomar will cover somewhat smaller volumes more completely.

What can we find out about these distant objects so far beyond the Milky Way? It seems to me that the studies which have already been undertaken, and which are now under way, can be grouped in this manner, although there is some overlapping: First, we can find out more about *individual* extragalactic nebulae, their distances, sizes, masses, forms, and contents; second, as with any large class of objects, we can try to group them into further meaningful *subclasses;* third, we can study their *motions,* so far as they can be measured, and finally, their *numbers and distribution in space.* This last problem, literally the biggest in modern science, turns out to be linked with our fundamental notions of space and time.

Although it may seem simple, in principle, to determine the linear size of an object from its angular size and its distance, there are serious practical difficulties in the case of the nebulae. They have no clearly defined edges. Photographs of longer exposure show greater extensions, and there are reasons to believe that the Andromeda nebula, for example, is well over five times as large as what we can see in a telescope. The best photographs of this spiral show an angular extent corresponding to a diameter of about 40,000 light-years, at its distance of over 700,000 light-years. This is roughly the same size as the Milky Way system, which seems reasonable enough. (In fact, our picture of the Milky Way system has been developed partly by analogy to the form of spiral nebulae; in other words, it has long been in the back of astronomers' minds that the galaxy and the spirals are the same class of objects.) But other spirals and the elliptical nebulae are found to have diameters much smaller than this; from 2,000 light-years to 10,000 light-years. We are thus forced to the conclusion that our galaxy is a giant among the spiral nebulae.

How can we "weigh" a nebula consisting of billions of stars? The method is similar to that for determining the mass of the sun; it depends upon measuring the motions of other masses in the vicinity. Since the outer stars in a nebula are attracted by the rest of the nebula, just as the planets are attracted by the sun, they would "fall" into the center were they not in motion in an orbit around that center. The motion is a measure of the gravitational pull of the nebula, which in turn is a measure of its mass. We can scarcely hope to see — or photograph — such motion as a change of position in the sky; at a distance of a million light-years a star would have to be moving at about 9,000 miles per second across the line of sight to change its position by even 1 second of arc in

ILLUS. 3—Messier 31 in the constellation Andromeda, an extragalactic nebula far beyond the confines of the Milky Way system. Because other similar nebulae are seen at all angles of tilt (from circular form, as on Illus. 4, to lenticular forms seen edge-on), Messier 31 is interpreted as a circular disk, tilted with one edge toward us. The two smaller bright fuzzy patches are other extragalactic nebulae (of elliptical type) at about the same distance as Messier 31. (Photograph Yerkes Observatory.)

a century! Luckily there is a more sensitive method of measuring motion along the line of sight (toward or away from us) by its effect on the spectrum. This "Doppler effect," which may be deduced from basic notions of the nature of light, space, and time, consists of a slight change in color, toward the red for recession and toward the blue for approach, which can easily be detected with a spectrograph, if the light source has readily identified original colors in its spectrum. Early work at the Lowell Observatory and more recent work at the Lick Observatory have established from this effect that the spirals are rotating — at least, the ones viewed edge-on show more approach at one end than at the other. The amount of rotation of the outermost parts indicates a mass about 100 billion times that of the sun for the Andromeda nebula, and smaller masses, about 1 billion to 10 billion suns, for other nebulae. Similar reasoning leads us to expect that the Milky Way system is also rotating; this has been measured, and leads to a mass of over 200 billion suns. Again we find our own galaxy larger than the rest, which seems to leave us in a "preferred" position in the universe. Moreover, there are other reasons to feel dissatisfied with these small measured values of nebular masses, as will become apparent later on.

The form and content of the extragalactic nebulae have contributed largely to their classification. Although there are others, the most meaningful classification seems to be one proposed by Hubble. He recognized three broad classes, based on form alone: the elliptical nebulae, the spirals, and the barred spirals. Within each of these classes there is a continuous sequence from "early" to "late" types — from smaller, more compact forms to larger, looser forms in the spirals, and from circular to more elliptical forms in the elliptical nebulae. The terms "early" and "late" seem to have been unhappily chosen, as it now appears that the "late" types, if anything, are younger in age. This conclusion is based by the German astrophysicist von Weizäcker on dynamical arguments, by Baade and others on the content. Baade, at Mount Wilson, has superimposed on Hubble's classification a distinction between two types of stellar population: type I, associated with spiral arms, consists primarily of gas clouds and large, hot, blue stars which are thought, from considerations of stellar evolution to be young; type II population, associated with the elliptical nebulae and the cores of spirals, consists primarily of cooler stars, which may be quite as old as the earth and sun — a good 3 billion years. Hubble's three classes can be arranged in a kind of sequence, from the globular (circular-appearing) elliptical nebulae, through the more and more elliptical types, through a transition type neither elliptical nor spiral, and then, in two parallel "branches," through the later and later types of spirals, both normal and barred. If the more recent ideas are correct, spiral evolution is taking place in the reverse direction; late-type spirals are collapsing to the final stage of globular nebulae.

One aspect of the content of extragalactic nebulae has received but scant attention until recently. Just as in our own galaxy, there is interstellar gas and dust in the other nebulae. The dust shows up as dark streaks on photographs; the gas emits light of the characteristic colors of hydrogen, oxygen, nitrogen, and other gases. In the extragalactic nebulae we have an excellent opportunity to study the distribution and physical conditions of these interstellar gases, and work now in progress at the McDonald Observatory is directed to this end.

We have already seen how one component of the motion (the radial velocity) of nebulae can be measured by the Doppler effect, and how their distances can be estimated by the brightness method. In 1925, Hubble and Humason at the Mount Wilson Observatory noted a correlation between these two, in the sense that velocity of recession for nebulae on all sides of us increases with increasing distance. The later work of Hubble and Humason has shown a remarkable relation which holds as far as the spectra of nebulae can be observed: the velocity of recession on every side is proportional to the distance, and increases about 100 miles per second in each million light-years.

At first sight, this observation seems to leave us — or our galaxy — in a central and highly repelling position, with all the rest of the universe "running away from us." A moment's reflection shows, however, that the "velocity-distance law" implies a symmetrical view from any other nebula; an observer there, considering himself "at rest," would see the others "running away" from him, and with velocities proportional to their distances. As for explanation of this strange behavior, there are several. The most easily visualized is based on the simple assumption that a cosmic explosion started the nebulae moving apart from a common starting point with speeds which have since remained roughly constant, and that the fastest moving ones have naturally got the farthest. From this simple concept, together with the rate of increase of recessional velocity with distance, we can readily compute that the explosion must have taken place some 2 billion years ago, a figure in fair agreement with the age of the earth determined from quite different data (radioactive decay in minerals). However, there are further complications which cast doubt on this simple explanation.

There are so many nebulae that a plot of each one's position in space would be literally an endless task. The best means of representing their distribution in space so far devised has been to count, or estimate, the numbers out to various distances. For instance, a survey by Shapley and Ames at Harvard showed over a thousand nebulae actually brighter than "thirteenth magnitude" (visible in a 6- or 7-inch telescope), another by Mayall at the Lick Observatory shows an estimated 9 million over the whole sky brighter than "nineteenth magnitude" (corrected for obscuration by local interstellar dust) from sample plates taken with the 36-inch reflector, and two other sampling surveys by Hubble with the 100-inch telescope at the Mount Wilson Observatory indicate that there are an estimated 70 million brighter than the "twentieth magnitude" — as faint as the 100-inch telescope can conveniently photograph. From the average intrinsic brightnesses of nebulae we can convert these figures to (roughly): 2,000 within 13 million light-years, 9 million within 200 million light-years, and 70 million within 450 million light-years.

These numbers are about what we would expect if the nebulae were *evenly* distributed, about 2 in each 10-billion-billion cubic light-years. The numbers would then increase with the cube of the distance, since the volume of a sphere is proportional to the cube of its radius. The two deepest surveys, however, depart slightly from the cube law, indicating a thinning out of nebulae the farther we go from our galaxy. Now it has been repugnant to astronomers since the time of Copernicus to consider ourselves "at the center," as this thinning out would imply; hence a number of efforts have been made to interpret this last result, tentative though it may be, in such a way that no "center" is necessary. A number of difficulties arise; for instance, we are seeing the distant nebulae not where they are now, but where they were 13 to 450 million years ago, the time required for their light to reach us. Their intrinsic brightness, too, may not be constant in time. And it is certain that their light is so changed toward redder color by

ILLUS. 4—a. Messier 51 in the constellation Canes Venatici, an extragalactic
nebula of spiral form seen square-on.
b. NGC 1300, a barred spiral. (Photographs McDonald Observatory.)

the Doppler effect that a correction must be made for its reduced power to blacken the photographic plate. What is more, a receding source should theoretically be fainter than the same source of light at rest.

Using the best data available in 1935, Hubble and Tolman concluded that these deepest surveys can be understood if space itself is "curved," somewhat as a two-dimensional surface can be curved into the form of a sphere. Just as there is not as much area in a circle on the surface of a sphere as there is within a circle of the same radius on a flat surface, so, too, there would be less "room" in "curved space" than in "flat space," as we normally conceive it, for spirals at great distances from us. This conclusion was inspired by Einstein's General Theory of Relativity, which ascribes what we normally call gravitation to a kind of curvature of space; in other words, space is expected to be curved by the mass of matter contained in it. Unfortunately the curvature of space necessary to explain Hubble's counts of the nebulae is very large — corresponding to a radius of only 500 million light-years or so, which implies a very large amount of matter, not at all in agreement with the observed space density of spirals and the (small) masses measured from their rotations.

This is the impasse we have reached in our attempt to understand the universe beyond the Milky Way. It may be removed by improving the observational data; by better measurement of the masses of spirals, including the faint outer parts, as we are trying to do at the McDonald Observatory; by finding evidence for matter between the spirals; by improving the correction for the Doppler effect as Stebbins and Whitford of Wisconsin are doing in their color work at Mount Wilson; or by better and more complete surveys of the nebulae which are soon to be expected from the 48-inch Schmidt telescope and 200-inch telescope at Palomar. Or it may be removed by some new line of theoretical reasoning such as the Kinematical Relativity of Milne, in England, or by taking account of the clustering of nebulae, in a revision of Tolman's calculations, as now being undertaken by Omer at Chicago. Probably the solution will be found through some combination of these, but I have no doubt that, when it is reached, some even larger problem will be found to take its place.

SUPPLEMENTARY NOTE

In the 15 years since this article was written, a good deal more has been learned about galaxies. More accurate measurements of brightness show that distant ones are over five times farther from us than Hubble thought. Thus, the "velocity-distance law," now called the Hubble law, states that the recession of galaxies increases about 19 miles per second in each million light-years, that the radius of space curvature is several billion light-years, and that the age of the universe since the "Big Bang" is 10 billion years instead of 2 billion. (New radioactive dating of rocks by geophysicists shows the age of the earth to be about 4 billion years.) These large distances, now accepted as commonplace, culminated in the recent discovery of peculiar galaxies with very large redshift velocities which imply enormous distances and extremely high candlepower. In fact, the Quasi-Stellar Objects (QSO's, for short) are very compact, and radiate about 100 times more strongly than ordinary giant galaxies such as our Milky Way.

Radio telescopes, which first detected the QSO's, have also been used to survey the gas in the Milky Way, showing its spiral structure and "splashes" indicating an explosion near the center 200 million years ago. Several other galaxies show similar evidence of explosions, and there are vast regions around many others from which radio waves are emitted, but no light. These are possibly clouds of ionized gases blown out by huge explosions in earlier times.

Masses of 25 individual galaxies have been measured from their rotations, and over 100 others have been "weighed" by their motion in pairs. These results show that elliptical galaxies are about 50 times more massive than spirals, which casts doubt on the evolution from spiral to elliptical form. In fact, the problem of evolution is now receiving a good deal of attention. It is generally assumed that a large cloud of gas and dust condensed into the billions of stars we now see as a galaxy. In some cases this led to a violent explosion; the QSO's may be in this stage of evolution, and other radio galaxies have already had their explosions. In every case, the stars age, the larger ones blow off most of their mass as an interstellar gas cloud, and the smaller ones grow redder and fainter. Thus, older galaxies are expected to be redder and fainter.

The distribution of galaxies in space is not as "even" as we thought in 1949. Most of them tend to be grouped in clusters of various sizes. The motions in clusters can be used to "weigh" the cluster, and it appears that many of the clusters contain more mass than the sum of all their galaxies. Yet we find no visible evidence of material between galaxies. The "larger problems" predicted in 1949 are at least three: (1) What causes the explosions? (2) Are all galaxies the same age? (3) What is the nature of the "hidden masses"?

ADEN B. MEINEL

Advances in Astronomical Technology

[FROM THE SMITHSONIAN REPORT FOR 1963]

THE DIRECTOR *of the Steward Observatory of the University of Arizona, Dr. Aden B. Meinel, presents in this article a survey of the latest methods of obtaining better results from our present earth-bound telescopes. The two main difficulties in telescopic observation of celestial objects are their faintness and their apparent small size. These difficulties are compounded by the necessity of looking through our atmosphere, which results in an unavoidable blurring of images. Dr. Meinel discusses the steps taken to minimize this handicap, but it cannot be completely eliminated as long as telescopes are restricted to the earth's surface. This consideration leads to the very recent actual and proposed placing of large telescopes outside our atmosphere through the use of large balloons and space vehicles. Not only will this eliminate the "seeing" problem created by the atmosphere, but it will also make possible important studies of the ultraviolet which is largely cut off from the earth's surface by the atmosphere. The author describes the immense hazard to a space telescope, including the 10-g thrust in launching and the destructive effects of the vacuum of space on lubricants and even metals, but these problems will doubtless be overcome eventually.*

ASTRONOMY is a branch of science that has contributed much to the rapid expansion of the frontiers of modern technology. The unique technical problem faced by the astronomer is the faintness of the stars and other objects with which he must work. Telescope mirrors measured in meters across are needed to gather enough flux of this faint light to permit its study. Celestial objects are also so far away that their apparent size is so small that the astronomer's telescope must, in addition, focus the faint light it gathers to a sharp focus.

Most celestial objects are in reality very hot and luminous but appear faint because of their great distances from us. The brightest star, Sirius, with an intrinsic luminosity 28 times that of our sun is approximately 10,000 million (1 followed by ten zeros) times apparently fainter than the sun, and it is one of the closest of the visible stars. The faintest galaxy of stars that can be detected with the 200-inch Palomar telescope is so remote that its light has taken over 1 billion years traveling at the velocity of light (300,000 km./sec.) to reach us from the depths of space. These two problems, faintness and small angular size, set the unusual characteristics of astronomical instrumentation and research.

The eye is little used in astronomical work today except in the examination of the moon and planets. While the eye is exceedingly sensitive to light it does not have the property of integration. In other words, the eye will not detect any star fainter than one it can see in the first second of time. A photographic plate, on the other hand, will record the picture of stars 100 times fainter in 100 seconds than it will record in 1 second. In recent decades the astronomer has principally worked with the photographic process to determine the position, motion, and brightness of celestial objects. Photography still represents a method of information storing unrivaled for pictorial display, as is evidenced by the accompanying photographs. The fastest photographic emulsions, however, utilize only about 1 percent of the incident light. The best photoelectric devices available to the astronomer today can utilize approximately 30 percent of the light.

TELESCOPES

The principal auxiliary instruments currently used on a telescope are the photoelectric photometer and spectrophotometer, the photographic spectrograph, the photographic camera, and recently a new device, the image intensification tube. A spectrograph is a most powerful device in the hands of the astronomer. It can reveal many interesting properties of a star, such as temperature, mass, chemical composition, the extent of its atmosphere, whether the star is single, a binary system, etc., its motion toward or away from the observer and indirectly, but effectively, the absolute brightness, distance and even the age of the star. I cannot go into the many interesting details of how each of these things is learned, but I hope that the recitation of this list will give the reader a glimpse into the fascinating world open to the astronomer.

The astronomer has pushed the telescope close to its maximum useful size in the current century. At this time we have four telescopes that have been built with mirror diameters of 100 inches or more. In order of size these telescopes are the 200-inch Hale telescope on Mount Palomar, completed in 1947; the 120-inch on Mount Hamilton, in 1959; the 104-inch now being placed in operation in the U.S.S.R.; and the famed 100-inch on Mount Wilson, completed in 1919 and which did much to revolutionize observational astronomy in the hands of Hubble and Baade. A giant telescope of 240-inch aperture and of revolutionary design is reported under design by the Institute of Optics in Leningrad. A new telescope of 150-inch aperture has also reached the design stage at the Kitt Peak National Observatory in the U.S.A.

Since new and larger telescopes cost much in return for a relatively small gain in distance reached and in new knowledge, astronomers are now concentrating upon the use of new methods to make better use of the starlight that is collected by our terrestrial telescopes. They are also looking forward to the utilization of space telescopes, but before I speak of these new telescopes it is necessary to appreciate the handicaps with which the astronomer is faced with his telescopes located upon the surface of the earth.

The atmosphere limits the usefulness of a large telescope even on the clearest night atop a mountain. The small turbulences present in the atmosphere that are accompanied by thermal differences make it impossible to sharply focus a telescope. The air itself will not permit the far ultraviolet light or the infrared light to reach the highest mountain. In addition, the night sky background is not entirely dark. Far from the lights of the city and on a moonless night one can see with the dark-adapted eye well enough to read the large headline type of a newspaper. The stars are therefore seen by a telescope as upon this faintly luminous background. This diffuse "light of the night sky" and the lack of sharpness of focus from atmospheric turbulence combine to set the limit in faintness to which a telescope can reach.

The total brightness of the night sky background with a large telescope is approximately equal to that of one 20th magnitude star per square second of arc. It is obvious, therefore, that we cannot tolerate many square seconds of arc in a detector when we wish to observe a 23d magnitude star. Since the light of the night sky is a diffuse source, its brightness does not depend upon the mirror diameter of the telescope but only upon the ratio of the focal length divided by the aperture, called the f-ratio or f-number of the telescope.

INCREASING THE EFFICIENCY

Faced with the above limitations the astronomer has four means at his disposal where gains can be made as follows:

1. Increase the size of the telescope mirror;
2. Increase the efficiency of the detector;
3. Decrease the aperture, and thereby the night sky noise at the detector;
4. Place the telescope above the atmosphere, either on a high balloon or a satellite.

The first alternative, building a larger telescope, has been considered. While it is within the scope of present technology to build a 400-inch telescope, its cost would be in the vicinity of $40 million. Its ultimate benefits would be doubtful in terms of the great expense because of the limitations imposed by atmospheric seeing unless a site with unprecedentedly fine seeing could be found.

The term "seeing" is used by the astronomer to refer to two disturbances caused by the atmosphere. They are (a) time fluctuations in the intensity of the wavefront arriving at various points at the telescope aperture, and (b) time fluctuations in the direction of arrival of the wavefront. The first is called "scintillation" and is readily seen with the unaided eye as twinkling. The second effect is usually referred to as "seeing" since it affects the ability of the telescope, especially a large one, to focus sharply. Research into seeing has shown that these effects are most serious close to the land surface. To minimize these effects telescopes are now located, at no small inconvenience and expense, upon the summits of mountains in relatively smooth air. In the best sites the average seeing diameter for a large telescope is between 1 and 2 seconds of arc. Upon rare occasions the seeing may approach 0.2 to 0.3 second of arc, as has been noted at Pic du Midi in France; however, this size is still much larger than the theoretical resolving power of a large instrument. As a consequence a very large telescope can promise only a larger picture of the same blurred celestial object as would be obtained with one perhaps only one-half as big.

The second possibility for improvement is in the efficiency of the detection of the photons. The photographic process, widely used for many years, has the ability to record stars over a wide range of brightness, although the accuracy of the measure of brightness is relatively low. One photograph may record star images over a range of 20 magnitudes (10^8 in intensity) and also record a million information elements per square millimeter. Information densities up to 5 million elements per square millimeter are possible under laboratory conditions. The quantum efficiency of a photographic emulsion is low, ranging from 0.1 to 1.0 percent. There is little hope for a large improvement in the photographic process itself since individual silver grains in the emulsion are quite good detectors. The quantum efficiency for a single grain to be developable in terms of absorbed photons is 25 percent. One developed grain, however, does not provide a detectable quantity since every grain produced by chemical reaction called "fog" would be indistinguishable from a "star." Only when groups of 20 or more grains are developed does one recognize the clump as an entity on the background of fog grain clumpiness.

In recent years much effort has been devoted to the utilization of the high quantum efficiencies approaching 30 percent for the photoelectric detector. The photomultiplier is a commercially available device of high efficiency and built-in amplification which has been widely used in astronomy and nuclear physics. The internal amplification of such a device of 10^6 produces a measurable pulse each time a photoelectron is emitted from the cathode. The cathode will occasionally reject a "thermal" electron spontaneously as a consequence of the low work function of the caesium compound emitting surface. These thermal electrons produce what is called the "dark current," which adds a noise background to the signal. A good photomultiplier at room temperature will have a dark current of 10 to 20 electrons per second from a 1 cm.^{2} photocathode surface. Because the dark current emission is temperature dependent, the astronomical use of photomultipliers for use on faint objects is always with the device cooled to dry-ice temperature ($-80°$C.). At this low temperature a good tube will have a dark current of about 0.2 electron per second per cm.^{2}

The photomultiplier is an excellent detector of a single object at a time. The output current is accurately linear over a wide range of intensities; hence, the brightness of a star can be measured very accurately. In practice, the photoelectric photometer isolates a single small region of the sky at the focus of the telescope. The size of the diaphragm of the photometer is kept small in order to reduce the noise signal from the background of the sky, but large enough to permit the blurred image of the star to pass completely through the hole and to allow for inaccuracies in the guiding of the telescope. The usual size of the diaphragm is 1 to 2 mm. diameter.

The high efficiency of the photoelectric surface has led to efforts to construct an imaging system where the astronomer could take a "picture" of many stars at a time rather than one by one. While the theory of an image tube is very simple — one needs only to electronically accelerate and focus the electrons emitted from the cathode upon a fluorescent screen or directly upon a photographic emulsion — the practical attainment of an image tube proved full of technical difficulties. The earliest use of an image tube in astronomy was by Krassovsky (U.S.S.R.) who adapted an infrared snooperscope tube to photograph the infrared airglow spectrum,

ILLUS. 5—*The summer Milky Way photographed with an all-sky camera in infrared light. The brightness at the horizon is due to the upper-atmosphere airglow of the earth.*

a task not possible at all with the photographic emulsion since it is not sensitive to the infrared beyond 1 micron wavelength. The first image tubes to rival and exceed the direct photograph were made in France by Lallemande. While the use of these in astronomy has permitted unusual observation such as the rotational velocity of the nuclear regions of the Andromeda nebula by Walker (U.S.A.), each tube must be made minutes before use — hardly like taking a photographic plate out of a box purchased months beforehand.

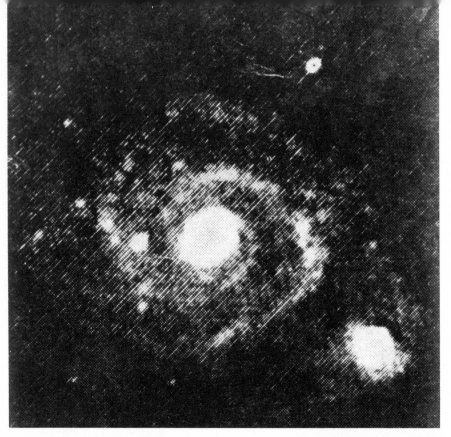

ILLUS. 6—Image orthicon telescope picture of the Whirlpool Nebula taken with an image orthicon tube attached to the 20-inch reflector at the Organ Pass observing station of the Dearborn Observatory. This picture would require a 100-inch telescope to photograph this object in the same exposure time with ordinary photographic plates.

The adaptation of the television tube method to astronomy has recently become possible by the development of tubes with high sensitivity to low levels of light and with integrating properties. Many astronomers in the U.S.A. are now experimenting with systems using commercial tubes with good success. The promise of this type of image tube is foreshadowed by the time in the near future when astronomers will want to have their "photograph" taken from a space telescope transmitted back to the earth.

A vast technology has developed for infrared detection in the region from 1 to 12 microns and which has only recently been applied to astronomy. The principal reasons for the lack of development of infrared astronomy are that the atmosphere transmission is highly variable in these wavelengths and detectors are still sensitive enough only to permit one to reach the brightest stars with a large telescope. To illustrate the problem of background noise, in the case of an infrared telescope it is only necessary to remember that the maximum of the infrared emission from material at room temperature is at 10 microns. The detector therefore looks at the star through a telescope that is literally glowing with its own light even though it is night and completely dark to the eye. As a consequence, much remains to be explored of the heavens when infrared telescopes can be flown from balloons or space telescopes where the telescope can be made very cold.

BALLOON TECHNOLOGY

The third possibility for improvement in the operating efficiency and research potential of a telescope has now been opened through advances in balloon technology. As mentioned earlier, the efficiency of a telescope increases when the "seeing" image size is decreased. Much effort has been expended in the location of the Palomar and Kitt Peak observatories to find a site with the best seeing conditions. It does not appear that much can be gained in this direction for future telescope locations as long as the terrestrial atmosphere is involved. Only when one can place his telescope above the atmosphere does the theoretical resolving power of a telescope become obtainable. Balloon-borne telescopes offer this possibility.

At balloon altitudes of approximately 80,000 feet there is effectively no seeing disturbance even from direct sunlight on the telescope. While visual observations have been made from balloons, the first successful demonstration of high-resolution photography was made with the 12-inch Stratoscope I by Schwarzschild (U.S.A.). This unmanned photographic telescope has taken superb direct photographs of the sun, achieving the full theoretical resolution of the telescope.

At the present time (1962) the 36-inch Stratoscope II system is nearing completion. This instrument is large enough to permit the observation of planets, stars, and nebulae, and it is designed to yield a guidance accuracy of 0.1 second of arc over extended periods. The achievement of this accuracy should, for instance, permit the solution of the existence or nonexistence of the "canals" on the planet Mars. Other balloon-borne telescopes are planned and several have failed. The launching and operation of as precise an instrument as a telescope from the tenuous platform provided from a balloon are complicated, and the probability for a malfunction of some portion of the system is a real threat to the success of the flight.

Rockets have been used for the last decade to obtain brief glimpses of the sun and stars from completely above the atmosphere. Even though a rocket-borne telescope has only 3 to 4 minutes of observing time, such a telescope is the only device that astronomers have had to observe the far ultraviolet beyond the atmospheric cutoff at a wavelength of 3000A. Beautiful far ultraviolet spectra and Lyman alpha photographs of the solar disk have been obtained by Tousey (U.S.A.). The recent flights by Stecher and Milligan (U.S.A.) have observed the spectrum of stars in the far ultraviolet. Since their observations showed that the theoretical predictions of the ultraviolet brightness of the hot O and B type stars was incorrect by a large factor, much interest now exists in the pending operation of the first space telescopes. Telescopes as developed for use in the early rocket vehicles have been severely limited by the space available in the nose cone of the rocket. The accompanying photograph shows the instrument flown by Stecher and Milligan to illustrate this point. Their instrument was designed very compactly. A 10-inch telescope and diffraction grating was fitted into a space 14 inches in diameter and 12 inches in length.

The success of the rocket experiments and the great promise for the exploration of the universe in the far ultraviolet has led to the initiation by NASA (U.S.A.) of a spacecraft system capable of carrying a 36-inch telescope and all its related instrumentation. The program plans three such systems at an expected cost of $100 million. This is a large amount of money on any monetary scale and is justified by the fact that in no other way is it possible to learn what such an instrument will be able to tell us. The payload for the OAO telescope will be in excess of 4,000 pounds.

The most obvious gain to be had from a space telescope is, of

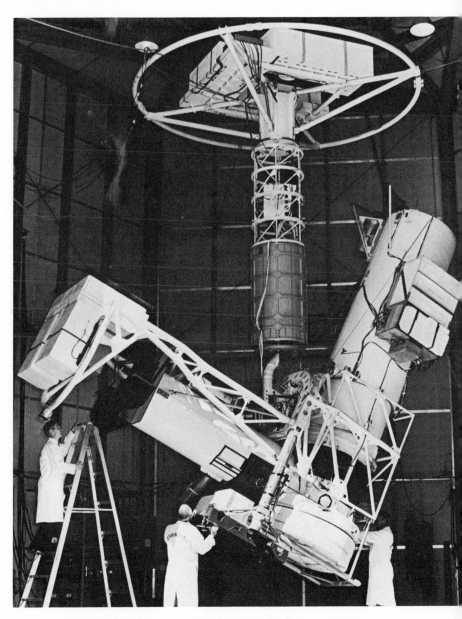

ILLUS. 7—*The 36-inch stratoscope II balloon-borne telescope. It will operate from 80,000 feet. The telescope and its balloon stand 562 feet high at launching. The telescope is shown at the right, with the projection to the left containing the auxiliary cameras and instruments. The vertical column contains the pointing-control system.*

ILLUS. 8—*Direct photograph of M 33 at the Cassegrain focus of the Kitt Peak 84-inch telescope by C. R. Lynds.*

course, the accessibility of the ultraviolet. This region of wavelengths is of great interest to the astrophysicist since the resonance absorption and emissions from atoms occur in this region. A less obvious advantage, and one that will require more technological development, is that an orbital telescope can work at the theoretical resolving power of the optical system, since no "seeing" disturbance is present. Given sufficient guiding accuracy, possible in free space, one could use diaphragms of very small angular size and increase the star-to-sky signal by 5 magnitudes over the same

ILLUS. 9—Artist's conception of the OAO (Orbital Astronomical Observatory).

telescope on earth. If TV devices of sufficient information handling capability become available, then high resolution studies on a full-time basis will be possible. This possibility is of special interest for the observation of time-variable phenomena at a predetermined time or for long periods of time since neither weather nor daylight will interfere with the work of a space telescope.

Space telescopes pose engineering problems that are not encountered in terrestrial telescopes and whose solution is required before successful missions can be made. The launching g-forces are

ILLUS. 10—Photograph of the spiral nebula in Ursa Major (M 81) taken with the 200-inch Palomar telescope.

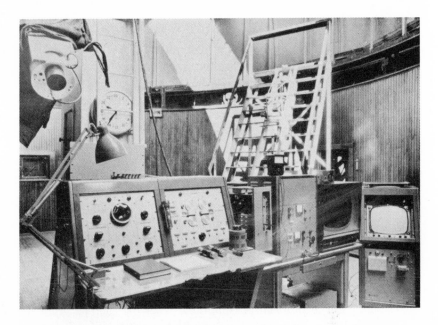

ILLUS. 11—*Dearborn Observatory telescope control console.*

ILLUS. 12—*Inflation of the launch balloon. Stratoscope II is in the center of the photograph.*

an example. During the launching phase the telescope will be subject to thrust and vibration forces up to the order of 10 g's. As a consequence, either the engineer must find a structural design that will preserve optical collimation or the astronomer will have to have controls to permit him to realign his optical systems after the telescope arrives in orbit. The lack of proper collimation could seriously degrade the performance of a space telescope.

The second major problem in the design of the space telescope is that produced by its thermal environment while in orbit. Sunlight intermittently illuminates one side or the other of the space craft. This variable heating on one side coupled with the intense cold of outer space on the other produces a large and changing temperature gradient between the outer skin of the space craft and the telescope. It will be necessary to keep the thermal gradient small in the optical system if high-resolution performance is to be obtained. The problem of computing what the thermal gradients will be before the space craft is in orbit is a difficult mathematical problem, and one that must be done with accuracy before the engineers can design a structure to meet the requirements.

The third problem area, one common to all complicated mechanisms, is that of lifetime. Even when the probability of failure is very small for any one component of a system, when several hundred thousand components must function correctly the probability of failure of the system becomes large enough to present trouble. In the case of the orbiting astronomical observatories, the design lifetime is to be one year — an exceedingly difficult specification to design with confidence in the results. The environment of the hyper-vacuum of space causes many problems that have no counterparts on earth. Lubricants evaporate; even gross metal, like magnesium, evaporates at such a high rate as to weaken structures. Moving parts tend to weld together since all the surface contaminants that contribute to low friction on earth evaporate. Primary cosmic rays can ruin the best high-voltage insulation at a single impact, not to mention the gradual destruction of electronic components by the energetic particles in the Van Allen radiation belts. The list of problems rapidly extends as one looks closer into the actual design of a space telescope, yet the rewards of a new view of the universe draw astronomers onward.

ROBERT C. SEAMANS, JR.

The Challenge of Space Exploration[1]

[FROM THE SMITHSONIAN REPORT FOR 1961[2]]

THE GREAT ADVENTURE of our time, both from the standpoint of science and of human achievement, is the already begun exploration of space. The author, Robert C. Seamans, Jr., is the Associate Administrator of the National Aeronautics and Space Administration, and has played an important role in furthering America's participation in this scientific adventure. The previously held belief that mankind is eternally confined to the earth's surface is no longer valid. Psychologists hold that the human spirit requires the stimulus of obstacles to overcome and new frontiers to explore, and outer space provides both in abundance. If further justification is needed for the vast expenditure of effort and money involved in the conquest of space, it is already amply provided in the enormous technological advances thus far achieved and in the certain future results of great value to medicine, communications, and materials. The first goal — manned landings on the moon — may reveal secrets of the origin not only of our solar system, but

---

[1] Address before the 1961 Air Force/Aerospace Corporation Symposium on Ballistic Missile and Aerospace Technology, Los Angeles, Calif., Aug. 29, 1961. The original presentation has here been somewhat updated.

[2] Revised as of January 1965 by the addition of a supplementary note at end of article.

also of life itself, for the reason that the moon's surface, where there is no atmospheric erosion, will yield a sample of matter just as it was billions of years ago. The author discusses the exceedingly complex technological requirements for manned journeys into space and, in doing so, explains why space flights must be manned to achieve the desired results. The text of the article is presented just as it was written in mid-1961, with later developments summarized in a supplement at the end.

I<small>T</small> IS here proposed to discuss the program of the National Aeronautics and Space Administration (NASA) for space exploration — a program designed around the concept that men must participate directly in this exploration. Let me say at the outset that there is no dichotomy between manned and unmanned spaceflight in NASA's thinking and planning. Each of these approaches contributes important information, techniques, and developments to the other. We are convinced that concurrent advancement of both unmanned and manned spaceflight will pay off in a total science and technology of far-reaching, even revolutionary, importance to mankind.

WHY WE MUST ACCELERATE OUR SPACE PROGRAM

I will first review the major reasons behind the President's decision to accelerate our space program, including the landing of a team of United States astronauts on the moon in this decade. The United States must make this effort for urgent scientific, technological, political, and economic reasons. In his May 25, 1961, state of the Union message, President Kennedy said:

> Now is the time to act, to take longer strides — time for a great new American enterprise — time for this nation to take a clearly leading role in space achievement . . . I believe that the nation

should commit itself to achieving the goal, before the decade is out, of landing a man on the moon and returning him safely to earth.

Four major reasons underlie the national decision to marshal the resources required for leadership in space: (1) the quest for scientific knowledge; (2) direct and immediate application of satellites into operational systems; (3) the risk of delay in our space competition with Communism; and (4) the technological advances and stimulus to our economy that will emerge from the space effort.

SCIENTIFIC KNOWLEDGE

Space research is a vigorously expanding field, whose growth is comparable to the development of nuclear physics after World War II. It is a field which cuts across the established areas of astronomy and physics and the earth sciences, and draws together scientists of varied backgrounds. The close interaction and exchange of ideas among scientists from many different fields have proved to be highly stimulating.

One of the goals of the NASA scientific program involves lunar exploration, manned and unmanned. From the scientific standpoint, exploration of the moon is of great importance. The moon may hold the answers to some of the key questions in science. How was the solar system created? How did it develop and change? Where did life originate? The moon is devoid of atmosphere in the terrestrial sense. Having neither winds nor rains, its surface is almost changeless. Thus the moon offers scientists a chance to study the very early matter of the solar system in practically the form in which it existed billions of years ago.

The great volume of United States research in the space sciences demonstrates the intense interest of American scientists. Data flowing into astronomy and the earth sciences from United States space experiments are providing significantly new ideas and concepts to these traditional disciplines.

DIRECT APPLICATIONS

Space itself, when instrumented by man, will provide system capabilities not previously possible. Early returns from NASA experiments are already leading to early implementation of communications and meteorological satellite systems.

In 1960 NASA's Echo I passive communications satellite appealed to the world's imagination. The huge aluminized plastic sphere has been seen by people in many countries. Echo proved that it is possible to communicate between distant areas on the earth by reflecting radio signals from a satellite.

Private companies have shown interest both in the Echo concept and in "repeater" satellites that can receive messages at one point over the earth's surface and retransmit them to ground receiving stations thousands of miles distant. Satellite communications will make worldwide telephone and television services realities and will accommodate growth of global communications. This enhanced communication could well be a bond drawing people of the world closer together.

NASA's Tiros series of satellites has demonstrated the possibilities of vastly more accurate and longer-range weather forecasting. Tiros I transmitted nearly 23,000 television pictures of the earth's cloud patterns. Tiros II, launched in November 1960, has transmitted more than 40,000 pictures and has reported important information about the atmosphere and the radiation of solar heat back from the earth.

The Weather Bureau made use in 1961 of Tiros III pictures of storm Eliza in the Pacific and hurricane Anna in the Atlantic. NASA also used Tiros III for weather support of Astronaut Grissom's July 21, 1961, Mercury suborbital flight. Twice a day as the satellite passed over the Caribbean, one of its two TV cameras was triggered to report weather conditions in the area of the flight. Also, when Major Grissom was briefed just prior to his flight, he was shown TV pictures obtained from Tiros for visual comparison during the actual flight.

According to the House Committee on Science and Astronautics, "An improvement of only 10 percent in accuracy [of weather forecasting] could result in savings totaling hundreds of millions of dollars annually to farmers, builders, airlines, shipping, the tourist trade, and many other enterprises."

RISK OF DELAY

It is not my place to discuss military missions, but there is an important interchange of components and vehicles between the NASA and the Department of Defense programs. United States mastery of space is essential insurance against finding ourselves with a technology inferior to that the Communists will develop as they press forward on the space frontier. If we allow them to surpass us, their space technology in its military aspects could jeopardize our security.

In addition to potential direct military conflicts, the free societies are in deadly competition with the Communists for the support of the uncommitted peoples of the world. Space activity has great emotional appeal, and we cannot afford the risk of being passed or appearing to be passed. Today, prestige is one of the most important elements of international relations. Essential is the belief of other nations that we have capability and determination to carry out whatever we declare seriously that we intend to do.

In the minds of millions, dramatic space achievements have become today's symbol of tomorrow's scientific and technical supremacy. There is, without a doubt, a tendency to equate space and the future. Therefore, space is one of the fronts upon which President Kennedy and his administration chose to act broadly, vigorously, and with continuous purpose. No other single field offers us the opportunity to gain more of what we need abroad and at the same time to achieve such a wealth of both practical and scientific results at home.

STIMULUS TO ECONOMY

Our nation needs the stimulus, the knowledge, and the products that will evolve as we carry out our program of space exploration. The influence of the technical progress that will come into being through the integrating force and drive of a major space effort will be felt throughout the economy. Many of the instruments, equipment, power sources, and techniques that we devise to make space expeditions possible will be adaptable to other uses. The result will be substantial scientific advances and a variety of new consumer goods and industrial processes that will return tremendous benefits to us in practically every profession and activity.

Two decades ago the theme of the Temporary National Economic Committee hearings was that America's frontiers had closed and that this was what had caused the stagnation of the thirties. All frontiers then seemed to have been passed, all new territories explored, with very little left for inquiring intelligence beyond applying and developing what has already been discovered. Psychologists and philosophers have recognized the need of man's mind for new frontiers to cross. In this connection, manned and unmanned exploration of space is already stimulating basic and applied research throughout our educational, governmental, and industrial systems. The concept of an eternally shut-in human race has been proved superficial. The prospect of exploring space is providing the catalyst and tonic for new adventures of the mind and spirit.

UNMANNED SPACE FLIGHT

Since January 31, 1958, this country has successfully launched 46 earth satellites, 2 solar satellites, and 2 deep space probes. A recent one is Explorer XII which is making simultaneous measurements of many aspects of the space environment between altitudes of about 200 and 50,000 miles from the earth. The early years of space exploration have provided scientific knowledge important to direct application of satellites in operational systems for communication and weather forecasting, and have contributed to the technology needed for more advanced manned and unmanned spacecraft to come.

Some of the scientific findings are:

Discovery of two intense radiation zones trapped around the earth — the Van Allen belts.

Determination that the earth is slightly pear shaped, with the stem at the North Pole.

New data regarding the makeup of the fields of magnetism in space. For example, Explorer X, a 78-pound NASA satellite, transmitted highly meaningful data on solar-terrestrial relationships — such as magnetic fields and solar winds.

Discovery that sunlight exerts appreciable physical pressure on objects in space. This pressure is shifting the orbit of the Vanguard I satellite about a mile per year and has affected the orbit of the 100-foot-diameter Echo I satellite at a rate 300 times greater.

Among our most successful experiments to date has been the Pioneer series of space probes. Pioneer V, for example — launched into solar orbit on March 11, 1960 — was tracked into space to a distance of 22.5 million miles, then the greatest distance any manmade object had been tracked. Pioneer V sent back scientific data on conditions in space until communication contact was lost on June 26, 1960. This space probe gave us new and valuable information about cosmic rays, the earth's magnetic field, and solar "storms" and evidence of the existence of a large "ring current" circulating around the earth at altitudes of about 30,000 to 60,000 miles.

Advanced launch vehicles are becoming available for both scientific missions and operational systems. They will have greatly improved load-carrying capability for unmanned space experiments. For example, detailed plans have been made and work has begun on an Orbiting Geophysical Observatory, based on the use of the Agena. This observatory will be one of our first standardized satellites, with a stock-model structure, basic power supply, attitude control, telemetry, and a command system. Its modular compartments are capable of carrying out 50 different geophysical experiments on a single mission. The observatory itself will be about 6 feet long by 3 feet square. The two solar "paddles" which collect energy from the sun will be about 6 feet square. The satellite will weigh 1,000 pounds and will include 150 pounds of scientific equipment.

NASA's plans for extending unmanned space exploration to the moon and beyond are maturing. Ranger spacecraft — successors to the one flown in a test on August 23, 1961 — will land instruments on the moon. These instruments will determine the nature and extent of tremors and measure the force of gravity on the lunar surface.

Following Ranger will come Surveyor, a spacecraft that will be able to make a so-called "soft landing" on the moon. More delicate scientific instruments than those in Ranger can thus be employed. Surveyor will have aboard scientific instruments, including drills and tapes, to analyze the lunar surface and to determine its make-up. At the same time, high-resolution television cameras will transmit to earth pictures of the lunar terrain.

Also under way is a spacecraft that will fly close to Venus and Mars, and later perhaps other, more distant planets. This space-craft, called Mariner, will carry instruments to measure planetary atmosphere, surface temperatures, rotation rates, magnetic fields, and surrounding radiation regions. (See supplementary note at end of article.)

The NASA experimental program for developing operational systems includes, as already stated, communication and meteorological satellite projects. Our communications satellite program encompasses a coordination of passive experiments as well as investigations with active repeaters at medium altitudes — 2,000 to 4,000 miles — and at synchronous altitude. NASA has arranged for two experimental projects at medium altitudes, one under government contract and one financed by private industry. Both experiment satellites will include, in addition to the communication payload, instruments for measuring the effects of radiation on performance and life expectancy of the payload. Ground stations in this country, Europe, and South America will be employed for both projects.

A synchronous orbit system may provide world coverage, with fewer satellites, thus avoiding large costs and complexities of tracking and switching. We face technical difficulties, however, in placing and maintaining satellites in such orbits for long periods. NASA is initiating a series of experiments that will employ 40- or 50-pound payloads in synchronous orbits. The ground facilities which the Army has been developing for its Project Advent have been made available to NASA for the synchronous satellite experiment.

The Tiros series of meteorological experiments will be followed by a series using an earth-stabilized spacecraft — called Nimbus — in polar orbit. The Weather Bureau of the Department of Commerce, the responsible organization for United States weather-forecasting activities, is following through on an operational meteorological satellite system based on Nimbus. As agent for the Weather Bureau, NASA will specify the launch vehicles and spacecraft, conduct the launch operations, and control the satellites in space.

MANNED SPACEFLIGHT IS ESSENTIAL

Frequently I have been asked why we are preparing to send men on hazardous spaceflights when instrumented satellites and probes have proved so versatile and have returned such quantities of information on the near-space environment of the earth and on conditions in the vast reaches of deep space.

First, integration of a human pilot into an onboard spacecraft system greatly improves reliability. The man can make not only in-flight tests but also in-flight repairs. We have striking examples of this in missions of NASA's X–15 rocket airplane which has been flying to the fringes of space and has achieved a speed of over 4,000 miles per hour. In at least 8 out of 38 X–15 flights to date, flights would have failed without a pilot in the cockpit to correct malfunctions of equipment, instruments, or powerplant. In at least as many other cases, if X–15 missions had been unmanned, we would have obtained no information because either instruments or telemetry failed. The X–15 pilot, however, was able to land with valuable flight information recorded by his own senses.

Second, while instruments can perform many tasks of sensing and measuring better than men, the statistical information gathered and transmitted to earth by these devices constitutes only a part of the basic research necessary for understanding the larger realities of space. The most advanced apparatus can perform only as it is programed to do. Instruments have no flexibility to meet unforeseen situations. Scientific data acquired in space mechanically must be balanced by on-the-spot human senses, human reasoning, and by the power of judgment compounded of these elements.

A man's capacity for storing information is enormous. He requires a minimum of programing. He can change his mind without elaborate and time-consuming reprograming. His mind is an excellent filter, discarding redundant data with great speed. Man also far outstrips any computer in the ability to make decisions. In this connection, I should like to quote what Dr. Carl Sagan, of the Department of Astronomy, University of California, recently wrote to Senator Paul Douglas of Illinois, to emphasize scientific reasons for manned spaceflight.

> The scientific value [of spaceflight] comes when the men perform scientific tasks. There are large numbers of mineralogical, micro-biological, and astronomical questions which trained scientific personnel on the moon will be able to answer far more reliably than any presently conceived automatic instruments. . . .
>
> I feel strongly that, while an enormous amount of very significant scientific information can be obtained by unmanned vehicles, there are certain problems of the greatest significance which may well elude any unmanned system. If indigenous life exists on the planet Mars — and the bulk of contemporary evidence suggests that this is indeed the case — any but the most preliminary investigations will require a human experimenter.
>
> It is very difficult to imagine a sophisticated experimental program on the biochemistry, morphology, physiology, genetics, ecology, or behavior of even simple extraterrestrial organisms carried out by a preprogramed instrumented package. If the extraterrestrial organisms are very different from familiar life-forms — and with 5 billion years of independent evolution, this may well be true — it is possible that an instrumented landing vehicle will not even be able to identify them as alive. A human scientist who can draw conclusions . . . on the spot is an enormous asset in all aspects of lunar and planetary exploration. . . .

Third, we must recognize that manned flight in space has a much greater impact on the world's populace than unmanned flight.

The United States has congratulated the Soviet Union on the orbital flights of cosmonauts Gagarin and Titov. These achievements did not surprise us. We had been expecting them. Because the Russians have a significant lead on large boosters, we should be prepared for other Soviet "firsts" in space in the immediate future. This serves to underline the urgency of President Kennedy's decision to accelerate our own manned space program.

Finally, it must be realized that in the long run man cannot, by his very nature, be kept out of space. The same drive that led Columbus to explore the outer reaches of the known world will induce modern man to explore the deeps of the solar system.

MANNED SPACE FLIGHT

The historic flights of American astronauts Alan Shepard and Virgil Grissom on May 5 and July 21, 1961, respectively, were so completely reported that I shall not repeat the details. As you know, these flights were important steps in Project Mercury, which is the first phase in the United States program for manned spaceflight.

The spaceflights of astronauts Shepard and Grissom were made to test the man and the Mercury spacecraft, and to determine the quality of the vehicle and its systems and man's ability to handle them in space. In other words, the flights were made to learn how the astronaut, his capsule, and his equipment can best function together, as preliminary steps to putting an astronaut in orbit around the earth.

The value of these preliminary flights is attested by the success of astronaut John Glenn's orbital flight on February 20, 1962, in which the initial objective of Project Mercury was achieved. Further three-orbit 4½-hour flights are planned in Project Mercury. Then late in 1962 or early in 1963 we will begin flights with a Mercury spacecraft modified so that it has the capability of remaining in orbit up to 24 hours.

To follow Mercury, we are developing the two-man spacecraft Gemini, in which we will conduct orbital flights up to a week in duration, and test out techniques of maneuvering and joining spacecraft in orbit about the earth.

The third phase of our manned spaceflight program is called Project Apollo. The Apollo spacecraft will be large enough for living and working quarters to accommodate three men who will be able to operate in a "shirt-sleeves environment." The Apollo spacecraft will be injected into earth orbit by the Saturn launch vehicle which has an eight-cluster first stage with a thrust of 1,500,000 pounds, compared to the Russian booster with about 750,000 pounds of thrust, the Atlas with 360,000 pounds, and the Redstone with 78,000. The Redstone was used for the Shepard and Grissom flights, and the Atlas will be the booster for Mercury orbital flights.

The Apollo-Saturn combination will provide a manned earth satellite, in which the three-man team can perform a great variety of scientific experiments while training for sustained spaceflight. Next will come voyages deeper into space including a three-man voyage around the moon and return to earth, and finally an actual moon landing and return, planned late in this decade.

The Saturn launch vehicle which is now under development will not provide the capability for circumlunar flight and lunar landing. In the near future, we will commence the development of larger launch vehicles. Implementation of this program will result in the investment of large sums for research, development, and capital equipment. We must select the vehicle configurations wisely in order to fulfill our immediate objectives and to maximize our capabilities for other possible missions involving large payloads.

The design of the Apollo spacecraft itself must be kept as flexible as possible to meet the requirements of an orbiting laboratory, as well as circumlunar and lunar-landing flights. To achieve this flexibility, the so-called "modular concept" will be employed. In other words, various building blocks or units of the vehicle systems will be used for different phases of missions. The first component, which we call the "command center module," will house the crew during launching and entry. It will also serve as a flight control center for the remainder of the missions.

The second module is a propulsion unit. In earth-orbital flights, this unit will return the craft to earth under either normal or emergency conditions. It will also be used for maneuvering in orbit and for orbital rendezvous with other satellites. For circumlunar flights, the propulsion module will return the spacecraft to earth safely from any point along the lunar trajectory and will provide midcourse and terminal guidance corrections. In addition, the propulsion module will inject the Apollo spacecraft into an orbit around the moon and eject it from that orbit toward earth. For the lunar landing mission, the propulsion unit will serve as the takeoff stage.

The third module is a propulsion stage that will decelerate the spacecraft as it approaches the moon, and will gently lower it to the moon's surface.

For the earth-orbital laboratory an additional module may be added to the spacecraft to provide capacity for scientific instrumentation and for life support during a reasonably long-lived orbit.

It is important to note that the command center module for lunar flights will have to be designed to permit entry into the atmosphere at 25,000 miles per hour, or at nearly 1½ times the speed of a satellite returning from orbit. Developing protection against entry heating will be one of our most difficult problems. The spacecraft must have a moderate amount of maneuverability within the atmosphere to control the flight path and to allow landing at a preselected site. All designs being considered must be capable of surviving either ground or water landings.

Among requirements for the Apollo system are the following:

1. A life support system to provide a suitable environment for periods of several weeks.

2. Radiation shielding to give sufficient protection during passage to and from the moon as well as on the lunar surface.

3. A navigation system which will give position fixes, and which will compute the amount and direction of thrust for course correction when required.

4. An attitude stabilization system to be used throughout the flight. This system will permit orientation of the spacecraft for thrust control as well as for lunar landing and reentry through the atmosphere.

5. Communications for all phases of the flight.

Feasibility studies for Project Apollo were under way for many months. Initial studies were carried out in NASA's research and development centers and by industry. On July 18–20, 1961, more than 1,200 representatives of firms in the aerospace industry attended a NASA–Industry Technical Conference in Washington, where they were briefed on Apollo requirements. In mid-August, proposals were solicited from a number of industry teams for design and fabrication of the Apollo spacecraft system.

THE CHALLENGE TO THE AEROSPACE INDUSTRIES

Of the $1,671,750,000 NASA budget for fiscal year 1962, $206,750,000 was for salaries and personnel expenses of the NASA organization. Contract effort provided for the construction of new facilities and the support of the research and development activities. The fiscal year 1962 budget included $245 million for construction of new and supporting facilities and $1,220 million for research and development. This research and development encompassed propulsion systems, propellants, power supplies, structures and materials, guidance and control, instrumentation and telemetry, and aerodynamics, as well as launch vehicles and the satellite program.

The 1962 program was approximately twice the 1961 program. Funding requirements will increase still further in 1963 if we are to meet the goals recommended by President Kennedy. NASA, other Government agencies, universities, and industry all have important responsibilities in the conduct of this rapidly expanding effort. We feel that the NASA staff should be kept at a level necessary to plan the space exploration program and to organize, contract for, and oversee it, while conducting enough in-house work to maintain the caliber of our scientific and technical personnel. However, contract participation by universities and industry currently amounts to more than 85 percent of NASA budget dollars. This percentage will increase.

The special responsibilities of the aerospace industries in this prodigious undertaking involve the following important areas that deserve special attention:

Working with universities to educate greatly increased numbers of scientists, engineers, and technicians for roles in space exploration but broadly trained for other major technological developments of future importance to this country.

Utilizing technical personnel effectively, thereby minimizing the time spent by these specially trained people on routine effort.

Organizing teams of technical and administrative personnel in imaginative ways, both within the corporate structure and between corporations working toward common objectives.

Providing technical and administrative competence in new geographic areas when special site locations are required for fabrication, testing, and tracking.

Improving the reliability of newly developed equipment by greatly increased emphasis on sound engineering, individual workmanship, and extensive testing.

Initiating research programs aimed at enhancing our space effort and modernizing facilities for fabrication and testing of components.

Utilizing the technology developed for the space program in other fields to build our economy.

CONCLUSION

I would like to conclude with thoughts that concern all who are working in the national space effort.

The first is from Dr. Guyford Stever of the Massachusetts Institute of Technology. He has said:

> We aerospace engineers have a tremendous responsibility to everyone. We are the ones entrusted with the future of mankind in this field. We have a need for broader, more balanced people in the aerospace professions, those with a social awareness and an understanding of nontechnical, as well as technical subjects. The aerospace engineer must get the most out of the field and fit it into the needs of society.

He believes that aerospace scientists and engineers will bring an incredible revolution in medicine, communications, and materials — to mention only three.

A month ago the National Science Foundation issued a study called *Investing in Scientific Progress*, from which I should like to quote a few lines:

> From the time of Franklin and Jefferson the people of the United States have had faith in both the intellectual and the material benefits that science can bring. We have continually expanded our scientific knowledge of the physical universe, of living things, and of social organization. Our past investment in science has brought us double reward: a highly developed technology which has helped to keep us free, and a continuing enlargement of our understanding which has helped to enrich our freedom.
>
> Today, far more than in the past, scientific progress determines the character of tomorrow's civilization.

Space exploration in general, and manned spaceflight in particular, offers us the chance for unparalleled progress. I am firmly convinced that, as a nation, we shall respond boldly and with de-

termination to the call President Kennedy issued in his inaugural
address when he urged the world —

> To invoke the wonders of science instead of its terrors . . . to ex-
> plore the stars, to conquer the deserts, eradicate disease, tap the
> ocean depths and encourage the arts and commerce.

SUPPLEMENTARY NOTE

Since this paper was prepared in 1961, the nation's program of
space exploration has realized many of the promises foreshadowed
four years ago.

The area of communication satellites has seen successful flights
of Telstar, Relay, and Syncom; the Communication Satellite Corporation has been established to exploit this technology on a worldwide basis; and the developmental satellites that have completed
their research tasks are currently in use as forerunners of an operational system. In the area of meteorology, six additional Tiros
satellites, all successful, have been flown since 1961, and the first
Nimbus satellite was successful. This activity, including advances
in automatic picture transmission, has established the foundation
for an operational Weather Bureau system to be implemented
shortly.

In the area of the space sciences, we have achieved a Venus probe
and the first spacecraft to explore Mars is on its course and operating satisfactorily. Over 4,000 photographs of the lunar surface, some
with resolution less than 3 feet, were received from the Ranger
missions. Since 1961 NASA has successfully launched 18 scientific
satellites, including solar observatories and interplanetary monitors.

In the area of manned flight, Project Mercury has been successfully completed with four manned earth orbital flights, the longest
being over 34 hours. The Gemini program successfully completed
its unmanned flight qualification tests, and Project Apollo, whose
manned lunar landing is still to come, has become clearly defined
in the last three years. The spacecraft configuration is based upon
lunar orbit rendezvous for the mission, and consequently there will

be a command module to carry the astronauts to the moon and back, a service module to provide life support and propulsion, and a lunar excursion module to permit descent from the lunar orbit to the lunar surface and return to the orbiting command module. The new launch vehicle foreseen to be necessary is now defined as the Saturn V, capable of placing over 120 tons into earth orbit and 45 tons on a trajectory to the moon.

Enormous progress has been made; even larger horizons for future progress have been opened to us by the advances in science and technology that have occurred since 1961.

RALPH S. COOPER

Rocket Propulsion

[FROM THE SMITHSONIAN REPORT FOR 1962[1]]

A COROLLARY *of the subject of space exploration, or rather a pre-requisite to it, is the theme of rocket propulsion. The velocity of a rocket provided by the propellant determines whether the rocket will orbit the earth, escape the earth's gravity, or escape from the solar system entirely. Ralph S. Cooper, the author of this readable account of propellants, their present types and purposes, and prospects for advanced types such as atomic and electrical power sources, is a staff member of the Theoretical Division, Los Alamos Scientific Laboratory at Los Alamos, New Mexico. His research is in the fields of solid state and electrochemistry, and he works and publishes in reactor physics (cross sections and criticality) and in many phases of nuclear rocket propulsion (reactor concepts, mission and systems studies, radiation, etc.). He reviews briefly the history of rockets, which strangely enough date back to the 13th century, and compares the merits of liquid and solid propellants. For the purpose of putting very large payloads into space, such as those required for the proposed lunar landing, larger and larger rockets are being built, the largest to achieve a thrust of 7½ million pounds. At the same time, research is being rapidly pressed forward toward*

---

[1] Revised as of February 1965.

the development of nuclear and electric propulsion systems. The article makes it clear that rocket development and deep space exploration depend wholly on the efficiency and capability of rocket propellants.

IN THE exploration of space, propulsion — the means of getting there — has always been the crucial problem. Inspection of any of our space vehicles shows that the bulk (over 90 percent) of their volume and weight is devoted to the propulsion systems, mainly to the propellant itself. The extent of space exploration in the future will depend primarily upon the sizes and efficiencies of the propulsion systems that will be developed.

One might wonder whether large-scale space operations are economically feasible in terms of their apparently high energy requirements. But in fact, the electrical energy used by a typical American household during one month is sufficient to put about 75 pounds into orbit about the earth. The same amount of energy is contained in only six gallons (50 pounds) of gasoline plus the oxygen (150 pounds) needed to burn it. Rockets, being far from 100 percent efficient in transferring the energy to the payload, require about five to 10 times as much as this, but still the requirements are not unreasonable. Furthermore, atomic nuclei represent a very compact, almost limitless, source of energy if we can find ways to utilize them efficiently.

VELOCITY REQUIREMENTS

Space travel is dynamic in the sense that velocities rather than positions are significant. The important effect of propulsion is to change the vehicle velocity, which then results in an appropriate change in position, and thus one usually expresses the propulsion requirements for various missions in terms of a velocity. For example, the velocity required for a low earth orbit is about 26,000 feet per second (or 18,000 miles per hour). In addition, one must lift the vehicle to some height and overcome certain gravitational and atmospheric losses (such as aerodynamic drag). These losses are frequently evaluated in terms of velocity and included in the mission requirement. Table 1 gives the approximate requirements for some missions of interest. A lunar round trip has only twice the velocity requirement of orbital missions, and interplanetary trips need only three times orbital velocity. However, this implies that the rockets must be respectively four and nine times as large as the orbital vehicles for the same payload and propulsion system.

TABLE 1. — *Mission velocity requirements*

Mission	Velocity, ft./sec.[*]
Low earth orbit	30,000
Earth escape } Lunar hit }	42,000
High earth orbit } Lunar orbit } Mars, Venus probes }	45,000
Lunar landing	50,000
Lunar round trip } Escape from solar system }	60,000
Mars, Venus round trip	60,000 to 90,000

[*] *Including losses.*

ROCKET PRINCIPLES

Almost all types of rockets are based on the principle of action and reaction, and are similar in action to the recoil of a gun or to the motion of a balloon which is rapidly losing its gas. The motion depends upon expelling some material (propellant), be it gas, solid, or charged particles, from the vehicle. Thus rockets carrying their own propellant are able to operate in a vacuum outside the atmosphere, just as a gun's recoil is independent of the air about it. The velocity of the expellant with respect to the vehicle (called the exhaust velocity) is a measure of how effectively the propellant is used, and is comparable to the miles per gallon of an auto engine.

The higher the exhaust velocity, the more effectively the propellant is being used, and although this requires more energy per unit mass of propellant, it is advantageous to have high exhaust velocity. Note that the original source of energy does not have to be in the ejected material, although this is true for chemically propelled rockets. In our earlier illustrations, the energy was stored in the gunpowder, not the lead projectile, and in the stretched rubber of the balloon as well as in the compressed gas. The initial gross weight of a rocket for a given payload depends exponentially upon the ratio of the mission velocity requirement and the exhaust velocity, making the results quite sensitive to these quantities. Since the mission velocities are relatively fixed, major reductions of vehicle sizes for given payloads and missions can come only through increasing the exhaust velocity.

The final mass includes the "dead" weight of the rocket (engines, tankage, unused propellant), as well as the payload. For some value of the ratio of the velocity requirement to exhaust velocity, the dead weight required for the propulsion system leaves nothing remaining for the payload. This problem is circumvented by jettisoning used portions of the propulsion system, resulting in a number of stages. Usually the tankage and engines of a given stage are dropped when it has exhausted its propellant. Occasionally, as with the Atlas, which drops two of its engines, only portions are released. Staging permits arbitrary mission velocities to be attained, although the payloads may be small. One can find in general an optimum number of stages for a given mission and propulsion system. A high exhaust velocity allows one to use few stages, which results in a simpler, as well as a lighter, vehicle.

CHEMICAL PROPULSION: SOLID PROPELLANTS

Solid propellant rockets are the simplest, and were first historically. They were used in both China and Europe in the 13th century. Used sporadically for centuries, they became very popular in warfare about 1800 ("the rockets' red glare") but were displaced by rifled artillery which was much more accurate. They continued in use in a number of minor applications as well as in warfare where

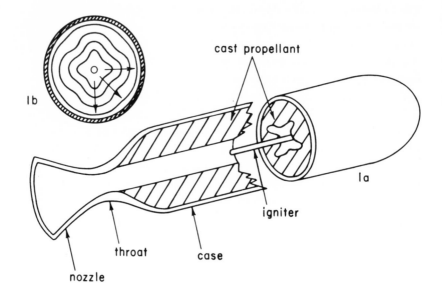

ILLUS. 13—a. Typical modern solid propellant rocket; b. recession of internal surface with time.

much cheap, lightweight, but inaccurate firepower was acceptable. These "powder" rockets contained black powder and, later, smokeless powder grains loosely packed in their cases, necessitating short burning periods to keep the rockets from bursting because of the high temperature.

During World War II, solid rockets using an asphalt base were developed for assisting airplane takeoffs (JATO units). This propellant could be cast in a single piece but tended to crack or soften with temperature changes. The development of rubber-based propellants after the war, combined with a design which kept the wall cool, opened the way for large solid rocket engines. The propellant is cast in place in a single mass with a central hole. The igniter in this hole ignites the inside surface, and the burning surface moves outward toward the case which remains cool until the propellant is almost completely burned. During the entire burning period, the case must be able to contain the high pressure (hundreds of pounds per square inch) which originates in the hot gases and is transmitted through the rubberlike propellant. Thus lightweight, high-strength materials are an important requirement for solid rockets, which tend to have high dead weights due to the case. The primary requirement for nozzle materials is ability to withstand extremely high temperatures, and for this purpose, inserts of special refractory materials (e.g., graphite or tungsten) are often placed in the nozzle throat.

The propellant itself must contain both a fuel and an oxidizer, which supplies the oxygen for the combustion process. Both can be contained in the same molecule (such as nitroglycerine-nitrocellulose) which forms a homogeneous "double base" propellant. For large motors, a rubberlike fuel with small, discrete particles of oxidizer dispersed throughout ("composite" propellant) is more appropriate, since large pieces can be cast in place with little danger of cracking or softening. The exhaust velocity for such materials is in the range of 7,000 to 8,000 feet per second, which is not as good as many liquid propellant combinations. To place a payload in orbit (at a mission velocity requirement of 30,000 feet per second), four solid propellant stages are required, and such a vehicle (Scout) has been developed by NASA. Although it puts less than 1 percent of its initial weight in orbit, it has many of the favorable characteristics of solids — simplicity, ease of handling and launching, relatively low cost, use of various stages for different missions — which commend it to scientific research work with small payloads (about 100 pounds). The ease of scaling up or clustering solid rocket motors has led to their consideration as large boosters. When used as first stages only, their lower performance and higher dead weight are less significant. In very large sizes, the propellant cost (about $1.00 per pound) becomes significant, as does the difficulty of handling the large quantities of potentially explosive material.

LIQUID PROPELLANT ROCKETS

In order to achieve higher exhaust velocities, it is necessary to use propellants with combustion products of low molecular weight, and these chemicals are generally liquid or gaseous at room temperatures. The gases (such as oxygen) would require too much volume and weight to be contained in that state, and thus are liquefied and kept at low (cryogenic) temperatures, in contrast to so-called "storable" propellants which are liquid at room temperatures. The first liquid propellant rocket engine was made about 1900, and in the 1920's and 1930's work on them was carried out independently in Germany and in the United States. Little was done in this country except the work of Prof. Robert Goddard.

A variety of applications and propellant combinations were evolved, including an antiaircraft missile using aniline as the fuel and nitric acid as the oxidizer, aircraft rocket engines utilizing alcohol and concentrated hydrogen peroxide, and finally the V–2, an alcohol and liquid oxygen missile. Based on research of the 1930's, its design was begun in 1938, and the first experimental flight was in 1942. Fortunately, internal political squabbles prevented its completion until late in the war. A 3,000-mile range, two-stage missile was being designed for bombarding the American Continent.

With the V–2, rocketry came of age. The Redstone missiles which were used for the U.S. suborbital manned flights were basically scaled-up versions of the V–2, as were early postwar Russian rockets. Long-range rockets with high explosive warheads are poor, expensive, inaccurate weapons, and probably would not have been developed except for the appearance of nuclear weapons, which gave the final impetus that led rapidly to space exploration capability.

The variety of propellant combinations and types of liquid rocket engines rapidly multiplied, and so a brief discussion must select and oversimplify. The propulsion system includes tankage, propellants, pumps to bring propellants to the combustion chamber where they are burned, and a nozzle to expel the gases efficiently. The fluid propellant can be used before combustion to cool the nozzle and combustion chamber, allowing longer periods of operation than un-cooled solid rocket motors. The propellants may be forced into the engine under the pressure of gas in the tanks, but since this requires heavier tankage, for large rockets the propellant is pumped into the combustion chamber. Propellants enter through an "in-

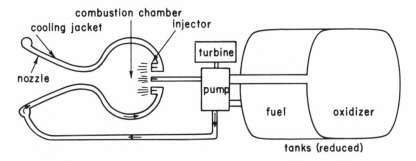

ILLUS. 14—Simplified schematic of a typical liquid propellant rocket.

jector" which is similar to a showerhead and serves to disperse and mix the propellants for efficient combustion. The pump, which requires considerable power in large engines, is usually powered by a gas turbine. The turbine may have its own gas generating system or utilize the propellant combustion products to supply its working fluid. The nozzle or entire engine can be swiveled to provide flight control for the vehicle.

The dead weight of a large liquid rocket propulsion system is 5 to 10 percent of the stage gross weight. The most commonly used propellant combinations (for example, "RP," a kerosenelike hydrocarbon, and oxygen) yield exhaust velocities of about 10,000 feet per second, while the use of liquid hydrogen as a fuel yields 14,000 feet per second, which is close to the maximum possible with chemical propulsion. Hydrogen has a very low boiling point and very low density, but its high performance has led to its choice as the fuel for future U.S. spacecraft. For liquid chemical propulsion, two or three stages are optimum for the earth orbit mission, and only a high energy fueled rocket with a light structure can place itself in orbit with only a single stage. The liquid propellants are less expensive than solid fuel, but the engines are more complicated and therefore more expensive to develop and build. At this time, it is not clear whether it will be economically feasible to reduce costs by recovering spent boosters for reuse.

OTHER CHEMICAL SYSTEMS

Naturally many proposals have been made for improving the performance of chemical systems by increasing their exhaust velocity, reducing dead weights or complexity. Specialized systems have been or will be developed for particular purposes, including monopropellants (single chemical liquids which decompose to give hot gas), hybrid solid-liquid rockets, engines with controllable thrust levels for landing. Relatively little improvement can be expected in the exhaust velocity, even with quite exotic propellant combinations, and it is this which primarily determines the performance. Many advances in simplicity, reliability, and structural weight can be expected, but a "breakthrough" in performance of chemical propulsion seems unlikely.

One area where great improvement is possible is in "aerospace" vehicles, which use air-breathing engines (turbojets or ramjets) for a portion of the boost phase of flight. Since only the fuel need be carried in the vehicle, much greater efficiency is possible in the region up to 10,000 feet per second (7,000 miles per hour) which is one-third of orbital velocity. If sufficiently large, high-speed aircraft engines and airframes could be built, they could be used as flyable, recoverable boosters. In combination with rocket propulsion such "planes" might even be powered into orbit (the so-called "aerospace plane"), although this seems a very formidable task.

NUCLEAR PROPULSION

Nuclear energy can be a very compact type of almost limitless energy, and it is natural to seek some way of utilizing it for space propulsion. Any form of rocket will require some form of propellant to provide the thrust by being expelled from the vehicle, but with a separate energy supply, this could be used much more effectively (i.e., with higher exhaust velocity). There are many methods of nuclear propulsion, with efficiency and complexity generally increasing together. Emphasis here is on those which are closest to becoming a practical reality.

The simplest and most straightforward way of using nuclear

power in a rocket is to replace the liquid rocket combustion chamber with a nuclear reactor to supply heat to the propellant. The reactor is an array of solid nuclear fuel elements containing a fissionable fuel. When the reactor is brought to power, the heat generated in its fuel is transferred directly to the liquid propellant which is pumped through the reactor. The liquid is vaporized, heated to a very high temperature, and expelled through a nozzle to provide the thrust. Since the heat energy is supplied by a source independent of the propellant (rather than by the propellant's chemical energy), one has a freer choice of propellant.

By choosing hydrogen, which has the lowest molecular weight, one can readily achieve exhaust velocities of 25,000 to 30,000 feet per second, about twice those of the best chemical propulsion system. This high performance is partially offset by the heavier dead weight (10 to 15 percent necessitated by the reactor and H_2 tankage) and by the complications arising from the nuclear radiation emanating from the reactor. Nevertheless, the high performance is invaluable for missions in the interplanetary class and useful for less ambitious ones.

The nuclear reactor is basically a simple device and its chain reaction can be easily controlled through the movement of neutron-absorbing materials in the core (the fuel-bearing region) or the reflector (an outer layer of material which helps to keep the neutrons from escaping). Since there is no combustion, explosions are unlikely, and the nuclear engine should prove to be quite reliable from that standpoint. To obtain the high thrust and high exhaust velocity, the reactor must run at much higher power and temperature than do ordinary power reactors, but this is partially ameliorated by the short lifetime (about 10 minutes) required of rocket reactors. Each cubic foot of the reactor core must generate energy equivalent to the electricity used in many thousands of homes. Furthermore, it must do this while much of the reactor core, several cubic feet and several thousand pounds, is at the temperature of an electric light bulb filament (2,000 to 3,000° C.)! This is far above the melting points of most common materials (such as steel, quartz sand, and most refractory materials) and limits the choice of fuel elements to very few. Graphite (the most familiar), tungsten (used in lamp filaments), and a few metal carbides are about the

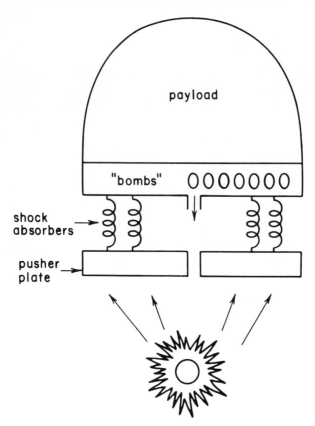

ILLUS. 15—A nuclear explosive-propelled vehicle. The nuclear explosive heats the propellant, which impinges on the "pusher plate," transferring momentum to the vehicle. A set of shock absorbers smooths out the force on the payload.

only candidates. These must contain the fissionable material in a refractory form such as uranium oxide or carbide, which also have high melting points.

The liquid hydrogen presents several difficulties. First, it is only one-fourteenth as dense as water (or most chemical fuels) and thus requires relatively larger and heavier tankage. Secondly, it boils at −423° F., which is close to absolute zero (−459° F.), and thus requires special insulating and handling techniques. It is cold enough not only to liquefy air, but to freeze it solid. Nevertheless, hydrogen is being used as a liquid fuel in the chemical rocket program, and techniques are being developed which should make its use routine.

The nuclear radiation presents a number of problems, but these

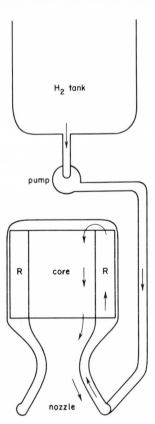

ILLUS. 16—Simplified schematic of a nuclear propulsion system. The H_2 propellant is pumped from the tank, cooling the nozzle and reactor reflector (R), before being heated in the core and expelled through the nozzle.

can be met with straightforward solutions in most cases. It has been shown that even with regular launchings in the atmosphere, the worldwide contamination would be negligible. Hazards for manned operations must be minimized, but the problems may not be very different from those associated with chemical propulsion. Manned space flight may require extensive shielding against space radiation, which will be effective against the nuclear engine as well.

The exhaust velocity for nuclear propulsion is about equal to the velocity increment needed to achieve earth orbit, and therefore a single nuclear stage is capable of going into orbit with considerable (about 20 percent) payload. For difficult missions, only about half as many nuclear stages as chemical stages need be used, increasing reliability and decreasing launch costs. Finally, operation in space reduces many of the radiation problems and weight penalties associated with nuclear propulsion (lower thrust, lower weight engines can be used, lighter structured H_2 tanks employed).

ADVANCED PROPULSION SYSTEMS

Since the nuclear heat exchanger engine uses less than 0.1 percent of the fission energy available, we can see that only the beginnings of nuclear propulsion have been touched upon. The problem lies not in obtaining the energy as much as in dealing with the higher temperatures involved when this energy is transferred to the propellant. An additional incentive for seeking temperatures above 3,000° C. is the disassociation of the H_2 molecules into H atoms; disassociation occurs over a range of temperatures, which allows much greater storage of energy in the propellant at these temperatures. This could lead to exhaust velocities of up to 50,000 feet per second. There has been hope of making gaseous core reactors, operating at up to 10,000° C., but the problem of separating the gaseous fuel from the propellant appears insurmountable if reasonable thrust is desired. One possibility for circumventing the material temperature problem is the use of small nuclear explosions in what might be called an "external combustion engine." The nuclear explosive heats the propellant behind the vehicle. The propellant impinges on a large, heavy "pusher plate," transferring momentum to the plate which is coupled to the rest of the vehicle through a shock-absorbing system. Space ships utilizing such a propulsion system could carry millions of pounds of payload throughout the solar system with quite small nuclear explosives.

There are no workable methods of utilizing nuclear fusion (thermonuclear) energy for space propulsion presently in sight.

There is another class of propulsion devices which will ultimately rely on nuclear energy as the power source and which is best termed "electrical propulsion." This includes a wide variety of engines which heat and/or, more importantly, accelerate the propellant electrically. By accelerating the propellant directly, one can get it to very high velocities (50,000 to 500,000 ft./sec.) without raising its thermal (random molecular motion) energy. One volt of electrical potential corresponds to 10,000° C. of thermal energy. The propellant can consist of electrically charged ions, fine particles, gases, etc., which are accelerated by electrical or magnetic fields using the same principles applied in "atom smashers" and television tubes. There are two major problems associated with these engines. First, although their exhaust velocity is very high, they are limited to very small total thrust compared to the weight of the engine and power supply. Thus they can be used only in space where the vehicle is already in orbit and a very small acceleration (less than one-thousandth that of the earth's gravity) acting over a long period (months or years) is acceptable. Secondly, the long period of operation has several unfortunate consequences. Electrical power sources must be available which are very light in weight and capable of operating many months to several years with little or no attention. This leads to a small nuclear reactor as the only energy source with either a turbine-generator or a thermo-electric system to convert the reactor's heat to electricity. The latter, with no moving parts, would be preferable for a long-lived operation. For electrical propulsion, the power/weight of the energy source is the measure of performance rather than the exhaust velocity. The long period of thrust and low acceleration also implies long periods spent in the radiation belts and in transit to planets, which is undesirable for manned flight. Nevertheless, the high exhaust velocity makes this form of propulsion attractive for very high velocity missions such as exploration of the solar system with probes or manned vehicles. Both the engines and the power sources (which are the crucial components) are being developed.

There are other low-thrust propulsion systems which may be of interest for scientific payloads. One type would use solar energy to heat hydrogen with a plastic mirror system replacing the reactor as the energy source. The weight of aluminized plastic film and the relatively low energy rate in solar radiation limit this to low thrust/weight ratios. A very intriguing propulsion technique, based on the momentum carried by solar radiation, has been called "solar sailing." Here a very large aluminized plastic sail is used to catch and reflect sunshine much as ship sails catch the wind. The accelerations are small, but significant as has been shown by the effects of the sun upon the large Echo balloon satellite, which also demonstrated that present materials could withstand the space environment for long periods. Note also that the "propellant" is composed of particles of light ("photons") supplied by the sun and thus the solar sail need not carry any propellant or ever need refueling.

PERFORMANCE COMPARISON

There is as much variety in space propulsion as in surface transportation, and consequently there are varied performance levels and areas of application. The method of propulsion used in practice is dependent upon availability, cost, and other criteria, as well as performance simply on a gross weight basis. Table 2 gives ap-

TABLE 2. — *High-thrust propulsion system parameters*

	Solid	Liquid RP-O_2	High energy H_2-O_2	Nuclear H_2
Exhaust velocity, ft./sec..............	8,000	10,000	13,500	27,000
Percent dead weight.................	8	5	7	15

proximate representative parameters for four propulsion systems currently under development. The gross weights of vehicles to send a 10,000-pound payload on various missions are given in Table 3. A 10,000-pound payload was chosen for consistency and as a reasonable manned vehicle size, although the more difficult missions may require greater payload for radiation shielding and life support systems. Results are scalable to other payloads. The necessity for staging leads logically to the use of early, low-power versions of advanced propulsion systems in upper stages resulting in hybrid vehicles with intermediate performance. Each replacement of a chemical by a nuclear stage leads to reductions of 2½ in vehicle gross weight as can be seen in Table 4 for the lunar mission. Thus the booster size can be reduced and the payload increased considerably with nuclear upper stages. For manned vehicles, a chemical last stage would be desirable to act as an escape vehicle, and for the shielding its propellant would provide.

There are no unclassified performance figures available for the nuclear explosion scheme, and low-thrust nuclear-electric propulsion performance depends crucially on the specific weight of the power plant. If the desired values can be achieved, orbital start electric spacecraft could carry about one-third of their gross weight as payload on interplanetary round trips.

To summarize the situation, most of these propulsion systems can be used exclusively for any vehicle, but combinations will be used which reflect their attributes and state of the art. Liquid propellant rockets will be the most used of the 1960's, with high-energy propel-

TABLE 3. — *Performance of high-thrust systems*

Mission	ΔV, ft./sec.	Vehicle gross weight for a 10,000-pound payload			
		Solid	O_2-RP	H_2-O_2	Nuclear H_2
Earth orbit......	30,000	780,000	280,000	130,000	43,000
Lunar round trip..	60,000	60,000,000	8,000,000	1,700,000	190,000
Martian round trip............	90,000	....	....	22,000,000	800,000

TABLE 4. — *Vehicles for a lunar mission — 55,000 pounds landed on the lunar surface*

Vehicle	All chemical 4 stages	3 chemical 1 nuclear (3d stage)	1 chemical 2 nuclear upper stages	All nuclear 2 stages
Vehicle gross wt./lbs.........	10,000,000	4,000,000	1,700,000	860,000
Vehicle dead wt.............	500,000	220,000	110,000	125,000
Propellant volume, ft.^{3}......	200,000	100,000	80,000	160,000

lant being used in upper stages. Solid propellant rockets will be used for small final stages (e.g., retro rockets), low total cost, low payload research rockets, and possibly as large, first-stage boosters. Nuclear propulsion will be used in upper stages for difficult missions (lunar and interplanetary). The low-thrust electric propulsion systems will be limited to orbital start interplanetary missions.

AUXILIARY POWER SUPPLIES

Up to the present, electrical power has been supplied to spacecraft mainly by chemical batteries or solar cells. The former are relatively heavy per unit of output, and have short lifetimes. The latter are limited to low powers which will fluctuate with the spacecraft's orientation and position, and are affected by radiation. Some of these difficulties are relieved by using the two in conjunction, allowing the solar cells periodically to charge the batteries, which supply continuous power. Nuclear energy represents a way to circumvent the lifetime and power limitations. One method, which has already been put into practice, is to use the heat generated by radioactive isotopes to supply energy to thermoelectric generators. These convert heat into electricity in the same manner as do temperature-measuring thermocouples. Radioisotope sources are somewhat limited in power (several hundred watts) but can have lifetimes ranging from 100 days to 100 years or more in practice, depending upon the isotope chosen.

For high powers (kilowatts) and long times (years) nuclear reactors are the only practical source. A nuclear electric power supply must include power conversion equipment, radiators to reject unusable heat, and possibly some shielding, as well as the reactor. This leads to system weights of the order of 1,000 pounds, useful only in large payloads. At present, only rotating electric generators are sufficiently developed to handle the high power. These will have a metal vapor (such as mercury) heated by the reactor, to power a turbine which drives a generator. The vapor is condensed and cooled in the radiator to complete the cycle. Eventually, high-power thermoelectric conversion systems will be developed with lower weight, higher efficiency, fewer moving parts, and greater reliability than the turbo-generator system.

STATE OF THE ART AND PROSPECTS

In the early 1960's most large space boosters used liquid propellants with exhaust velocities of less than 10,000 feet per second. The solid propellant Scout rocket was used for small scientific payloads, and the Thor-Delta rocket for those up to 800 pounds. This latter is a vehicle with two liquid stages and a third solid rocket stage. The Thor-Agena has a larger second stage and can carry twice as much. The Atlas-Agena was the largest operational vehicle and was used for lunar and interplanetary probes. The Centaur high energy (hydrogen-oxygen) stage is being developed for the Atlas booster and has placed 8,500 pounds in orbit.

Larger engines and vehicles are being developed to implement the manned lunar exploration program. The Saturn I vehicle has a first stage using eight RP-oxygen engines giving a total thrust of 1.5 million pounds. With its hydrogen-oxygen second stage it has placed 39,000 pounds in orbit, about half of which was the spent second stage. An uprated version (S-IB) will be able to place 30,000 pounds of payload in orbit and will be used to test the Apollo spacecraft. The S-IB will use a 200,000-pound-thrust H_2-O_2 engine in its second stage.

The manned lunar mission will be carried out with the much larger Saturn V rocket. Its first stage will be powered by five F-1 engines with a total thrust of 7.5 million pounds. This vehicle with high energy upper stages will place 200,000 pounds in orbit and send 90,000 pounds to the moon. Nuclear propulsion may be first tested and used in an advanced Saturn upper stage. With experi-

TABLE 5. — *Rocket engines*

	Propellants	Thrust	Use
H-1	RP-O_2	188,000 lbs.	Saturn I
F1	RP-O_2	1,500,000	Saturn V
ALGOL	Solid	86,000	Scout
RL-10	H_2-O_2	15,000	Centaur
J-2	H_2-O_2	200,000	Saturn IB (2nd stage) Saturn V (upper stage)
M-1	H_2-O_2	1,500,000	Engine development
NERVA	Nuclear-H_2	50,000	Engine development
PHOEBUS	Nuclear-H_2	250,000	Reactor development

TABLE 6. — *NASA launch vehicles*

	Thrust, lbs.	Payload 300-mile orbit	Escape	Type
Scout	86,000	240	. . . . .	4 solid stages
Thor-Delta	170,000	800	105	2 liquid, 1 solid
Thor-Agena	170,000	1,600	. . . . .	2 liquid stages
Atlas-Agena	368,000	5,900	950	. . . .
Atlas-Centaur	368,000	8,500	2,300	H_2-O_2 upper stage
Saturn I	1,500,000	15,000	. . . . .	H_2-O_2 second stage
Saturn IB	1,600,000	28,500	. . . . .	larger second stage
Saturn V	7,500,000	220,000	90,000	2 high-energy upper stages

ILLUS. 17—*Kiwi B4-a, one of the nuclear rocket reactors being prepared for testing at the Nevada Test site. (Courtesy of the Los Alamos Scientific Laboratory.)*

ence gained in the military rocket programs, larger solid propellant rockets are being developed for use as boosters. A vehicle is under development which has two 120-inch-diameter solid rockets strapped in parallel to a Titan missile, with payloads comparable to the Saturn I. Similar thrust augmentation has been applied by NASA to the Thor space boosters with three 33-inch solid rockets. The manned space program has relied in its early stages on rockets developed by the military. The Atlas and Titan rockets are both liquid propellant rockets with several hundred thousand pounds of thrust, with the Titan being somewhat the larger. In the 1960's the advances in chemical propulsion will be in switching to high-energy propellants and making larger sizes of the present engine and vehicle types.

Nuclear propulsion is in the early stages of engine development. A series of experiments culminating in the Kiwi B reactor (Illus. 17) has proved the principles, and the Nerva engine utilizing this reactor is being developed. The reactor is composed of uranium-fueled graphite which is protected from reacting with the hot hydrogen by a cladding of niobium carbide. The Nerva engine will have a power of 1,000 megawatts, equal to the Hoover Dam output, which corresponds to a thrust of 50,000 pounds. A reactor of five times this power, Phoebus, is being developed with the same basic graphite technology.

Several types of electric rocket engines are being developed and have been tested in space for short periods, using Scout rockets to loft them and batteries to power them. The Russians have reportedly used electric thrustors for attitude control on their manned orbital and interplanetary spacecraft. The thrusts for all of these are fractions of an ounce, and they await the arrival of large power supplies (many kilowatts) before they can be used for the spacecraft's primary propulsion.

We can expect liquid fuel chemical rockets to be the workhorses of the next decade, with solid rockets used in several special applications, for small rockets and for extra thrust on boosters. Nuclear engines will be developed and used in upper stages on large rockets. These will be applied to lunar transportation and planetary probes, with the main goal being their eventual use in manned interplanetary exploration. Electric propulsion will be applied to deep-space missions as the appropriate power supplies are developed. Hopefully, some of the more advanced systems may reach the engineering development stages in the coming decade.

CHARLES S. DRAPER

Navigation — From Canoes to Spaceships

[FROM THE SMITHSONIAN REPORT FOR 1960]

CHARLES S. DRAPER, *author of this article, which like the two preceding ones has a very important bearing on space exploration, performs the dual functions of Head of the Department of Aeronautics and Astronautics and Director of the Instrumentation Laboratory, Massachusetts Institute of Technology. Although the article describes briefly primitive navigation — hence the word "canoes" in the title — most of it treats fully of modern, highly sophisticated methods including navigation by radio and radar, loran, and the very new highly technical inertial-guidance systems. These last systems, based on geometric reference members established through gyroscopic action, have been developed as a result of the changed requirements of modern military operations and of space navigation. Bombers approaching enemy territory, missile-launching submarines on long underwater missions, ballistic missiles, and space vehicles for various reasons obviously cannot depend upon radio contact for guidance. Dr. Draper explains in some detail the workings of the inertial-guidance systems which well illustrate the highly complex technological advances that characterize the mid-20th century decades.*

In 1786 John Hyacinth de Magellan of London presented 200 guineas to the American Philosophical Society as a gift, through which special gold medals were to be awarded from time to time. Under the terms of the gift, each of these medals should go "to the author of the best discovery or most useful invention relating to navigation, astronomy, or natural philosophy (mere natural history only excepted)." This specification of conditions makes it very probable that the donor intended to honor his lineal ancestor Ferdinand Magellan, who was killed during a Philippine Islands battle in April of 1521, after having navigated across all the unknown longitudes of the world's oceans. This earlier Magellan, the illustrious first circumnavigator of the globe, was a man whose vision, boldness, leadership, steadiness in adversity, and actual achievements give him an unassailable position as a very great member of the human race. It is a high honor for the author of this paper to be identified in any way with the name of Magellan, and he is deeply grateful to the American Philosophical Society for the 1959 Magellanic Medal. The citation mentions contributions to inertial guidance, a field in which the author has been active for many years as director of the Instrumentation Laboratory at the Massachusetts Institute of Technology. In this position, he has been fortunate to have the collaboration of a dedicated and able group of scientists and engineers who must rightfully receive a great share of any credit that may be due for pioneering applications of inertial devices to the problems of navigation.

Inertial navigation is properly the subject of primary interest for this paper, but a brief discussion of guidance in general is needed to bring out an over-all picture, with the inertial method given its place as one segment of a generalized pattern. To be complete, this pattern must include the navigational means that have been used or are available for terrestrial, marine, aeronautical, and space vehicles ranging from the dugout canoes of our caveman ancestors to the interplanetary ships that will be built in the near future for explorations of the solar system. Historical coverage and details of particular devices are beyond the scope of this paper, which is concerned only with the basic principles and methods that are used to solve the problems of navigation. Accordingly, references are omitted from the text, but a short bibliography related to gyroscopic devices and inertial navigation is provided for the convenience of those readers who may be interested in pursuing the subject further.

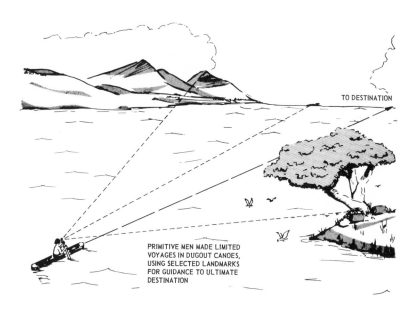

TO DESTINATION

PRIMITIVE MEN MADE LIMITED VOYAGES IN DUGOUT CANOES, USING SELECTED LANDMARKS FOR GUIDANCE TO ULTIMATE DESTINATION

ILLUS. 18–Visual line-of-sight navigation.

PRIMITIVE NAVIGATION

When one of our remote ancestors wished to go on a trip, he selected landmarks within sight and took his guidance from first one and then another, until he reached his destination (Illustration 18).[1] If night or bad weather prevented him from seeing any landmark, he was forced to stop until conditions improved. Navigation with restrictions of this kind limited voyages to waters near extended

---

[1] The figures are drawn so as to be self-explanatory; hence, little detailed discussion of the figures appears in the text.

shorelines and islands, except for a few special cases where boats might be moved by known wind and water currents. This complete dependence on currents or on visible terrestrial objects was relieved many centuries ago by the discovery that under proper conditions heavenly bodies could be used to assist travel over the surface of the earth. In effect, the stars were found to act as points in a knowable space located at a great distance from the earth (Illustration 19). The sun, the moon, and the planets did not appear to be fixed in this space, but followed paths that reduced their usefulness for the purposes of guidance. On clear nights, the star Polaris showed the direction of north and provided information on latitude by its angle above the horizon. Other stars with known positions in the pattern of the celestial sphere were also used, but celestial navigation remained an incomplete art for many centuries. The principal reason for this imperfection was the earth's rotation, which made it impossible to determine the angular position of the earth with respect to the stars. Without good information on this position, estimates of longitude necessarily remained of low quality.

CELESTIAL NAVIGATION

The key problem in longitude measurements was that of finding the rotational angle of the earth with respect to a reference position having known relationships to points fixed on the celestial sphere. Astronomical knowledge recorded in star tables and almanacs easily gave angles between lines of sight to celestial objects and the vertical at any terrestrial point, if the earth could be assumed to remain in a particular position. In practice, the earth never fulfilled this assumption, but continuously moved with respect to any possible reference position. Because the angular velocity of the earth among the stars was and is effectively constant and well known, an accurate means for indicating sidereal time (time based on rotation of the earth referred to the celestial sphere) would have made it possible to find longitude by fixing the angle of the earth from a selected reference position.

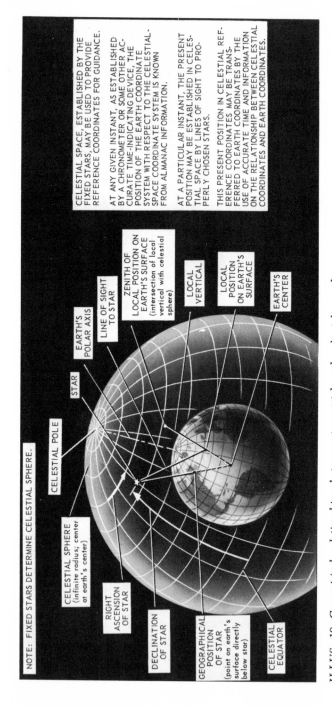

NOTE: FIXED STARS DETERMINE CELESTIAL SPHERE.

CELESTIAL POLE

CELESTIAL SPHERE
(infinite radius; center
at earth's center)

RIGHT
ASCENSION
OF STAR

DECLINATION
OF STAR

GEOGRAPHICAL
POSITION
OF STAR
(point on earth's
surface directly
below star)

CELESTIAL
EQUATOR

STAR

EARTH'S POLAR AXIS

LINE OF SIGHT
TO STAR

ZENITH OF
LOCAL POSITION ON
EARTH'S SURFACE
(intersection of local
vertical with celestial
sphere)

LOCAL VERTICAL

LOCAL
POSITION
ON EARTH'S
SURFACE

EARTH'S
CENTER

CELESTIAL SPACE, ESTABLISHED BY THE
FIXED STARS, MAY BE USED TO PROVIDE
REFERENCE COORDINATES FOR GUIDANCE.

AT ANY GIVEN INSTANT, AS ESTABLISHED
BY A CHRONOMETER OR SOME OTHER AC-
CURATE TIME-INDICATING DEVICE, THE
POSITION OF THE EARTH COORDINATE
SYSTEM WITH RESPECT TO THE CELESTIAL-
SPACE COORDINATE SYSTEM IS KNOWN
FROM ALMANAC INFORMATION.

AT A PARTICULAR INSTANT, THE PRESENT
POSITION MAY BE ESTABLISHED IN CELES-
TIAL SPACE BY LINES OF SIGHT TO PRO-
PERLY CHOSEN STARS.

THIS PRESENT POSITION IN CELESTIAL REF-
ERENCE COORDINATES MAY BE TRANS-
FERRED TO EARTH COORDINATES BY THE
USE OF ACCURATE TIME AND INFORMATION
ON THE RELATIONSHIP BETWEEN CELESTIAL
COORDINATES AND EARTH COORDINATES.

ILLUS. 19—Geometrical relationships between terrestrial and celestial coordinates.

The basic problem of timekeeping for navigation was first solved during the 18th century by John Harrison, who received a prize from the British Admiralty for his achievement. The 19th-century developments of instruments and other devices that accompanied and followed Harrison's work on the marine chronometer — improved sextants, logarithmic multiplication, almanacs, and other aids — brought the art of celestial navigation by visual observations very close to the high level that it has today.

Celestial navigation is basically the art of using the celestial sphere as a reference space in which visible stars provide geometrical points for relating positions in terrestrial space to a system of coordinates outside the earth. These star lines of sight are the directions from which angles to the local vertical are observed at the terrestrial point to be located, by means of instruments like the sextant (Illustration 20). Angle measurements of this kind are useful in navigation only if the positions that the observed stars occupy on the celestial sphere are known and if the instantaneous orientation of a selected meridian fixed to the earth is measured with respect to the celestial sphere.

Data on celestial-sphere points are available from the body of knowledge developed in descriptive astronomy and are recorded for the purposes of navigation in star tables and almanacs. The meridian selected as the reference for navigation is arbitrarily taken as the one passing through Greenwich. At any instant, the hour angle of this meridian may be determined with the aid of a chronometer reading, which provides knowledge of the time elapsed since the Greenwich meridian last occupied a reference orientation with respect to the celestial sphere. The hour angle, star observations, and almanac data are the elements used to find locations on the earth by conventional methods of navigation.

The geometrical principles associated with the use of a non-terrestrial reference space for the purposes of navigation have been known and applied for centuries. Many techniques for using these principles, differing in details from the process that has been described, are possible. This fact is not important for the purposes of this paper, which is primarily concerned with describing the place of inertial methods among other ways of locating points on the earth's surface. It will appear that inertial navigation is geo-

ILLUS. 20—Use of the sextant in celestial navigation.

metrically analogous to celestial navigation. The essential difference lies in the use by inertial systems of gyroscopically controlled, rigid body members to serve the functions of the celestial sphere as a nonterrestrial reference space.

NAVIGATION BY RADIO AND RADAR

Navigation by the use of terrestrial landmarks, a very old art, was revolutionized during the first decades of the 20th century by the new science of electronics. This revolution came from applications

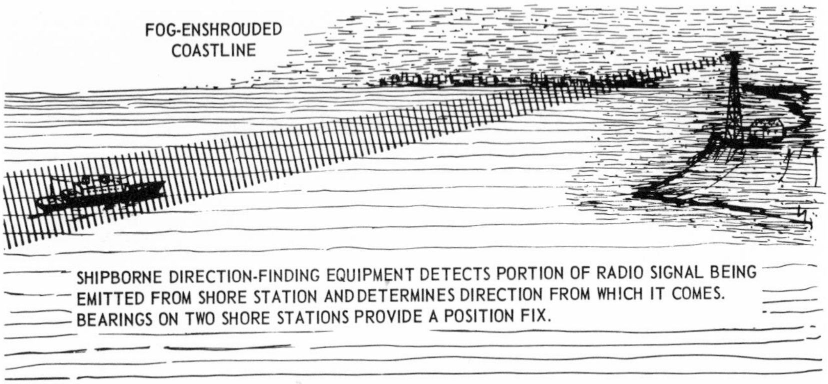

FOG-ENSHROUDED
COASTLINE

SHIPBORNE DIRECTION-FINDING EQUIPMENT DETECTS PORTION OF RADIO SIGNAL BEING
EMITTED FROM SHORE STATION AND DETERMINES DIRECTION FROM WHICH IT COMES.
BEARINGS ON TWO SHORE STATIONS PROVIDE A POSITION FIX.

ILLUS. 21—Application of radio techniques to terrestrial navigation.

of radio techniques to maintain radiation links between vehicles and points with known locations on the earth by the use of electromagnetic radiation having wavelengths much longer than those of visible light (Illustration 21). Darkness, bad weather, distance, and obstructions that affect visual observations do not interfere with these long-wavelength contacts with landmarks that are radio stations or reflectors.

Radio direction finders are now common equipment for aircraft and marine vessels and serve as basic aids to navigation by giving bearings to known stations. Signals set up in the fashion of the "A" and "N" quadrants that are associated with the radio beams of civil airways have been used for several decades to guide airplanes. Higher accuracy and wider coverage in fixes are possible by applying the principles of loran, and similar radio-navigation systems, in which the navigating vehicle receives synchronized pulse signals from at least three transmitting stations (Illus. 22). The time difference between the signals received from any two stations determines a hyperbola-shaped line of position on the navigation chart. Use of at least one other transmitting station determines a second such line of position. The crossing of these two lines of position on the navigation chart establishes a highly accurate fix. With this navigation technique, the difficulties that beset visual observations of landmarks are substantially eliminated. Navigation by such radio-navigation nets, which cover wide areas

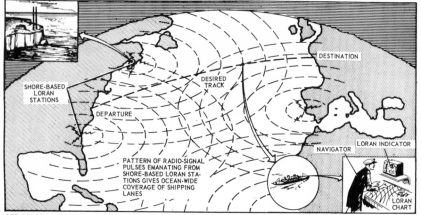

DESTINATION

SHORE-BASED LORAN STATIONS

DESIRED TRACK

DEPARTURE

LORAN INDICATOR

NAVIGATOR

PATTERN OF RADIO-SIGNAL PULSES EMANATING FROM SHORE-BASED LORAN STATIONS GIVES OCEAN-WIDE COVERAGE OF SHIPPING LANES

LORAN CHART

DEPARTURE AND DESTINATION ARE KNOWN IN EARTH COORDINATES (LATITUDE AND LONGITUDE). DESIRED TRACK IS ESTABLISHED FROM KNOWLEDGE OF DEPARTURE AND DESTINATION IN EARTH COORDINATES.

ACTUAL POSITION OF SHIP CAN BE DETERMINED BY MEANS OF LORAN. LORAN IS A HYPERBOLIC NAVIGATION SYSTEM IN WHICH THE NAVIGATING CRAFT RECEIVES SYNCHRONIZED PULSE SIGNALS FROM AT LEAST THREE KNOWN POINTS. TIME DIFFERENCE BETWEEN ARRIVAL OF SIGNALS FROM ANY PAIR OF THESE TRANSMITTING STATIONS IS MEASURED AND DETERMINES A HYPERBOLA-SHAPED LINE OF POSITION ON A LORAN CHART. BY MEANS OF ANOTHER PAIR OF STATIONS A SECOND SET OF SIGNALS CAN BE USED TO DETERMINE A SECOND LINE OF POSITION. THE CROSSING OF THE TWO LINES OF POSITION GIVES A POSITION FIX IN LORAN COORDINATES.

LORAN CHART SHOWS LORAN LINES OF POSITION SUPERIMPOSED ON GEOGRAPHIC PLOT. THEREFORE, LOCATION OF PRESENT POSITION IN LORAN COORDINATES GIVES DIRECTLY THE LOCATION IN EARTH COORDINATES.

ILLUS. 22—Navigation by means of loran.

of the earth's surface, is very useful for locating stationary points and slow-moving vehicles, but is not well adapted to situations that involve rapid maneuvers of fast vehicles.

Radar, which uses wavelengths shorter than those of the radio-navigation systems just described but longer than those of light, gives direct indication of distance from a single landmark. It is an excellent means for navigation by direct-line-of-sight contacts, with the restrictions associated with light substantially eliminated (Illus. 23). The landmarks for radar may be ordinary terrain features and artificial objects, such as lighthouses, buoys, or other vehicles. Radar devices usually operate by comparing transmitted and reflected pulses. The time between sending and receiving for a particular pulse gives the distance to the reflecting surface in terms of the velocity of light.

An alternative method of using wavelengths of the radar spectrum for the purposes of navigation is to transmit continuous waves instead of pulses. This technique is particularly useful when the transmitter and reflecting surfaces are moving so rapidly with respect to each other that a measurable shift in frequency between reflected and transmitted waves exists. This frequency shift is a

USE OF RADAR PROVIDES
DIRECT LINE OF SIGHT TO
KNOWN LANDMARK AND RE-
SULTS IN BOTH RANGE AND
BEARING INFORMATION

ILLUS. 23—Navigation by use of radar.

manifestation of the well-understood Doppler effect and is the basis for a number of radiation-contact guidance equipments that are classed as Doppler systems.

It is fair to state that toward the middle of the 20th century, radio and radar methods had substantially eliminated the difficulties that attend the use of visual contacts for the purposes of navigation by terrestrial landmarks. A number of other benefits had also appeared when visible light was replaced by longer wavelengths for navigational purposes: direct range and velocity measurements were available, working distances were greatly extended, direct-line-of-sight restrictions were removed, and complete automation of equipment became feasible. By about 1950, developments of equipment and methods had substantially exhausted the possibilities of improving navigation by terrestrial and celestial references. Improvements in details will always occur, but it is unlikely that these fields will see revolutionary changes in the future.

MODERN PROBLEMS IN NAVIGATION

All the advances in methods, theory, tables, instruments, and techniques that appeared during the course of several thousand years to perfect the art of navigation combined to solve the same problem that confronted the first caveman navigator. This problem was and still is that of finding position of the earth from information provided by time and by radiation contacts with objects having known locations in terrestrial space or celestial space. Navigation progressed with the perfection of chronometers and other instruments, and with improvements in the means for sensing radiation-contact information, until at the present time a state of development exists for these elements that approximates their ultimate possibilities. It now remains for new methods to overcome the problems in navigation that began to emerge during the last half of the fifth decade of our century. These problems, which are not solvable by radiation-contact methods, originated largely from needs associated with modern military operations and flights by vehicles moving in the emptiness of space outside the earth's atmosphere, although civilian applications will surely become important in the future. The new difficulties in navigation appear because the vehicles involved must operate in situations where it is undesirable or impossible to maintain radiation contacts of any kind with outside points.

Bombers flying to attack targets deep within well-defended enemy territory will surely not have an environment of cooperative ground stations and can expect the enemy to take all possible measures for interfering with the operation of such radiation-contact equipments as radios and radars. Submarines designed for the underwater launching of ballistic missiles must have an accurate and continuous knowledge of position during long periods of submerged cruising near enemy shores. Ballistic missiles, which to be effective must be designed for simultaneous launching in salvos of considerable numbers, need to have self-contained guidance systems in order to keep ground installations within feasible limits of size and cost. Satellites, lunar craft, and interplanetary vehicles need navigational equipment designed to make the most effective use of the available weight and volume capacity, so that there are strong reasons for working out designs based on the best possible combinations of radiation-contact components and inertial elements.

These examples serve to illustrate the nature of the new requirements on navigation equipment that have developed during the past 10 years. These requirements reduce to the necessity for navigation systems capable of giving high-quality performance during periods that include a considerable number of hours without radia-

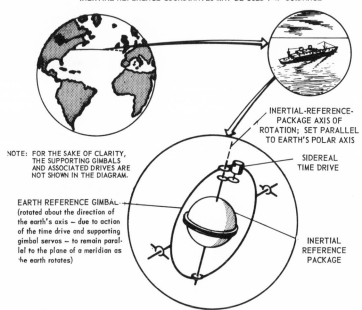

CONTACT AND DIRECT RADIATION CONNECTION IS NOT POSSIBLE, INERTIAL REFERENCE COORDINATES MAY BE USED FOR GUIDANCE

INERTIAL-REFERENCE-PACKAGE AXIS OF ROTATION; SET PARALLEL TO EARTH'S POLAR AXIS

SIDEREAL TIME DRIVE

NOTE: FOR THE SAKE OF CLARITY, THE SUPPORTING GIMBALS AND ASSOCIATED DRIVES ARE NOT SHOWN IN THE DIAGRAM.

EARTH REFERENCE GIMBAL (rotated about the direction of the earth's axis — due to action of the time drive and supporting gimbal servos — to remain parallel to the plane of a meridian as the earth rotates)

INERTIAL REFERENCE PACKAGE

INERTIAL-REFERENCE-PACKAGE ORIENTATION IS INITIALLY ACCURATELY ESTABLISHED WITH RESPECT TO INERTIAL SPACE, THAT IS, WITH RESPECT TO CELESTIAL SPACE (FOR THE PURPOSES OF PRACTICAL GUIDANCE, INERTIAL SPACE AND CELESTIAL SPACE ARE EFFECTIVELY IDENTICAL). THIS MAY INVOLVE THE USE OF DEVICES NOT INCLUDED IN THE INERTIAL GUIDANCE EQUIPMENT.

HIGH-PERFORMANCE INERTIAL-REFERENCE GYRO UNITS (GYRO UNITS WITH LOW DRIFT RATES) SUPPLYING CORRECTION SIGNALS FOR SERVO-DRIVEN GIMBALS OPERATE TO ACCURATELY HOLD THE INERTIAL-REFERENCE-PACKAGE ORIENTATION WITH RESPECT TO INERTIAL SPACE DURING THE PERIOD GUIDANCE IS REQUIRED.

A SPECIFIC FORCE RECEIVER SYSTEM WITH SCHULER TUNING MAY BE USED TO ACCURATELY INDICATE THE VERTICAL IN MOVING VEHICLES.

MEASUREMENT OF THE ANGLES BETWEEN THE VERTICAL AND A MEMBER FIXED WITH THE PROPER ORIENTATION TO THE EARTH REFERENCE GIMBAL GIVES PRESENT POSITION OF THE VEHICLE ON THE EARTH.

ILLUS. 24—Guidance by substitution of inertial reference coordinates for celestial coordinates.

tion contacts. In terms of the basic geometry involved, this means that navigation equipment must include a completely self-contained means for providing geometrical references (Illus. 24).

Inertial principles applied through the medium of gyroscopic action (see bibliography) make it possible to realize geometrical reference members, in the form of rigid bodies, that are capable of serving the functions of celestial space in navigation. To be satisfactory, these reference members must hold initially established orientations with high accuracy under conditions of opera-

tion. The essential features of systems based on reference members
of this kind are discussed in the sections that follow.

SELF-CONTAINED GEOMETRICAL REFERENCES FOR
NAVIGATION BY APPLICATION OF GYROSCOPIC
PRINCIPLES

Gyroscopic effects are mainly associated with the mechanical behavior of a balanced, symmetrical rotor spinning rapidly about its
axis of circular symmetry and mounted in gimbals, or carried by
some other means, that allow it to have rotational freedom about
directions at right angles to its spin axis. The action of such a gyro-
scope (a name applied by Foucault to devices with the features
just described) depends on Newton's law of motion, which states
that a particle of mass acted on by a force has a rate of change of
its velocity vector in the direction of the applied force. The magnitude of this rate of change is directly proportional to the magnitude of the force and is inversely proportional to the moving mass.
Any space in which Newton's law of motion applies is by definition an inertial space. The possibility of inertial navigation depends
on the fact that matter used for equipment parts responds to applied forces by motions with respect to an inertial space that is
essentially identical with the space determined by the fixed stars.

In a moving, rigid body, such as a gyroscopic rotor, interactions
among individual particles combine to give the rotor an angular
momentum that is equal to the product of the moment of inertia
about the spin axis and the angular velocity of spin. The consequence of Newton's law of motion as far as it pertains to a gyroscopic rotor is that a torque applied to the rotor about any axis at
right angles to the spin axis causes the spin axis to rotate toward
alignment with the torque axis. The angular velocity associated
with this rotation, which is called precession, is proportional to the
magnitude of the applied torque and is inversely proportional to
the magnitude of the rotor angular momentum.

When the torque applied to a gyroscopic rotor is zero, the angular velocity of precession is zero, and the spin axis perfectly

holds its existing orientation with respect to inertial space. For the purposes of navigation, the important fact is that the space in which a torque-free gyroscopic rotor holds its spin axis in a fixed direction is identical with the celestial space associated with the fixed stars. This means that a geometrical reference member controlled by two or three gyroscopic rotors designed for substantially torque-free operation will hold its orientation almost perfectly with respect to celestial space. Thus, a mechanical member inside a navigation system can supply all the necessary geometrical-reference information, without the need for external radiation contacts of any kind.

In addition to this feature, which supplies the essential need of self-contained navigation equipment, gyroscopic inertial members are more convenient for reference purposes than celestial space, which must be used through the medium of a few nonsystematically located fixed stars. This convenience stems from the fact that torque-free gyroscopic rotors do not tend to move toward any preferred direction, but hold any orientation they may have when applied torques are reduced to zero. Therefore, the orientation chosen for any given situation may be the one that allows the simplest or most convenient configuration of the required mechanism. For example, causing one of the support axes of the gyroscopic package to operate in parallelism with the earth's axis of rotation makes it possible for a simple sidereal clock drive (such as represented in Illus. 24) to compensate for the rotation of the earth. The orientation of the reference member remains fixed with respect to inertial space about this polar axis, so that the first support gimbal outside of the sidereal time drive remains parallel to some meridian on the earth. By mechanical adjustments, this artificial meridian may be aligned with any selected earth meridian. The combination of this artificial meridian inside the navigation equipment and the artificially established direction of the earth's polar axis provides an adjustable earth reference space that is derived from an adjustable inertial reference space and a time drive. Positions on the earth are fixed by determining the direction of the local gravitational vector with respect to this mechanically established earth reference space (Illustration 25).

The inertial-system configuration just described was chosen because of its simplicity for the purposes of explanation. Various other configurations are possible. For example, the gyro units of the inertial reference member may be designed to receive continuous torque inputs that cause the member to change its orientation with respect to inertial space so that it indicates the direction of the local vertical as the system moves over the earth's surface. In a system of this kind, changes in position with respect to the earth are indicated by integrations of torque-controlling signals to calibrated gyro units. Each signal corresponds to an angular velocity component of the reference member with respect to inertial space, and one integration gives the associated angular displacement. Correction of this displacement for rotation of the earth by a time signal and multiplication by the radius of the earth gives a component of distance traveled over the earth's surface. The same procedure applied to the other components of inertial-reference-member rotation gives the corresponding components of travel. Combining all the travel components gives the indicated resultant movement of an inertial navigation system over the earth. Relating this indicated movement to the point of departure gives the indicated position of the vehicle carrying the navigation equipment at any instant.

Another configuration of inertial navigation equipment places the inertial reference member in an arbitrary orientation and employs computers to produce information on indicated position. This arrangement is often used for the guidance of ballistic missiles.

PRACTICAL ASPECTS OF INERTIAL REFERENCES

In practice, inertial references involve many factors that cannot be mentioned in this paper because of space limitations. Some of these factors are associated with design details, while others are common to all systems. One of these common factors is the necessity for establishing the desired inertial-reference-member orientation prior to any period of use for the system containing the member. This orientation must be based on inputs generated by means

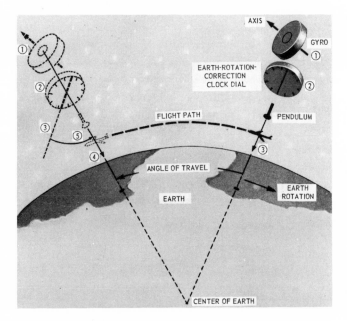

① GYRO HOLDS AXIS DIRECTION CONSTANT WITH RESPECT TO FIXED STARS, THAT IS, WITH RESPECT TO AN INERTIAL REFERENCE SPACE.

② DIAL ROTATION WITH SIDEREAL TIME CORRECTS FOR EARTH ROTATION TO GIVE AN EARTH REFERENCE SPACE.

③ DIRECTION OF GRAVITY AT START OF FLIGHT, WITH RESPECT TO THE EARTH REFERENCE SPACE.

④ DIRECTION OF GRAVITY AT FLIGHT POSITION REPRESENTED BY DOTTED LINES, WITH RESPECT TO THE EARTH REFERENCE SPACE.

⑤ INDICATED ANGLE OF TRAVEL IS PROVIDED BY ANGULAR DISPLACEMENT, IN EARTH REFERENCE SPACE, OF DIRECTION OF GRAVITY WITH RESPECT TO ITS POSITION AT THE START OF THE FLIGHT.

ILLUS. 25—Inertial system simplified to illustrate elements of navigation for vehicles moving at substantially constant altitude.

outside the gyro units of the reference member and supplied to these units as angular-velocity command signals that become zero when the proper orientation is reached. For example, an optical system using a light-sensitive cell tracker pointed toward Polaris and a servomechanism arrangement can be used to drive an axis of the inertial reference member toward alignment with the earth's axis of rotation. Similarly, pendulum signals can be used for properly setting the reference member in a selected angular position about the polar axis.

Any actual gyro unit is imperfect in the sense that its rotor can never be completely torque-free, with the result that the spin axis does not hold its direction perfectly with respect to inertial space. However, by proper design and construction, it is possible to make the resultant of undesired torque components very small and to keep the uncertainty parts of these components at still lower levels. Drift rates having an order of magnitude of one one-thousandth of earth's rate (earth's rate is 15° per hour) can now be expected from commercially available gyro units. For high performance, the rotors of these units cannot be used directly to generate motion-resisting torques sufficient to control heavy supporting gimbals. However, techniques are available that make it feasible for the member carrying the spin-axis bearings of the rotor to operate under conditions of substantially complete freedom from interfering torque components. In units that take advantage of this possibility, deflections of the case of the unit with respect to the rotor do not provide heavy torque but are used only for the generation of control signals, a service that imposes virtually zero torque loads. By using these signals as command inputs to amplifiers controlling the servomotors that drive the supporting gimbals, the effects of friction and other disturbing torques may be overcome so completely that the structure carrying the gyro units remains accurately in an orientation determined by the gyro spin axes.

SPECIFIC-FORCE-RECEIVER SYSTEMS FOR INDICATIONS OF THE VERTICAL AND THE DISTANCE TRAVELED

Inertial navigation systems designed to operate on or near the earth's surface must have some provision for indicating the direction of the local vertical. This direction gives indicated position through its orientation with respect to the artificially established earth coordinate reference of the system. On a platform fixed to the earth, the problem of indicating the vertical is easily solved by means of a simple pendulum. On a moving platform subjected to horizontal accelerations, a simple pendulum is no longer satisfactory, because of interfering effects introduced by these accelerations. This interference is unavoidable because, by Einstein's principle of equivalence, the mass of any body in its response to a gravitational field is identical with the mass associated with inertia-reaction effects. Thus a pendulum bob hanging along the vertical under gravity is deflected when its point of support is given any horizontal acceleration. Under the accelerations usually experienced by moving vehicles, a simple pendulum may well have erratic deflections of several degrees. Disturbances of this magnitude are completely unacceptable for the purposes of navigation where the required maximum accuracy magnitude is of the order of 1 mile. When it is remembered that on the earth's surface 1 minute of arc between local-vertical directions corresponds to a distance of 1 nautical mile, the uselessness of simple pendulum arrangements for navigation is apparent.

Errors in local-vertical indications under conditions of erratic acceleration of a moving vehicle may be reduced to satisfactory limits by designing the indicating system so that it has a proper dynamic behavior. The required characteristic is that of responding to a horizontal linear acceleration component by an angular acceleration about a horizontal axis at right angles to the linear acceleration. When the angular acceleration has a magnitude equal to the linear horizontal acceleration divided by the radius from the center of the earth to the moving platform, vertical indications change in step with variations in position. A system with performance of this kind is said to have Schuler tuning; this is in recognition of Prof. Schuler, who first published the theory of such arrangements. When Schuler tuning is used, indications of the vertical remain accurate in the presence of arbitrary horizontal accelerations. On the surface of the earth, Schuler tuning corresponds to a period of about 84 minutes. Any practical system possessing the features suggested in Illus. 25 would have to use a pendulum with this characteristic.

Because of the small distance between the pivot and the center of gravity that would be required in a simple physical pendulum with Schuler tuning, a pendulum of this kind is not physically feasible. The practical solution for this problem is to use an equivalent pendulum system based on a servodriven gimbal-supported platform carrying sensing elements that respond to gravity and acceleration. Amplifiers in the feedback loops are designed so that electronic circuits act to introduce the required dynamic performance. By variation of circuit parameters, it is possible to adjust both the period and the damping so that optimum results are achieved under operating conditions.

The sensing components required for Schuler-tuned equivalent pendulum systems are arrangements in which gravitational and inertia-reaction forces acting on a seismic mass (a body designed to act as the receiving element of a sensor) cause deflection against some restraining means in a way that generates an output signal representing the resultant input force. This resultant is made up of the force acting to move the seismic element in the direction of the gravity field and the inertia-reaction effects that tend to cause the seismic element to lag behind the linear acceleration of the sensing unit. It is convenient to consider gravity and inertia-reaction effects as combining to form the specific force, which is the resultant force per unit mass acting on a body due to gravity and acceleration. A simple pendulum is a specific-force receiver in which the suspended mass tends to align itself with the direction of the specific-force input vector. Many other kinds of specific-force receivers are in use in which the output signal represents the specific-force component acting along an input axis that has a fixed direction with respect to the case of the sensing component. Devices of this kind appear as essential elements in all inertial navigation systems.

INERTIAL NAVIGATION SYSTEMS FOR VEHICLES
MOVING AT SUBSTANTIALLY CONSTANT ALTITUDE

Navigation systems used in vehicles supported by ground, air, or water normally move in surfaces that are substantially spherical about the center of the earth, so that the specific-force input for specific-force receivers is practically identical with gravity. This means that it is feasible to indicate the direction of gravity by means of an equivalent pendulum system with Schuler tuning. Inertial equipments for use in ground vehicles, aircraft, surface ships, and submarines all take advantage of this fact by basing their indications of vehicle location on the orientation of an indicated vertical member with respect to an earth reference member positioned by a gyroscopic inertial reference system and sidereal time. In some cases, the inertial reference member holds its physical orientation among the stars, while in other cases the member moves, and its rate of change of orientation with respect to inertial space acts as the input for a computer whose output is navigational information.

Many designs are possible for inertial systems based on indications of the local vertical by an equivalent pendulum with Schuler tuning. Several different equipments have been constructed by various commercial organizations and tested far enough to prove the feasibility of inertial navigation, but it is to be expected that several years of effort will have to pass before final decisions as to the best type of equipment can be made.

INERTIAL GUIDANCE SYSTEMS FOR BALLISTIC MISSILES AND SATELLITES

Ballistic missiles are subjected to high accelerations for short periods of high thrust during the phase of boosting through the atmosphere and then coast in free fall until they reenter the air before striking target areas. In this situation, it is not feasible to base guidance on indications of the local vertical. During the boost phase, the inputs for specific-force receivers are greatly different from gravity, both in direction and in magnitude. During the coasting phase, free fall reduces the net specific force to zero, so there are effectively no inputs for specific-force receivers. Reentry and the terminal phase are again subject to accelerations due to air resistance that cause the specific force available as the input for guidance equipment to be greatly different from gravity. These facts combine to prevent systems that operate by indicating the local direction of gravity from being useful in equipment for guiding ballistic missiles. Some other mode of operation must therefore be used to meet the operating requirements of such equipment.

Inertial guidance for ballistic missiles is achieved by eliminating terrestrial-space reference equipment and solving the guidance problem by means of specific-force receivers fixed in an artificially

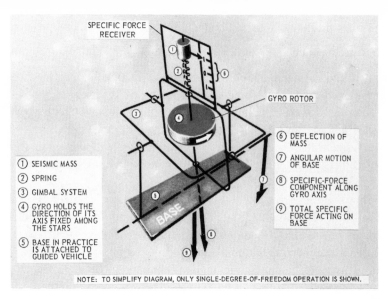

SPECIFIC FORCE
RECEIVER

GYRO ROTOR

① SEISMIC MASS
② SPRING
③ GIMBAL SYSTEM
④ GYRO HOLDS THE
  DIRECTION OF ITS
  AXIS FIXED AMONG
  THE STARS
⑤ BASE IN PRACTICE
  IS ATTACHED TO
  GUIDED VEHICLE

⑥ DEFLECTION OF
  MASS
⑦ ANGULAR MOTION
  OF BASE
⑧ SPECIFIC-FORCE
  COMPONENT ALONG
  GYRO AXIS
⑨ TOTAL SPECIFIC
  FORCE ACTING ON
  BASE

NOTE: TO SIMPLIFY DIAGRAM, ONLY SINGLE-DEGREE-OF-FREEDOM OPERATION IS SHOWN.

ILLUS. 26—Two-degree-of-freedom gyro and single-degree-of-freedom specific force receiver illustrating elements of inertial guidance for vehicles in arbitrary motion with respect to the earth.

oriented space that is associated with a gyroscopic reference member (Illus. 26). To mechanize this arrangement, a rigid body member supported by a servodriven gimbal system carries the necessary gyro units and, in addition, serves as the mounting for a set of three single-degree-of-freedom specific-force receivers with their input axes set at right angles to each other (Illus. 27). With this configuration, the total specific force acting on the gyro-oriented reference member is sensed in three components in a special set of coordinates having known geometrical relationships to terrestrial space and to celestial space. Signals representing these components are generated by the specific-force sensors and transmitted to a computer. This computer, acting on these inputs and on information stored in its memory banks, works out the instantaneous location of the missile under guidance, compares this location with the desired location on the proper path, and generates command signals for correcting the direction of the missile. These command signals are received by the missile control system, which changes the orientation of the thrust vector with respect to the missile so that the necessary changes in the missile path are made.

Ballistic-missile guidance is carried out in artificially established inertial-space coordinates, with the target considered as a moving

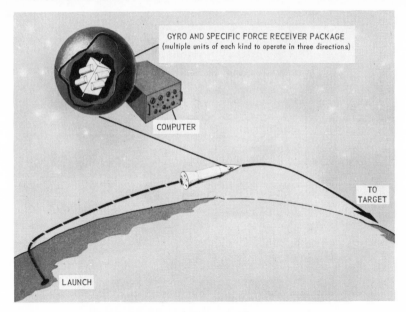

ILLUS. 27—Inertial guidance for a ballistic missile.

point because of the earth's rotation. For the purposes of this guidance method, gravity is regarded as merely one component of the resultant specific force, without any particular attention to its direction as it is related to location on the earth. Time is also an input to the system, but it is one of several factors for the computer, rather than the means for determining the orientation of the earth.

Satellites may be put into orbit by inertial guidance, but inertial equipment is not essential but may be helpful during long periods of coasting flight. Very probably, inertial devices will be useful in sensing angular-velocity inputs for control purposes. It is also likely that gyroscopic stabilization will be utilized to assist radiation-contact devices carried by satellites in tracking the earth and other celestial bodies.

INTERPLANETARY GUIDANCE

Interplanetary vehicles must operate for long periods of time with only tenuous radiation contacts with either their points of departure or their destinations. During the midcourse phases of long interplanetary trips, it may be desirable for the guided vehicle and

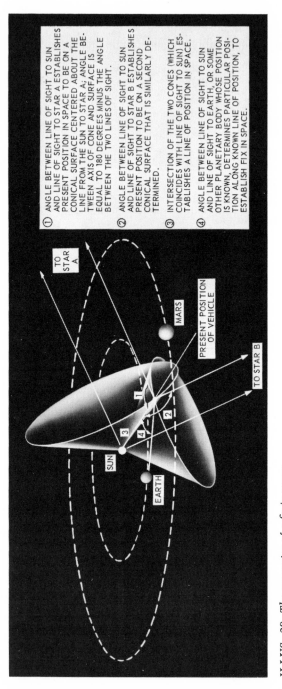

① ANGLE BETWEEN LINE OF SIGHT TO SUN AND LINE OF SIGHT TO STAR A ESTABLISHES PRESENT POSITION IN SPACE TO BE ON A CONICAL SURFACE CENTERED ABOUT THE LINE FROM THE SUN TO STAR A; ANGLE BETWEEN AXIS OF CONE AND SURFACE IS EQUAL TO 180 DEGREES MINUS THE ANGLE BETWEEN THE TWO LINES OF SIGHT.

② ANGLE BETWEEN LINE OF SIGHT TO SUN AND LINE OF SIGHT TO STAR B ESTABLISHES PRESENT POSITION TO BE ON A SECOND CONICAL SURFACE THAT IS SIMILARLY DETERMINED.

③ INTERSECTION OF THE TWO CONES (WHICH COINCIDES WITH LINE OF SIGHT TO SUN) ESTABLISHES A LINE OF POSITION IN SPACE.

④ ANGLE BETWEEN LINE OF SIGHT TO SUN AND LINE OF SIGHT TO EARTH, OR SOME OTHER PLANETARY BODY WHOSE POSITION IS KNOWN, DETERMINES PARTICULAR POSITION ALONG KNOWN LINE OF POSITION, TO ESTABLISH FIX IN SPACE.

TO STAR A

MARS

PRESENT POSITION OF VEHICLE

TO STAR B

SUN

EARTH

ILLUS. 28—The geometry of a fix in space.

its equipment to be able to operate without outside assistance from manned installations. Conditions will be close to ideal for radiation contacts with celestial bodies, and techniques are well developed for acquiring and tracking sources of optical wavelengths. Data from the operation of optical trackers, combined with accurate time from devices based on the natural-frequency vibrations of atoms or elastic bodies and with almanac data stored in digital computer memories, provide all the information needed for the accurate navigation of space vehicles. In effect, celestial-space coordinates are used for this purpose, with locations of the guided vehicle determined from the angular relationships among lines of sight to the sun, the stars, the observable planets, and satellites such as the moon. These lines of sight can be automatically sought out by optical trackers and may be maintained either by continuous tracking or by the use of gyroscopically controlled reference members with their orientations set from radiation-contact information.

For example, the process of navigation might start by acquiring and maintaining the line of sight from the vehicle to the sun by means of a heliotracker (Illus. 28). The second step would be searching for a selected star over a conical surface about the heliocentric line by means of a star tracker whose angle setting is based on an accurate indication of time and data stored in the memory of a computer. The angle measured between the lines of sight to the sun and this star establishes in celestial coordinates one of the cones of position shown in Illus. 28. This process is repeated with a second star. Then the angle between the sun line of sight and a planet line of sight is used to determine the location of the vehicle along the line of intersection of the two cones.

CONCLUSION

Navigation has been discussed in general terms, with emphasis on the geometrical aspects of the problems involved. Radiation contacts with terrestrial and celestial points provide means for navigation under ordinary circumstances. In the special situations that arise when radiation contacts are not feasible, inertial methods are available. Practical applications of these methods are too new for details of equipments to be settled, but it is certain that navigation of the future will employ many different arrangements, ranging from all-radiation-contact systems to all-inertial systems with various compromise arrangements in between. We can look forward with confidence to rapid and interesting developments in the old art of navigation.

REFERENCES

DRAPER, C. S. 1958. Self-contained guidance systems. Inst. Radio Eng., Trans. Military Electronics, MIL, vol. 2, No. 1.

DRAPER, C.S., and WOODBURY, R. B. 1946. Geometrical stabilization based on servodriven gimbals and integrating gyro units. Paper presented at the AGARD Symposium, Venice, Italy; published by the Instrumentation Lab., Massachusetts Inst. Techn., Cambridge, Mass.

DRAPER, C. S.; WRIGLEY, W.; and GROHE, L. R. 1955. The floating integrating gyro and its application to geometrical stabilization problems on moving bases. Inst. Aeron. Sci., S.M.F. Fund Paper No. FF-13, New York.

DRAPER, C. S.; WRIGLEY, W.; and WOODBURY, R. B. 1958. Principles of inertial guidance. Paper presented at the 1st Inst. Congr. Aeronautical Sci., Madrid, Spain; published by the Pergamon Press, London, England.

RAWLINGS, A. L. 1944. The theory of the gyroscopic compass and its deviations. New York.

SCHULER, M. 1923. Die Störung von Pendul- und Kreiselapparaten durch die Beschleunigung der Fahrzeuges. Phys. Zeitschr., vol. 24.

WRIGLEY, W. 1941. An investigation of methods available for indicating the direction of the vertical from moving bases. Sc.D. thesis, Massachusetts Inst. Techn., Cambridge, Mass.

1950. Schuler tuning characteristics in navigational instruments. Navigation, Journ. Inst. Navigation, vol. 2, No. 8.

WRIGLEY, W.; HOUSTON, F. E.; and WHITMAN, H. R. 1958. Indication of the vertical from moving bases. Inst. Radio Eng., Trans. Aeron. and Navig. Electronics, A.N.E., vol. 5, No. 4.

WRIGLEY, W.; WOODBURY, R. B.; and HOVORKA, J. 1957. Inertial guidance. Inst. Aeron. Sci., S.M.F. Fund Paper No. FF-16, New York.

SU-SHU HUANG

Some Astronomical Aspects of Life in the Universe

[FROM THE SMITHSONIAN REPORT FOR 1961[1]]

"STARS ARE FIREPLACES *in the cold and dark of space," writes the author. One of the most fascinating aspects of space exploration is the possibility of contact with intelligent beings on other planets of our solar system. Although we will never be sure one way or the other until our astronauts land on Venus or Mars and return with the verdict, nevertheless many phases of modern astronomical research have a bearing on the problem. The author of this very revealing article, Dr. Su-Shu Huang, until recently associated with the Institute for Advanced Study at Princeton, is now professor of astronomy at Northwestern University, Evanston, Ill. During the present year (1965), he is on leave from the university and serves jointly at Goddard Space Flight Center, Greenbelt, Md., and at Catholic University of America. He assesses the likelihood of the development of life, not only on our neighboring planets, but on the possible planets of stars other than our sun. Many lines of reasoning are brought to bear on the problem, even to the calculation of the number of stars within 16 light-years of us, that would be likely to possess a system of satellite planets. Of our own*

[1] Revised as of February 1965.

*planets, of course, Mars and Venus come the nearest to possessing
conditions even remotely resembling those of earth. Even if no intelligent life exists there now, Dr. Huang does not exclude the possibility that it may have flourished there millions of years ago
under more favorable environmental conditions. He concludes
with his ideas as to the best method of attempting to communicate
with possible intelligent beings elsewhere in the universe.*

T HREE DIFFERENT WAYS by which matter interacts are
gravitational, nuclear, and chemical. As our knowledge now stands,
it appears that the behavior of all matter in the universe — from
shining stars to exuberant life on the earth — may eventually be
explained in terms of these interactions. Indeed, the emergence of
life in general, and on earth in particular, is a net result of all three.

All forms of life must rely for maintenance on a stellar source
of energy. Therefore, the nature and evolution of a star control the
emergence and development of life. There is no doubt now that
stars condense from gas and dust in the interstellar clouds, a newly
formed star's temperature being very low because the interstellar
gas is quite cool. As the star contracts, its temperature increases. In
the early stage, the contraction takes place in the form of cata-
clysmic collapse because there is nothing to prevent the stellar
material from the free fall. The collapse slows down when the
opacity becomes appreciable. According to a recent theory by C.
Hayashi, the star is fully convective when it reaches the state of
quasi-equilibrium of slow contraction. Therefore, contrary to the
previously held view, the evolutionary track on the Hertzsprung-
Russell diagram is downward in a nearly vertical direction in the
early phase. It turns to a slightly slanted direction when the convection gradually retreats. The evolutionary tracks of different
masses are schematically shown in Illustration 32.

Gravitational contraction stops when the internal temperature
becomes high enough for thermonuclear reactions to begin to convert hydrogen into helium. These reactions supply energy equal to
that radiated by the star, which therefore maintains an equilibrium

condition with constant luminosity for a long time. Such a state of affairs corresponds to a star on the main sequence.

A star of a certain mass will arrive at the main sequence with a definite spectral type and luminosity, and its character changes only slightly during the long period in which the hydrogen in its core is being consumed. Once the central hydrogen is exhausted, the star evolves quite rapidly toward the right, to become a giant or supergiant — very different in size and surface brightness from before.

Both the time of contraction to the main sequence and the time that the star stays on the main sequence depend upon the mass. They are roughly given in Table 1 for different stellar masses together with the characteristics that the corresponding stars will assume at the main-sequence stage.

It is obvious from the table that time scales on the main sequence are much longer than those of contraction. This explains why about 90 percent of observed stars are to be found on the main sequence. The stay of a more massive star on the main sequence is shorter than that of a less massive star, as it dissipates its energy much faster. Thus, an O star remains in this state for only a few million years, compared to an M star's 100 billion.

From this brief look at stellar life histories, it is clear that gravitation holds a star together while nuclear interactions release the energy it radiates. The third kind of reaction, chemical, does not play a significant role in shaping a star, yet chemical action is responsible for the emergence and evolution of living organisms. And although we can predict that in about 10 billion years or less our sun will become a white dwarf, there is no way of telling how man will evolve in even 10 million years.

What is the reason for this? Gravitational interaction is very simple and is described by Newton's law of gravitation. The number of possible nuclear interactions is very large indeed, since there are hundreds of different atomic nuclei; nevertheless, we could still list all conceivable reactions. Hence we can compute them and even predict the evolution of stars by the law of gravitation and our knowledge of nuclear physics.

But how big is the total number of chemical reactions — both inorganic and organic — that one may conceive? Unable to estimate

ILLUS. 29—*The delicate, dusky markings of the cloud-covered planet Venus are well shown in these photographs taken by H. Camichel with a 15-inch telescope at Pic du Midi Observatory in France. The narrow crescent (above) was recorded on October 3, 1943; the other view on the 6th of the following month. Venus's high surface temperature makes it ill suited as an abode of life.*

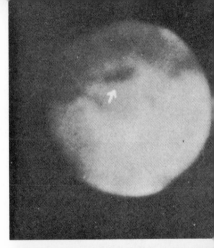

1911

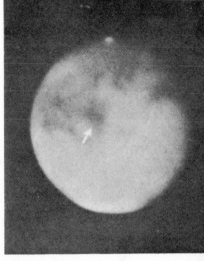

1926

ILLUS. 30—*Changes in the size and form of Solis Lacus and in the strength of the canals and oases thereabout. (Photograph by E. C. Slipher, Lowell Observatory.)*

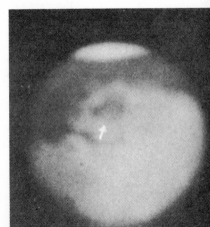

1939

ILLUS. 31—*This Sproul Observatory model made by Sarah Lee Lippincott shows the arrangement in space of all the stars known to lie within 16 light-years of the sun, which is at the center. The plexiglas sphere is 36 inches in diameter, and the distance scale is one inch per light-year. Wooden beads are used to represent the stars, with Sirius (right below center) the largest. To the right above center is Procyon, shown, like Sirius, with its white-dwarf companion. The large star at the left is Altair. Among these stellar neighbors there are 53 visible stars, including Tau Ceti and Epsilon Eridani which satisfy the author's criteria for possibly having planets where intelligent life may exist. These two stars were selected for special scrutiny in the Project Ozma attempt to detect extraterrestrial radio transmissions. (Photograph from Sproul Observatory of Swarthmore College.)*

such a number, I am probably safe in saying that it is larger than any astronomical figure we can find in our textbooks. It is this wealth of chemical activity that makes a prediction of the emergence and evolution of living organisms difficult, if not permanently elusive.

If we cannot compute the time scale of biological evolution, we must find it out empirically. Here on earth it took about 3 billion years for humans to evolve from atoms. I have suggested earlier that since biological evolution occurs through the random processes of mutation and selection, its average time scale is probably of the same order of magnitude — a few billion years. On this basis, for successful biological evolution on a planet, the luminosity of its parent star must be constant for at least this long. Thus we see from the table that only those main-sequence stars at and below spectral type *F* can support life. Others evolve too fast and do not maintain constant luminosities long enough.

A second limitation on the development of life on a planet is its star's ability to warm up a large space around it. Stars are fireplaces in the cold and dark of space, each having a region of propitious temperature in which life may develop and survive. It is evident, for example, that the habitable zones of cool stars of spectral type *M* are much smaller than that of the sun. Therefore, the

TABLE 1

Mass (sun=1)	Time scale		Characteristics on main sequence		
	Gravitational contraction (in 10^6 years)	Main-sequence stage (in 10^9 years)	Spectral type	Radius (sun=1)	Luminosity (sun=1)
17.0.........	.02	0.008	B0.........	9.0	29,000
6.3.........	.14	.08	B5.........	4.2	980
3.2.........	.62	.4	A0.........	2.8	100
1.9.........	1.9	2	A5.........	1.51	12.0
1.5.........	3.2	4	F0.........	1.25	4.8
1.3.........	4.3	6	F5.........	1.24	2.7
1.02.........	7.4	11	G0.........	1.02	1.2
1.00.........	7.9	13	G2 (sun)....	1.00	1.0
0.91.........	9.8	17	G5.........	.92	.72
0.74.........	15	28	K0.........	.74	.35
0.54.........	29	70	K5.........	.54	.10

chance of finding a planet revolving permanently inside the habitable zone of an M star is less than for somewhat hotter stars. However, M-type dwarfs are far more numerous than any other single spectral type, and the total number of them supporting life may be appreciable.

Combining the previous two arguments, we conclude that intelligent life has the highest chance of being found in the vicinities of stars of medium temperature, like the sun. A further limitation applies to binary and multiple systems, which constitute about one-third of all stars. A planet associated with a binary may or may not have a stable orbit, and in the latter case could wander out of the habitable zone and destroy life that might have developed earlier.

As for a life-supporting planet itself, one of its most important qualifications is maintenance of an atmosphere suitable for the chemical processes of living beings. An atmosphere makes possible the existence of water or other substances in liquid form on the planet's surface; it is simply inconceivable that living organisms can be maintained without the aid of some substances in liquid form.

The earth holds its air because its gravitational attraction prevents gas molecules, which are in a state of thermal motion, from escaping. The moon and Mercury are devoid of atmospheres partly because of their smaller surface gravities; hence, a larger planet is required.

But it is not advantageous to the emergence of life, especially of a high form, if the planet is too big. Since the most abundant element in the universe is hydrogen, a newly formed planet must have a high percentage of it, particularly in its outer envelope, because of hydrogen's light weight. In other words, we expect a new planet's atmosphere to be chemically in a reducing state. As A. I. Oparin has pointed out, life may first appear under reducing conditions, but it seems unlikely that life of a high form would emerge under such a dominantly hydrogen atmosphere.

My tentative conclusion is based upon the energy metabolism of living beings. In an oxidizing atmosphere, like the earth's, the combustion of glucose,

$$C_6H_{12}O_6 + 6O_2 \rightarrow 6CO_2 + 6H_2O,$$

which supplies most of the body's needs for energy, yields about 700 kilogram-calories of free energy per mole. On the other hand, in a reducing atmosphere the free energy has to be derived from fermentation of glucose to ethyl alcohol and carbon dioxide, according to

$$C_6H_{12}O_6 \rightarrow 2C_2H_5OH + 2CO_2,$$

which amounts to only about 60 kilogram-calories per mole.

Consequently, under reducing conditions a living being has to consume more than 10 times as much food as in an oxidizing environment in order to derive the same amount of free energy. Therefore, it is doubtful that a mind such as man's would appear through evolution in a reducing atmosphere, because living beings would be too preoccupied with seeking food.

If hydrogen must first escape from the air before a high form of life emerges, the planet must not be too large. Plausible values for the radius would be between 1,000 and 20,000 kilometers, which includes the moon and Mercury. The former could hold air if its density were high, and the latter would have a suitable atmosphere if its distance from the sun were greater.

The problem of life on other worlds is ultimately related to the formation of the complex molecules that are essential to life processes. Life on the earth, as we all know, depends upon carbon-containing molecules and on water. The fundamental question of bioastronomy is whether living beings elsewhere must also depend on the carbon bond, with water as a solvent. Although a definite answer cannot be provided, I have several arguments in favor of an affirmative one.

From what other element can complex molecules be built? A glance at the periodic table shows silicon, located directly below carbon, to be a likely candidate. Indeed, silicon is largely responsible for the great variety of molecules found in the earth's crust. However, silicon appears to have a higher affinity for fluorine and other halogens than for hydrogen. While its cosmic abundance is as much as one-fifth that of carbon, the percentage of halogens in the cosmos is negligible compared with hydrogen. As a result, complex compounds of silicon have much less chance to form than do those involving carbon.

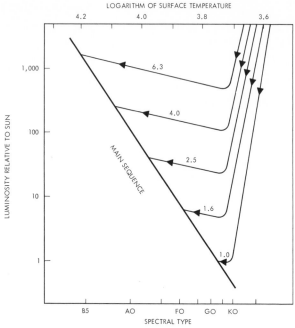

ILLUS. 32—A contracting newborn star evolves first downward along a nearly vertical line and then leftward to the main sequence, where a long stay should favor development of life on any planets the star may have. The number that labels each track denotes the mass of the star in units of the solar mass.

There are several empirical results favoring carbon as an essential life constituent. M. Calvin and his associates made the first successful experiment in prebiological chemistry when they obtained formaldehyde and formic acid in a cyclotron from a mixture of carbon dioxide and water. In 1953, S. L. Miller found that the amino acids — the building blocks of proteins — are formed, together with other organic compounds, when an electric discharge is passed through a mixture of methane, ammonia, and water vapor, in concentrations approximately equal to those given by H. C. Urey for the primitive atmosphere of the earth.

Calvin also discovered organic compounds in meteorites. Very recently B. Nagy, D. J. Hennessy, and W. G. Meinschein detected paraffinic hydrocarbons, closely akin to those found on earth in living matter, in a fragment of a stony meteorite that fell in France

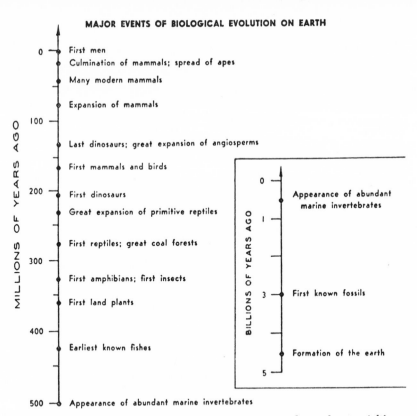

ILLUS. 33—*The author's chart of the major events in the evolution of life on our planet. The compressed scale (inset) shows some very early events in the earth's history.*

nearly a century ago. They believe this to be the first empirical evidence for the existence of life beyond our own planet. Such an interpretation has not been unanimously accepted by authorities on this subject. However, if the meteorite's hydrocarbons are not due to contamination, they indicate definitely that the formation of organic compounds is not limited to the surface of the earth, although the mechanism of formation may be debated for a long time to come.

All these results suggest that complex compounds of carbon can be formed easily from inorganic substances when conditions are suitable. We may not be seriously wrong if we assume that life everywhere in the universe depends on carbon compounds.

The question of life elsewhere in the solar system is no longer as speculative as it was even a decade ago, and in 10 years we may

have definite proof concerning the present existence of living beings on other planets. But if no life is found, it does not prove that
none ever appeared — such proof requires actual excavation of a
planet's surface, which may take a few decades to achieve.

Mars is most frequently mentioned as a possible former or present abode of life. Despite its small gravitational attraction (with only
10 percent of the earth's mass), its surface gravity is 37 percent of
ours and it retains an atmosphere. There is no hydrogen or helium;
none is expected. Spectroscopic observations show carbon dioxide
is present, but the search for oxygen has been negative. Mars' atmosphere contains less than one one-thousandth as much oxygen as
the earth's, yet there is doubtless much nitrogen.

Although spectroscopic observations have failed to detect water
vapor on Mars, its presence may be indicated by the seasonal variations of the polar caps. However, the physical nature of the polar
caps is still debatable. Some observers consider them to be made
of ice, but others, like C. C. Kiess and his collaborators (*Sky and
Telescope*, June 1960, p. 469), explain the caps as solid nitrogen
tetroxide.

The temperature of Mars' equatorial region can reach a maximum of about 30° C., but in general is lower than on earth. Since
not much water exists in the Martian atmosphere to keep heat
from radiating away into space at night, the temperature probably
reaches as low as $-100°$ C. Whether life can be maintained under
these conditions has interested astronomers for a long time.

Dark green areas in the equatorial regions suggest that plant life
of some form is present on Mars. The color and shade of these
markings change with the seasons in a way that indicates the
growth and decay of vegetation (darker in spring and lighter in
autumn). Because of the very severe climate, no higher terrestrial
plants could survive. However, special kinds, such as lichens, might
live. A lichen is a symbiotic plant composed of two different organisms: fungus and alga. These can flourish together under conditions that would be fatal if either had to meet them alone.

The fungus, which does not perform photosynthesis, derives food
from the alga, which does. But the fungus helps maintain the
water supply necessary for growth of the alga. Consequently, this
symbiotic plant occurs all over the earth, enduring many kinds of

extreme climate, from burning deserts to freezing mountaintops. However, it is not necessarily lichens themselves that we observe in the dark-green areas of Mars.

Rather, we wish to emphasize here that the severe climate on Mars does not exclude the possibility of the maintenance of life there. Indeed, observations by W. M. Sinton strongly imply that an infrared absorption band characteristic of many organic compounds is present in the Martian spectrum, which strengthens the belief in some form of vegetation on that planet.

Because Mars lacks oxygen, most astronomers agree that we should not expect to find a high form of life there, and I personally believe this conclusion is probably right. But there is the unlikely possibility that intelligent beings might have existed, or still survive, on Mars. This view does not need the support of the canals, whose interpretation has aroused much controversy. But since Mars' gravity is smaller than the earth's, it was easier for hydrogen to dissipate, and biological evolution could have started earlier on the red planet than here. It is not inconceivable that intelligent beings emerged on Mars millions of years ago. One might object that the rate of evolution would be slower because chemical reactions would occur less rapidly at the low Martian temperature. On the other hand, the development of the human brain may have been completed during the glacial ages here on earth.

The other neighbor of the earth is Venus. Carbon dioxide is abundant in its atmosphere, and water vapor has recently been established by John Strong, but oxygen has never been detected. There are extensive clouds that prevent us from seeing the planet's actual surface, and we can only measure the composition of the upper atmosphere. The clouds themselves probably consist of water droplets or ice particles.

Microwave observations of Venus by C. H. Mayer and his co-workers yield a temperature of more than 300° C. As Carl Sagan has pointed out, the high temperature of the planet is consistent with an abundance of carbon dioxide and water vapor below the clouds. Both these substances produce a very efficient greenhouse effect, letting visible sunlight pass through but preventing infrared radiation from going out. Hence Venus' surface temperature probably reaches such a high value that life is impossible there.

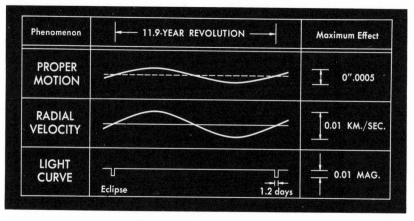

Phenomenon	⊢— 11.9-YEAR REVOLUTION —⊣	Maximum Effect
PROPER MOTION		0".0005
RADIAL VELOCITY		0.01 KM./SEC.
LIGHT CURVE	Eclipse 1.2 days	0.01 MAG.

ILLUS. 34—Three kinds of observational tests are presented for the detection of a planet similar to Jupiter revolving around a solar-type star 32 light-years distant from us. Even at best, the maximum effects (right) are very minute.

The existence of life on other bodies in our solar system cannot be categorically denied. However, because of their chemically reducing atmospheres and low temperatures (or very high, for Mercury's sunlit side), life must be very primitive, if present at all.

Elsewhere in the universe, the fundamental problem is the existence of planets. Are stars always accompanied by some smaller bodies? We don't have a definite answer, because of observational difficulties. No earthbound telescope could detect a planet of Jupiter's size even if it were associated with the nearest star, for the planet would be lost in the glare of the star's light. However, as Nancy G. Roman has suggested, a telescope installed in an artificial satellite would suffer much less from scattering of starlight in the earth's atmosphere and might be used for such a search.

What theoretical reasoning can be applied to this problem? Some 30 years ago astronomers felt that our solar system was formed when the sun encountered another star. Since the average distance between two neighboring stars is very large, a close encounter of this kind is a very rare event, producing only one planetary system among many millions of stars. But it has since been shown that the collision theory of planet formation is untenable.

Astronomers are now convinced that planets form from dust and gas that is either the remnant in the process of star formation or that has been acquired from the interstellar medium. If the cloud is massive enough, another star could be formed instead of planets.

Thus, binary and planetary systems apparently have the same origin, and they have other properties in common.

According to G. P. Kuiper, the average separation of all components in binary systems that have been studied is about 20 astronomical units, roughly the mean distance of the major planets from the sun. Also, there must be a wide range in the ratio of masses of binary star components. However, observational selection makes it difficult to detect a binary whose two components have greatly different masses. Actually, we are able to detect objects of small masses only in binaries located in the immediate neighborhood of the sun. Thus, unseen companions with masses about 0.01 that of the sun have been found by K. A. Strand (61 Cygni) and Sarah L. Lippincott (Lalande 21185). These objects perhaps still belong to the category of stars. But recently, P. van de Kamp has detected in Barnard's star a companion which is only 1.5 times as massive as Jupiter. An object of this mass must be regarded as a planet because its internal temperature cannot be high enough to ignite thermonuclear reactions. Therefore, van de Kamp's discovery provided a direct observational proof that the planetary systems and binary systems form indeed a uniform group. Since binary stars are very numerous, planetary systems should also occur frequently.

We can also make, heuristically, a prediction regarding the stars that have a good chance of possessing planets. Years ago Otto Struve pointed out that the rapid rotation of early-type main-sequence stars did not occur in classes later than $F5$. In other words, the average angular momentum per unit mass of main-sequence stars suffers a conspicuous discontinuity at this spectral subdivision. A reasonable possibility to explain this is that planetary systems are formed around stars of later spectral types, the unobservable planets absorbing the excess angular momentum in each case.

The available evidence, therefore, suggests that most single stars on the main sequence between $F5$ and perhaps $K5$ have a good chance of supporting life of an advanced form on their planets. Only a few percent of all stars fall in this range. Within 16.3 light-years (5 parsecs) of the sun, there are 58 other individual stars, 5 of which are unseen companions. Of 26 single stars in this group, only 2 besides the sun fall within our limitations for supporting life: Epsilon Eridani, a *K2* dwarf, and Tau Ceti, a *G4* dwarf.

Of course, the actual chance of intelligent life appearing is less than a few percent. Even if the size of a planet revolving within a habitable zone is right, its surface topography might not be. If the entire surface were water covered, for instance, a civilization like ours could not develop. Taking everything into consideration, I venture to state that no more than 1 to 2 percent of stars may have at one time or another supported intelligent life. On this basis, there are within 1,000 light-years a few thousand stars around which life of this nature could appear.

For us on earth, a most interesting question is whether or not intelligent life exists elsewhere right now. What is the chance of finding extraterrestrial contemporaries? No one dares guess how long our civilization will endure. Granted that man does not destroy himself, he still has to face natural calamities, such as a recurrence of the ice ages. Will man's tendency to overspecialization bring about his downfall? I incline to believe that the lifetime of a technological civilization occupies only a very small fraction of the entire period of biological evolution. If so, two such civilizations in different worlds would scarcely be simultaneous.

An interstellar journey will not be within our means for a long time to come. At the speed of artificial satellites that we have launched so far, it would take hundreds of thousands of years to cover the 10 light-years of distance to Epsilon Eridani or Tau Ceti. This leaves us with only communication by electromagnetic waves as possible means of contacting other intelligent beings. The problem of interstellar radio communication has been treated in detail in an article on Project Ozma, by F. D. Drake, in *Sky and Telescope* for January 1960 (p. 140). So far, Project Ozma observations have given negative results. Interstellar communication by lasers has been discussed by R. M. Schwartz and C. H. Townes in an article published in *Nature* (April 15, 1961), but no experimental attempt has yet been made in this direction.

It is generally agreed among radio scientists that the best frequency to employ is that of the 21-cm. neutral hydrogen line. It has been suggested that the value of *pi*, or the fine structure constant, or any other dimensionless constant, be transmitted in order to distinguish our signal from natural sources of radio noise. I personally think a great effort of this kind inadvisable, however fundamental the constant might be.

Instead, I suggest using simple numbers: 1, 2, 3, each represented by the corresponding number of dots. They are as good a sign of intelligence as any physical or biological constant. Then we could proceed to introduce the concept of equality and other algebraic symbols (as P. Morrison has also proposed). This can be done by coding such symbols and repeating a large number of examples, just as arithmetic is taught to children. At this stage the binary, decimal, or some other number system may be introduced, and finally the x, y concept of locating a point on a plane. Once this is established, a means for interchanging information follows easily.

While the chances of success in receiving intelligible signals from outer space are extremely small, even during a long search with larger and larger radio telescopes, it is worth trying because of its fundamental importance in understanding the nature of living beings and its impact on our philosophical beliefs.

KARL T. COMPTON

The Electron: Its Intellectual and Social Significance[1]

[FROM THE SMITHSONIAN REPORT FOR 1937]

THIS ARTICLE *on the electron was written nearly 30 years ago by the late Karl T. Compton, at that time the distinguished President of the Massachusetts Institute of Technology. Although the science and technology of electronics has since then expanded tremendously in ways not envisioned at that time, nevertheless the electron has become so embedded in every phase of our lives that a review of the intensive effort leading to its discovery and utilization seems not out of place in this* Treasury of 20th Century Science. *Dr. Compton goes back to the 1880's and 1890's to record the whole series of startling discoveries in the field of electric and radiation phenomena that transformed the then stagnant science of physics into a dynamic and fast-moving adventure. They culminated in 1897 in the discovery by J. J. Thomson of England of negatively charged particles which he showed to be the universal constituents of all matter and which he called "corpuscles." We now call them electrons. Dr. Compton then explains how the discovery of the electron aided in understanding the structure of atoms, with the consequent rapid*

---

[1] Address of the retiring president of the American Association for the Advancement of Science, delivered at Atlantic City on December 28, 1936.

development of modern physics and chemistry. He concludes with a brief review of the tremendous impact of the electron on technology and industry, calling it "the most versatile tool ever utilized." "... there is nothing so practical in its values as accurate knowledge, and the pursuit of such knowledge has been most successful when not fettered with the initial demand that it be directed toward practical ends."

In THIS CENTURY, centenaries, bicentenaries, and tercentenaries have been much in vogue. Every town or institution or event which has claim to distinction has sought the excuse of the calendar to remind the world of its claims to greatness. Thus we have celebrated the centenary of Faraday's discovery of the principles of electromagnetism and the bicentenary of Watt's invention of the steam engine — discoveries which have introduced the eras of electricity and of mechanical power. The city of Chicago sought to tell us that the progress of mankind really began with the founding of that community, and led us to spend millions of dollars to gain the impression that there is really some causal relationship between Chicago and world progress. In my part of the country, the city of Boston and its suburbs staged a succession of tercentenary celebrations, as proud of their past as Chicago is of its present. Greatest of all was the tercentenary celebration of Harvard University, signalizing the firm basis of intellectual freedom and leadership which is the prime requisite for a free people in a democracy.

Encouraged by the success of the Chicago Century of Progress and the Harvard Tercentenary, I venture to feature my address as signalizing an anniversary of the discovery of the electron. To be sure, it is only one generation old, and a generation is a sufficiently vague unit of time for my purposes. Yet, in spite of its youth, it bids fair to rival Chicago in its contributions to economic progress, and Harvard University in its contributions to the understanding of this world in which we live. So I venture to assert that no institution or community which has used one of these milestones to take stock of its achievements and plot its future course has stronger claims to intellectual significance and practical utility than I will claim for the electron.

The history of science abounds with instances when a new concept or discovery has led to tremendous advances into vast new fields of knowledge and art the very existence of which had hitherto been unsuspected. The discoveries of Galileo, Faraday, and Pasteur are such instances. But, to my notion, no such instance has been so dramatic as the discovery of the electron, the tiniest thing in the universe, which within one generation has transformed a stagnant science of physics, a descriptive science of chemistry, and a sterile science of astronomy into dynamically developing sciences fraught with intellectual adventure, interrelating interpretations and practical values.

I take particular pleasure in mentioning these practical values, for even the most unimaginative and short-sighted, hard-headed, "practical" businessman is forced to admit the justification for the pure research — of no preconceived practical use whatsoever in the minds of those who led in its prosecution, and of all degrees of success and significance — which has been directed at the electron. For out of this research have come the following things which all can understand and appreciate: a growing business in manufacture of electronic devices which now amounts to $50 million a year in America alone; a total business of some hundreds of millions of dollars a year which is made possible by these electronic devices; innumerable aids to health, safety, and convenience; and an immense advance in our knowledge of the universe in which we live.

THE BACKGROUND

In science, as in human affairs, great events do not occur without a background of development. The electron had an ancestry which can be traced back through the centuries. Its immediate progenitors were the electromagnetic theory of light, spectroscopy, and the leakage of electricity through gases. First cousins were X-rays and radioactivity and quantum theory, for, out of a background of long investigation of bewildering and apparently unrelated phenomena, there burst upon the scientific world the X-ray in 1895, radioactivity in 1896, and the electron in 1897 — all while investigators in the older fields of heat radiation and thermodynamics were finding those bothersome inconsistencies in these hitherto respectable subjects which led to that unexpected extension of Newtonian mechanics now called quantum mechanics. The concept of the electron, behaving according to the laws of quantum mechanics, is now the basis of most of our interpretation of all that falls under the good old name of natural philosophy.

That only the pioneers of the scientific world were prepared for these discoveries, however, is witnessed by the fact that a standard textbook of chemistry widely used in my student days in 1904 stated that, "Atoms are the indivisible constituents of molecules," and so late as 1911 a prominent physicist warned his colleagues not to be too hasty in accepting these new-fangled ideas.

The existence of electrons had been foreshadowed for a century by the facts of electrolysis, which led Davy and Berzelius to conclude that chemical forces were electrical in nature, and Faraday to conclude that electric charges exist only in multiples of some fundamental unit. For chemical acids and salts, dissolved in water, tend to split up into ions, that is, atoms or groups of atoms which move in an electric field in such directions as to indicate that they carry either positive or negative electric charges. Furthermore, it is found that the amounts of these ions which carry equal amounts of electricity are exactly proportional to the chemical combining weights of the ions. Faraday saw that this fact would be simply explained by assuming that every ion carries a charge proportional to its chemical valency, that is, the valency times a fundamental unit charge. But Faraday could not, from these facts, deduce the size of this unit of charge; he could only state the ratio of this charge to the mass of the chemical substance with which the charge was associated. Hydrogen, being the lightest of all ions, had of all known substances, therefore, the largest value of this ratio of charge to mass.

The first real evidence of particles of larger ratio of charge to mass than hydrogen ions came from the field of optics. Ever since Maxwell's equations of electromagnetism had predicted the existence of electromagnetic waves with the velocity of light, and Hertz,

17 years later, had discovered them experimentally, physicists had felt sure that light must be caused by some sort of oscillations of electricity within atoms. But only the vaguest and most unsatisfactory speculations, such as whirling vortices or pulsating spheres of electricity, had been suggested.

In 1896, however, Zeeman tried the experiment of examining the spectrum of a light source placed in a strong magnetic field, and discovered that the spectrum lines thus became split into components of slightly differing wavelength, and that these components of the light showed characteristic types of polarization depending on the direction in which the light emerged from the magnetic field. Almost at once, in January 1897, Lorentz showed that this experiment proved that light is caused by the oscillation of electric charges, the motions of which are affected by the magnetic field in the manner required to explain Zeeman's experiments. This much was not unexpected, but what was startling was Lorentz's proof that the Zeeman effect could only have been produced by electrified particles whose ratio of charge to mass is nearly 2,000 times larger than that of a hydrogen ion, and whose mass is therefore presumably nearly 2,000 times lighter than hydrogen.

Almost at once this conclusion was confirmed in a more dramatic and understandable way by J. J. Thomson, the then youthful director of the Cavendish Laboratory. But let me first pick up this thread of the story a little farther back.

DISCOVERY OF THE ELECTRON

All through the 1880's and early 1890's a series of most striking and unexpected discoveries followed from investigations of electric arcs, sparks, and especially the glowing discharges of electricity at high voltages through glass tubes containing various gases at pressures far below atmospheric pressure. The striking color effects, mysterious luminous streamers and entirely bizarre behavior of these discharges made them the most popular, yet most elusive, subject of laboratory research of those days.

It was these phenomena which led Crookes to postulate the existence of a mysterious "fourth state of matter," different from the solid, liquid, or gaseous states. (Of course, we now know that Crookes's fourth state is simply the ionized state of matter.) Once, while attempting to photograph the appearance of a discharge at very low gas pressure, Crookes was bothered by the fact that all the photographic plates in the room with his apparatus became fogged, as if light-struck in spite of their opaque wrapping. He avoided the trouble afterwards, however, by keeping his new supply of plates in another room until, one at a time, they were wanted for use. Thus he solved an experimental difficulty, and missed making a great discovery.

At about the same time Roentgen, in Germany, was trying the same experiment, and he too was troubled by the fogging of his photographic plates. But, as the story goes, his laboratory assistant directed his attention to the peculiar fact that these fogged plates, when developed, showed the image of a bunch of keys which had accidentally been lying on top of the box of plates while the electric discharge experiments were in operation. Roentgen immediately looked into this and discovered that the fogging was due to penetrating radiations produced in the discharge tube where the cathode rays struck the target or anode. Thus by accident were X-rays discovered — that type of accident not uncommon in science when an observant experimenter is at work.

While on the subject of accidents, I might digress to tell of another accident which did not happen, also in connection with X-rays. For more than 15 years after their discovery, disputes raged as to whether X-rays were radiations, like light but of very short wavelength, or electrically neutral particles of small mass and high speed. It was evident that they were not electrically charged, since their paths were unaffected by electric or magnetic fields. The leading advocate of the neutral particle theory was W. H. Bragg. In 1912, at Princeton, O. W. Richardson tried an experiment to see if X-rays could be refracted by a prism. A positive result would support the wave theory of X-rays. People had tried this with X-rays through glass prisms without success, but Richardson had an idea that an iron prism might be more effective. So he passed X-rays for hours and days through the tapering edge of a Gillette safety razor blade, but without finding any refraction. If he had happened to try the edge of a crystal instead of the edge of the razor blade, he would undoubtedly have discovered the peculiar diffraction of X-rays in passing through crystals, discovered a couple of years later by Laue, Friederich and Knipping and developed by father and son, W. H. and W. L. Bragg, which proved both the wave nature of X-rays and the atomic lattice structure of crystals. If Roentgen's discovery of X-rays was an accident, then I suppose Richardson's failure to discover diffraction of X-rays was a negative accident. I often wonder how many important negative accidents slip past us week by week!

But to get back on the subject of the electron: it was the cathode rays, which produce the X-rays, which finally turned out to be electrons traveling at high speeds. These cathode rays had been observed to shoot out in straight lines from the surfaces of cathodes in rarefied gases through which electric currents were forced by high voltage. Objects which they struck became luminous with fluorescent light, and objects in their paths cast shadows. But their true nature was disclosed when a magnet was placed near the discharge tube, for then their paths were curved in a direction showing that cathode rays were negatively charged. By measuring this curvature produced by a magnetic field of known strength, and making a pretty sure assumption that the kinetic energy of these rays was determined by the voltage applied to the tube, J. J. Thomson in 1897 first showed that cathode rays are negatively charged particles with a ratio of charge to mass nearly 2,000 times that of hydrogen. He furthermore showed that these particles are of the same type, as regards ratio of charge to mass, from whatever gas or cathode material they are produced. He therefore announced these particles, which he called "corpuscles," to be universal constituents of all substances. Thus was the electron discovered.

MASS AND CHARGE OF THE ELECTRON

Quick and fast came experiments of ingenious design to study the electrons more accurately. They were pulled this way and that by electric and magnetic fields. They were caught in miniature metal fly-traps, called Faraday cages, to measure their charge and kinetic energy. They were detected in their paths electrically, or by photographic plates or by fluorescence. Continually refined from that day to this, we now know that an electron has a ratio of charge to mass which is about 1,842 times the similar ratio for a hydrogen atomic ion.

It was also very desirable to know separately the charge and the mass of an electron, and not just the ratio between these quantities. So an even more interesting lot of experiments has been carried on to measure the electron's charge. They were begun in about 1900 by J. J. Thomson and his colleagues, Townsend, H. A. Wilson, and C. T. R. Wilson. I think a brief résumé of attempts to measure the electron's charge will throw an interesting sidelight on the versatility of scientific attack on a difficult problem.

The first attempts were by Townsend, by measurements on the motion and electrification of fog produced when electrolytic gas was bubbled into a region of air which was slightly supersaturated with water vapor, but too many uncertainties were involved to make this work convincing. The first accepted results were by J. J. Thomson, who, after an earlier attempt, employed a technique of producing fog under controlled conditions, developed by his colleague, C. T. R. Wilson, whose method was refined further by his pupil, H. A. Wilson.

It had long been known that water droplets of fog do not form in air which is somewhat supersaturated with water vapor unless there are nuclei, like specks of dust, on which the moisture can condense. Later, Townsend found that fog will also condense on ions, and more readily on negative than on positive ions. C. T. R. Wilson designed an apparatus in which dust-free air could be supersaturated with moisture sufficiently to permit condensation of fog droplets on negative but not on positive ions, which were produced by some convenient ionizing agent. So a fog was formed, in which each droplet of water was condensed on a negative ion. Thomson employed this apparatus in the following manner.

Of course, this fog gradually settled downward under the pull of gravity—slowly because the drops were small compared with the viscous resistance of the air through which they fell. It was like the slow settling of dust on the furniture and floor of a room. But the theory of the rate at which spheres move when a force drives them through a viscous medium was already well known, owing to Stokes's law. From this law, measurement of the rate of fall of the fog in centimeters per second as measured by a little telescope focused on the top edge of the fog, combined with knowledge of the force of gravity and the viscosity of air, enabled Thomson to calculate the size of the individual fog droplets. Dividing the total amount of water in the fog by the amount in one drop gave him the total number of fog droplets, and therefore the total number of negative ions. H. A. Wilson added the refinement of superposing an electric field on the gravitational field which pulled the drops through the air. Then, as the fog settled to the bottom of the apparatus, it deposited its electric charge, which altogether, was large enough to be measured with an electrometer. So, dividing this total charge by the number of ions composing it gave, as the charge of one ion, 3.4×10^{-10} electrostatic units. This was the first real measurement of the charge of an electron, and was the value quoted in the tables of physical constants when I became a graduate student in 1910.

About that time Millikan, who has always had a flair for picking strategically important subjects to which to devote his investigative talents, undertook with his students a revaluation of the electronic charge. Sources of error in the fog method were well recognized: Fog droplets were not all the same size, though measurements could only be made on those smallest ones which fell most slowly; also droplets did not remain of constant size, smaller ones tending to evaporate and larger ones to grow; also there were unavoidable convection currents in the air which modified the rate of fall of the fog; and some droplets might contain more than one ion.

Millikan cleverly avoided or minimized these difficulties by using only a single droplet of some relatively nonvolatile liquid like oil or mercury. By ionizing the surrounding air in an electric field he could put various electric charges on the drop. Illuminating it by a powerful light and viewing it like a star through a measuring telescope, he could measure its rate of fall under gravity and its rate of rise when pulled upward against gravity by an electric field, and keep repeating these observations for hours. These measurements were so precise that, to keep pace with them, he had to measure the viscosity of air with hitherto unequaled accuracy. When all this was done, he had proved conclusively that all electric charges are integral multiples of a fundamental unit charge, the electron, the value of which he set as 4.774 $\times 10^{-10}$ electrostatic units—about 40 percent larger than the earlier estimates and believed by Millikan to be correct within one part in a thousand.

Within the past half-dozen years, however, doubt has been thrown on the estimated accuracy of this value from quite a different direction, in work with X-rays. Originally, X-ray diffraction experiments in crystals proved the geometric arrangement of atoms in the crystals, but did not establish the scale of distances between atoms or the X-ray wavelength. These distances, once the arrangement of atoms was known, were calculated from absolute values of the weights of the atoms, which in turn were derived from electrochemical equivalents and the value of the electronic charge. Thus X-ray wavelengths, masses of atoms and distances between atoms in crystals all had values dependent on knowledge of the charge of the electron.

Recently, however, A. H. Compton, Bearden, and others have succeeded in making measurements of X-ray wavelengths by diffracting X-rays from a grating ruled with 15,000–30,000 parallel fine lines to the inch, and operating near the angle of grazing incidence. These measurements involve only knowledge of the number of lines per inch on the grating, and the angles of incidence and diffraction of the X-rays—both depending only on measurements of length and capable of high precision. X-ray wavelengths thus measured were a little different from the earlier accepted values, and this cast doubt on the accuracy of the electron charge value which had been used in the earlier X-ray estimates. The difference was not large, only about 1 part in 200, but it meant either that experiments had not been as accurate as believed or that there was some unrecognized complicating factor.

So Millikan's work has been repeated in various laboratories with refinements, such as the use of a remarkably nonvolatile oil for the drop. But the chief error was found to lie in the measurements of the viscosity of air. During the past year Kelletrop, of Uppsala, has thus published a revised "oil-drop" determination of electronic charge as 4.800$\times 10^{-10}$ E.S.U., which is in excellent agreement with the "X-ray" determinations. Bearden has just presented his own confirmation of this agreement before the American Physical Society.

It is an interesting coincidence that this best value of the charge of the electron is exactly the same as the figure given by Rutherford 30 years ago, though then determined with so much less precision that not much confidence was placed in it, except as to order of magnitude. It was then known that the alpha rays from radium are helium atoms which have lost two electrons and are therefore doubly positively charged. Rutherford caught a lot of these alpha rays in a metal trap, measuring their aggregate electric charge with an electroscope, and counting them by the scintillations which they produced on striking a fluorescent screen or otherwise. Dividing the total charge by the number gave him double the electronic charge, which he thus calculated to be 4.8×10^{-10} E.S.U. Already knowing the ratio of charge to mass with high precision, this value of the charge enables us to fix the electron's mass as 9.051×10^{-28} grams.

ELECTROMAGNETIC MASS

When we speak of the mass of an electron, however, we enter a whole new field of ideas. Some years before the discovery of electrons, J. J. Thomson had pointed out that an electrified particle will possess inertia, that is, mass, simply in virtue of its charge alone, irrespective of whether or not it has any mass of the gravitational type which we have been accustomed to think of. This "electromagnetic" mass comes about from the fact that any mechanical energy which is expended in accelerating an electric charge is transformed into the energy of the magnetic field surrounding the electrified particle in virtue of its motion. In fact, the kinetic energy of a moving electric charge is found to be simply the energy of its magnetic field and depends only on the square of the velocity of the charge, the amount of charge and the geometrical shape of the charge.

Making the simplest possible assumptions about the shape of an electron, such as a solid sphere or a hollow spherical shell of electricity, and assuming all its mass to be of electromagnetic origin, the diameter of an electron was calculated to be of the order of 10^{-13} cm. It must be emphasized, however, that this estimate of size is not, like the charge and mass, a definite measurement, but is simply an estimate based on assumptions, at least one of which is quite uncertain. For while we have both logic and experiment to back up the assumption that all the mass of the electron is of this electromagnetic origin, we must confess to utter ignorance regarding the shape of the electron. Indeed, some facts suggest that it may have different sizes and shapes in different environments, as in the free state or in an orbit of an atom or in the nucleus of an atom. So our estimate of 10^{-13} cm. for the size of the electron is, at best, very crude.

The idea of electromagnetic mass was strongly supported by the fact that measurements of the mass of very fast-moving electrons, through measurements of the ratio of charge to mass of beta rays from radium or cathode rays in high-voltage discharge tubes, showed that their mass is not really a constant thing but increases with the speed of the electron. The value of electron mass given above applies, strictly speaking, only to an electron at rest. Practically, however, it is accurate enough for practical purposes for electron speeds below about one-tenth the speed of light. At this speed the electron's mass is about half of 1 percent larger than if it were at rest. At still higher speeds, the mass increases more and more rapidly, approaching infinite mass as the speed of light is approached.

These facts, experimentally determined, were shown by Abraham to be of the type expected if the entire mass of an electron is of electromagnetic origin, due entirely to its electric charge. It was this argument, which has since received confirmation from other directions, which was the basis of the theory that all mass, that is, all matter, is electrical. However, the simple electromagnetic concepts were not quite adequate to give an accurate quantitative interpretation of these experiments, and it required the additional introduction by Lorentz of the concepts of the special theory of relativity to bring about complete interpretation of the experiments.

THE ELECTRON AND QUANTUM THEORY

Just two things more do we know accurately about the properties of electrons, in addition to their charge and mass. We know that they are also tiny magnets of strength equal to the basic unit of magnetic moment generally called the Bohr magneton. Once the electron had been discovered, it became natural to seek in it also the explanation of magnetic phenomena, since it was only necessary to assume that the electricity of an electron is whirling about an axis, and the electron becomes endowed with the properties of a tiny magnet. Parsons, Webster, and others examined the possibilities inherent in various assumed configurations, with interesting results. But it was only with the introduction of the quantum theory for the interpretation of atomic structure and spectra that the magnetic character of the electron has, within the last dozen years, been put on a well-established basis.

The other thing we know is perhaps the most unexpected of all the electron's properties — it behaves like a wave when it collides with other objects. Davisson and Germer discovered this in the Bell Laboratories, while examining the way in which a beam of electrons, incident on a solid surface, was scattered or reflected by it. They found, if the surface were crystalline, that the electrons were scattered just like diffracted X-rays, but that, unlike X-rays, the wavelength of an electron is not fixed but varies inversely as its speed. J. J. Thomson's son, G. P. Thomson, has made very illuminating studies of this phenomenon, which is the inverse of the Compton effect; together they have given physicists two mottoes: "Particles behave like waves and waves behave like particles" and "Here's to the electron; long may she wave." One of the triumphs of the new wave mechanics (a brand of quantum mechanics) is that it offers a medium of explanation of these strange phenomena. But my subject of the electron is too long to let me attempt a digression on wave mechanics.

SIGNIFICANCE OF THE ELECTRON CONCEPT

With this sketch of the electron itself before us, let us turn to some of the more important directions in which the electron has given us an interpretation of the physical universe generally. Immediately were explained the phenomena of electrolysis and of ionization generally, for ions were simply atoms or groups of atoms which had gained or lost one or more electrons. Primary chemical forces were explained as the electrostatic attraction between atomic groups which, respectively, contained an excess or a deficiency of electrons. (The more refined interpretation of chemical forces within the past half-dozen years, by Pauling and Slater, has been based upon the quantum theory of atomic structure.)

The three types of rays from radioactive substances were interpreted: alpha rays as helium atoms which had lost two electrons; beta rays as electrons; and gamma rays as X-ray-like radiations. In fact, Becquerel showed the magnetic deflection of beta rays in the same year, 1897, that Thomson showed the magnetic deflection of cathode rays and interpreted them as electrons.

For many years two unexplained phenomena had been studied in metals. When highly heated or when illuminated by ultraviolet light, metals had been shown to emit negative electricity. It was the work of but a year, after the discovery of the electron, for J. J. Thomson and his pupils to show that both these phenomena consist in the emission of electrons. But by what mechanisms are they thus emitted? That was a question the study of which has led to most important theoretical and practical consequences.

Richardson, first as a pupil of Thomson and then as a professor at Princeton in the early 1900's, developed the theory of thermionic emission of electrons, according to which the electrons are evaporated from the surface of a metal at high temperatures by a process very analogous to evaporation of molecules. The electrons are assumed to have the same distribution of kinetic energies that molecules possess at the same temperature in accordance with the principles of kinetic theory. They escape from the surface, if they reach it, with enough energy to take them away in spite of the attraction tending to pull the electron back into the metal. This attraction is expressed in terms of the now famous "work-function," a sort of latent heat of evaporation of electrons, which is the work that must be done to get an electron clear of the surface. With these simple assumptions, an equation was derived for the rate of

emission of electricity as a function of temperature which has stood
the test of perhaps as wide a range of experimentation as any other
equation of physics, a range of values of more than a million-
million fold in current without any detectable departure from the
theory, if this is properly applied.

Richardson's measurements of the "work-functions" of various
metals showed that these values run closely parallel with one of
the longest known but least understood properties of metals,
namely, their contact potential properties. By contact differences
of potential is meant the voltage difference between the surfaces
of two metals when they are placed in contact. Richardson found
that the difference between the "work-function" of two metals was,
within the limits of accuracy of the data, the same as their contact
difference of potential. He therefore proposed the theory that the
contact potential property of a metal is determined simply by the
work necessary to remove an electron from its surface.

As a beginning graduate student under Richardson in 1910, I was
given the job of undertaking a test of this theory through experiments on the other electron-emitting phenomenon, the photoelectric
effect. Einstein a few years before had proposed his famous photoelectric equation, which was a contribution to physical theory certainly comparable in importance and thus far more useful in its
applications than his more impressive and wider publicized general
theory of relativity. According to it, an electron in a metal may
receive from the incident light an amount of energy proportional to
the frequency of light — to be exact, an energy equal to Planck's
constant h times the frequency v. If it escapes from the metal, it
must do an amount of work w to get away, so that its kinetic
energy after escape from the metal would be the difference $hv - w$.
Obviously, by measuring these kinetic energies of electrons liberated from various metals by light of various frequencies, it should
be possible to find out if the "work-functions" w of different metals
are indeed related to their contact differences of potential in the
manner predicted by Richardson's theory.

In two papers, by me in 1911 and jointly with Richardson in
1912, it was concluded first that the contact differences of potential
are related to the "work-functions" as Richardson had predicted,
and secondly that Einstein's photoelectric equation, rather than a

rival theory then under discussion, properly described the facts. Practically simultaneously with this second paper, there appeared the report of a similar verification of Einstein's equation by A. L. Hughes, then in England, though lacking the quantitative connection with contact differences of potential.

This early work was not very accurate, partly because of lack of good vacuum technique for maintaining untarnished surfaces in a vacuum, partly through lack of constant sources of ultraviolet light and partly because the ultraviolet spectrographs used to isolate the various wavelengths of light gave a certain spectral impurity of scattered light of other wavelengths. These sources of error were recognized but not overcome when Millikan, in 1916, made a striking advance by using doubly purified light or otherwise correcting for the effects of impurity, and secured a verification of Einstein's equation which was far more accurate than the earlier work as regards the value of Planck's constant h. In fact, Millikan's work remains to this day as one of the best determinations of this important constant. In regard to the "work-function," however, this work of Millikan's was not so successful, for, after having apparently discovered facts at variance with Richardson's interpretation of the equation and its relation to constant potentials, these differences were ultimately found to reside in faults of experimental procedure or interpretation, so that Richardson's interpretation of Einstein's equation still holds.

In both thermionic and photoelectric effects, theoretical refinements have been introduced by the recent quantum mechanics, and great advances made in experimental technique. However, it is fair to say that their interpretations on the electron theory have been among the major achievements of this theory.

CONDUCTION OF METALS

While we are on the subject of electricity in metals, what constitutes the phenomenon of easy flow of electricity that is the distinguishing feature of metals? J. J. Thomson at once suggested that this must be due to the existence in metals of electrons free from their parent atoms, moving freely, except for collisions, whenever an electric field was applied in the metal. The theory thus worked out was attractive, but it encountered inconsistencies. There was not even any real evidence that electricity in metals was conducted by electrons.

Then along came Tolman with one of his brilliant ideas, skillfully followed by experiment. It had earlier been suggested that, whatever are the carriers of electric current in metals, it should be possible to centrifuge them toward the periphery of a disk if this were rotated very rapidly about its axis. To be more specific, if electrons are free to move in metals and if a wire connects the center and the periphery of the rotating disk through lightly pressing brush contacts, electrons should be thrown out of the disk at its periphery and pass back into the center of the disk through the wire. It would be rather analogous to a current of water driven by a centrifugal pump through a pipe circuit. But all attempts to detect such currents proved futile, because the currents produced by the friction of the contact against the periphery were far larger than the currents to be expected from the centrifuging of electrons.

But Tolman devised two methods of giving powerful accelerations to metal conductors in such manner that he was able to measure the feeble electric currents that were produced as the carriers of electricity in the metal were shaken back and forth, and his calculations showed that these currents were indeed of the size to be expected if the current is carried by electrons. This is our direct evidence that electrons carry the electric current in metals. The mechanism by which they do this is now beginning to be disclosed by Slater, on the basis of an application of quantum mechanics and spectroscopic ideas to metals, and again is an example of the refining power of the quantum theory to succeed where older classical theory was gropingly suggestive, but inadequate.

STRUCTURE OF THE ATOM

Now that I come to the most basic of all the phenomena which the electron has been called upon to interpret, I almost lose courage, for the subject is too vast and complex for anything but encyclopaedic treatment. I refer to the structure of atoms. Previous to the discovery of the electron, literally nothing was known of the internal structure or composition of atoms. With this discovery, however, it immediately became evident that all atoms contain electrons and an equivalent amount of positive electricity in some form. It was again J. J. Thomson's genius which began the investigation of the inner atom. This was only about 25 years ago.

Thomson reasoned that, if X-rays were made to fall on any substance, the electrons in the atoms of the substance would be forced to vibrate back and forth by the powerful alternating electric forces in the X-ray waves. But, in thus vibrating back and forth, these electrons would re-radiate secondary X-rays in all directions. He calculated just what fraction of the original X-ray energy ought to be thus re-radiated by each electron, and then set his pupils to measure just what this fraction was in specific cases. From the experimental results he was thus able to calculate the number of electrons which performed the re-radiation in each case. These results indicated that the number of such acting electrons in each atom was about half the value of the chemical atomic weight of the atom. Thus first were counted the electrons in an atom.

Rutherford and his pupils, aided by the mathematical analysis of Darwin, tackled the problem from a different point of view. They studied the distribution of deflection of alpha particles, shot out of radioactive materials, as these alpha particles traversed thin sheets of solid materials. They found that this distribution was quantitatively what would be expected if the deflections were produced by ordinary electrostatic forces, varying as the square of the distance, between the alpha particle and a very small object containing most of the mass in each atom. They were thus able to show that this small object is not more than one ten-thousandth of the diameter of the atom, that it contained substantially all the mass of the atom and that it carried a positive electric charge equal, in electronic units, to about half the chemical atomic weight of the atom.

Thus arose the concept that the atom is composed of a positive nucleus of small dimensions, surrounded by electrons to the number of about half the atomic weight.

This had scarcely become established when it was brilliantly refined and extended by Moseley, just before he went to his untimely death in the Great War in 1914. Moseley had made a most ingenious study of the spectra of X-rays of a large number of the chemical elements, using a modification of the X-ray spectroscopy technique developed by the Braggs. He found that the square roots of the frequencies of the characteristic X-ray lines were numerically very simply related to the number which gave the place of the element in the periodic table of the elements, so useful to chemists but so entirely without explanation. Thus this number acquired a definite physical significance and is now well known as the "atomic number."

For all the elements heavier than hydrogen, this atomic number is about half the atomic weight and, to make a long story short, this atomic number turns out to be exactly the number of electronic units of charge on an atomic nucleus, or the number of electrons in the atom outside the nucleus. At the same time, Moseley's work proved to be one of the greatest advances ever made in the basic interpretive side of chemistry.

Now that the number of electrons in each atom was known, the next step was to wonder how they were arranged, what held them in place and what they were doing in their spare time. Suggestions were not slow in coming. In fact, even before Moseley's work, two rival theories had appeared, one devised by chemist Lewis and extended by Langmuir to explain the directional symmetries of atoms as indicated by their molecular combining forms, and the other devised by physicist Bohr to account for spectra. Gradually the Bohr theory has been developed to include the symmetries of the Lewis-Langmuir theory, so that both may be said to be merged, with many major additions too numerous to mention.

It was Bohr's bold genius to cast off some of the fetters of classical mechanics, which had been fairly well proved inadequate to meet the situation, and to devise a new mechanics frankly to meet the simplest known facts of atomic structure and spectroscopy — the hydrogen atom and the atomic hydrogen spectrum. In doing so, he at one stroke brought into the same picture the quantum theory of radiation, the electronic structure of the atom and the facts of spectroscopy. He had his electron moving in a circular orbit around the nucleus under the regular laws of electrostatic attraction and centrifugal force. But he stipulated that only such orbits were possible in which the angular momentum of the electron was an integral multiple of Planck's constant h divided by 2π. He also stipulated that the electrons should not radiate energy while revolving in their orbits, but only when they jumped from one orbit to another. In this case the frequency of light radiated was equal to the change of energy of the electron between the two orbits, divided by Planck's constant h. With these assumptions, the spectra of hydrogen and of ionized helium were quantitatively explained in their main features, but not in their finer details.

Then came the Great War, and we heard little of atomic structure in the United States. But in Germany, Sommerfeld was extending Bohr's ideas in most interesting ways. He showed that, by considering elliptic as well as circular orbits, and taking account of the variation of the electron's mass with speed, the fine details as well as the main features in the spectra of hydrogen and ionized helium were accurately explained. He also showed how the theory could be extended to deal with atoms where there were many electrons moving in orbits. He showed that these additional concepts were in the right direction to explain the more complicated spectra both in the visible and in the X-ray regions.

SPECTRAL LINES

When this new work was first known in America, it started the most feverish and earnest scientific activity that the country has ever known, which is still in progress with undiminished zeal and with increasing productive effectiveness. I well remember when the first copy of Sommerfeld's *Atombau und Spectrallinen* came to America in the possession of Prof. P. W. Bridgman. Until later copies arrived, he knew no peace and enjoyed no privacy, for he was besieged by friends wanting to read the book — which he would not allow to go out of his possession. I recall, too, the sudden popularity of the only two or three men in America who knew what a spectral series was. Heretofore, practically our only interest in spectra had been in the culinary variety of spectroscopy used by chemists in identifying chemical elements. No interpretive quality to speak of had hitherto been attached to the peculiar numerical regularities which had been discovered in the vibration frequencies of groups of spectrum lines.

I recall, too, the dismay with which we found only a handful of mathematical physicists versed in the analytical dynamics underlying the new atomic structure theories. In the summer of 1921, having been taught by one of these few mathematical physicists, I went to the University of Michigan to lecture on Summerfeld's theory, and found there also F. A. Saunders, invited to impart his knowledge of spectrum series. In the winter of 1926, Born and Jordan having just announced a new development in quantum mechanics, I found more than 20 Americans in Göttingen at this fount of quantum wisdom. A year later they were at Zurich, with Schrödinger. A couple of years later, Heisenberg at Leipzig and then Dirac at Cambridge held the Elijah mantle of quantum theory. In America, contributions are coming rapidly, particularly in the fields of application to chemical interpretations, metals and other complex situations.

From all this has come the situation which permitted Dirac, a few years ago, to write: "The underlying physical laws necessary for the mathematical theory of a large part of physics and the whole of chemistry are thus completely known, and the difficulty is only that the exact application of these laws leads to equations much too complicated to be soluble." But if any ambitious young scientist be discouraged lest there be little left to do, let him consider the unexplored atomic nucleus, or the fact that every attempt to apply these laws, which look so satisfactory to us now, discloses new realms of knowledge still unexplored.

Time forbids mention of the most interesting work which was done to check and extend the theories of atomic structure, through direct measurement of the energy states of atoms and molecules by carefully controlled bombardment of these molecules by electrons. Begun by Franck and Hertz in Germany, much of this work was done in America by Foote and Mohler at the Bureau of Standards, by my students at Princeton and by Tate's group at Minnesota, all since 1920.

Before leaving the interpretive triumphs of the electron, however, I cannot refrain from jumping from the atom to the universe, to the interpretation of conditions on the stars. Spectra of stars had long been known, and these were interpreted as indicating that some stars consist principally of hydrogen, others of helium and others of many chemical elements like our sun. But in 1922, a young Indian physicist, Meghnad Saha, first applied atomic structure theory and knowledge of ionizing potentials to the sun and stars. He considered ionization in the hot vapors of the stars to be like a chemical dissociation produced by heat, in which the products of dissociation are electrons and the positive ionic residues of the atoms, and in which the heats of dissociation are given by the ionizing potentials of the atoms. In this way was developed a rational quantitative interpretation of stellar spectra which has thrown enormous light on the problem of conditions of temperature, pressure and condition of the chemical elements in stars. Russell in America and Milne in England have ably applied and extended this theory.

THE ELECTRON IN INDUSTRY

Finally, I come to the last phase of my subject, the social significance of the electron. By this I mean, of course, its useful applications. The first of these was Edison's invention of a thermionic rectifier, based on his discovery that negative electricity would flow across a vacuum from a hot filament to an adjacent electrode, but would not flow in the opposite direction. This was some years before the electron was discovered as the responsible agent in this phenomenon. But within a few years after the discovery of the electron, Fleming had shown that this same device will operate to rectify radio wave impulses, and thus permit their detection with a sensitive direct-current instrument. From this was patented the Fleming valve.

Once the basic character of thermionic emission was understood, and spurred on by the opportunities opening up in the radio field, new inventions, improvements, and applications of thermionic devices came rapidly. Of major importance was the three-electrode tube amplifier of De Forest. Industrial research laboratories in the communications and electric manufacturing business took the lead in developing techniques and in penetrating scientific exploration.

Noteworthy were the vacuum techniques and the monomolecular layers of activating materials developed by Langmuir and the high-vacuum thermionic X-ray tube of Coolidge. In the Bell Laboraties, oxide-coated filament tubes of good performance were developed and applied particularly to use in long-distance telephony. Let me give just two illustrations to the marvelous powers of some of these instruments.

It has been calculated that the energy of a transatlantic radio signal caught by the receiving station in Newfoundland comes in at about the rate required to lift a fly 7 inches in a year.

What is the largest number that has any physical significance? This is impossible to answer, being largely a matter of definition. But one common answer to this is 10^{110}, or one followed by 110 ciphers. This is about the number of electrons (the smallest things known) which would be required to fill up the universe to the greatest distances discovered by astronomy, if the electrons could be imagined to be closely packed side by side to fill up this whole space. Yet this number, large as it is, is very small indeed compared with the aggregate factor by which the energy of a voice striking a telephone transmitter in San Francisco is amplified by electronic tubes in the process of a long-distance telephone conversation to London. This amplification factor is about 10^{256}, or unity followed by 256 ciphers. If the universe were multiplied in size by the number of times it is larger than an electron, it could still not hold as many electrons as the number of this telephone amplification factor.

Then, mostly within 10 years or so, has come an active introduction of thermionic devices which are not highly evacuated, but operate with supplementary action of intense ionization of the gas in the tube. First of these were the low-voltage arc rectifiers, like the tungar. Most interesting and versatile are the thyratrons, which permit easy control of powerful currents and machinery, and give a new means of converting alternating into direct current, or vice versa. In this group also are some of the new types of lamps, of high efficiency or special color.

Not so striking, but equally interesting, have been the useful applications of the photoelectric effect. First was the use of sensitive photoelectric cells to replace the eye or photographic plate in astronomical telescopes. Then came sunshine meters, devices to open doors or count people or sort merchandise automatically, or to register the speed and license number of the unwary autoist. Most important thus far are the current-producing mechanisms in the sound-movie apparatus and in television equipment.

While, commercially, radio, sound movies, and long-distance telephony are at present of greatest importance, of no less importance, especially to us as scientists, are the marvelous tools which have been put into our hands for further research in practically every field of science, from physics and chemistry to psychology and criminology.

So we see how, within one generation, the electron has been discovered and examined, with its aid our intellectual outlook upon the universe has expanded in content and simplified in basic concept, and in its use mankind has the most versatile tool ever utilized. The end of the story is far from told. Every fact or relationship of the electron appears fuzzy with uncertainties when closely examined, for it can truly be said that every discovery discloses a dozen new problems. The field of practical and commercial uses of electronic devices is certainly still largely in its early stages of exploration.

This story illustrates in vivid manner a number of characteristics of scientific work, some of which I shall simply enumerate: (1) progress comes by spurts of advance as some big new idea opens up new territory, alternating with periods of consolidation; (2) progress comes not by revolution or discarding of past knowledge and experience, but is built upon past experience and is its natural extension once the vision from new vantage points is secured; (3) there is nothing so practical in its values as accurate knowledge, and the pursuit of such knowledge has been most successful when not fettered with the initial demand that it be directed toward practical ends.

I would not give the impression that it is only the electron which has given new life to the modern physical science. A story of similar interest could be built around the new concepts of radiation and atomic energy as expressed in the quantum theory, or about the electron's big brother, the proton, or his rather nondescript cousin, the neutron. In the atomic nucleus is a field of further exploration of enormous promise, now only beginning to be opened up by use of radioactive materials, cyclatrons and high-voltage generators.

Although these things have happened very recently, no one has better described the process and intellectual value of this type of scientific research than did Aristotle in the quotation which is inscribed in Greek on the façade of the National Academy of Sciences building in Washington:

> The search for truth is in one way hard and in another easy, for it is evident that no one can master it fully nor miss it wholly. But each adds a little to our knowledge of Nature, and from all the facts assembled there arises a certain grandeur.

ARTHUR R. LAUFER

Ultrasonics

[FROM THE SMITHSONIAN REPORT FOR 1951[1]]

"SOUND" WAVES *of a frequency higher than the human ear can hear have been found to exhibit some very remarkable properties. The term "ultrasonics" refers to the study and application of such high-frequency waves. As such frequencies are inaudible, it is questionable whether these waves can properly be called sound waves — Webster defines sound as "the impression made on the ear by the vibrations of the air." The author, Dr. Arthur R. Laufer, who was a member of the physics faculty at the University of Missouri when he wrote the original article, is now Chief Scientist of the Office of Naval Research at Pasadena, California. He reveals that although a few primitive methods of producing ultrasonic waves were developed prior to the opening of the 20th century, the first serious research in this new field dates from 1930. In the years following, many university and industrial laboratories, as well as military agencies, became interested, and today ultrasonics has a wide range of applications as a tool in scientific research, in medicine, and in industry. The author describes many of these surprising uses and indicates areas where further research may turn up even more im-*

---

[1] Revised as of March 1965 by the addition of a supplementary note at end of article.

portant applications. A science born only some thirty-odd years ago is still so young that, as Dr. Laufer concludes, it "holds the promise of exciting discoveries just beyond the horizon."

Some 3,000 years ago, according to the Old Testament, Joshua, the son of Nun, led the Israelites over the river Jordan into the promised land. And then, once each day for 6 days, seven priests carrying seven trumpets made of rams' horns circled the walled city of Jericho. And on the seventh day the priests circled the walls seven times, and on the seventh time the priests blew a loud blast on the trumpets, and the Israelites shouted a loud shout, and the walls of Jericho fell down flat. Thus must history reach back into antiquity to find the first allusion to the use of sound energy for a purpose other than hearing.

Thirty centuries later, in the field of ultrasonics, spectacular use is again being made of "sound" energy. Although inaudible to the human ear, ultrasonic "sound" waves have all the physical properties of audible sound waves, differing only in frequency. But it is this difference in frequency, and the consequent concentration of energy, which lead to the very different effects obtainable with ultrasonic waves.

Audible sounds, or sonic waves, range in frequency from about 20 cycles per second to about 20 kilocycles per second. Ultrasonic waves are defined as vibrational or "sound" waves which have a frequency higher than 20 kilocycles. Whether inaudible vibrational waves should be called sound waves is a debatable issue, depending for its resolution on the definition of sound on a physical or on a psychological basis. Not many years ago the waves now known as ultrasonic went under the name of supersonic. This latter name left a lasting impression in the field of radio. Although radio waves are electromagnetic rather than sound waves, the intermediate frequency used in the most popular type of radio receiver was in the "supersonic" frequency range and led to the designation of this receiver as a supersonic heterodyne, or, more briefly, a superheter-

odyne receiver. When the aviation industry appropriated the word
supersonic to refer to velocities greater than that of sound, physicists were forced to devise the word ultrasonic for frequencies
higher than those of audible sound. To retain its original meaning
the superheterodyne receiver should today be called ultraheter-
odyne!

PROPERTIES

The properties which give rise to the unusual effects of ultrasonic
waves follow from principles common to all wave phenomena. In a
given medium the wavelength of a wave is inversely proportional to
the frequency, so a high frequency implies a short wavelength.
Furthermore, the directional character of wave propagation is a
function of the wavelength. Suppose that a vibrating circular piston
is used to generate sound waves. If the frequency is low the waves
spread out from the source in all directions and bend around corners. As the frequency is raised the waves begin to assume directional characteristics, that is, more of the wave energy is propagated
in certain directions than in others and bending becomes less pronounced. At high frequencies most of the wave energy is concentrated in a truncated cone. The angle of the cone is a function of the
ratio of the wavelength of the wave to the diameter of the piston
source; the smaller the ratio, the smaller the angle of the cone.
Waves of high frequency, or short wavelength, will therefore be
propagated essentially in a given direction with negligible bending.
Ultrasonic waves have been generated at frequencies as high as 500
megacycles, corresponding to a wavelength in air equal to that of
visible red light. Such ultrasonic radiation has all the directional
properties of a beam of light. Unfortunately, the attenuation of the
radiation is also proportional to the frequency, or rather to the
square of the frequency, so that sharply defined beams cannot be
propagated over long distances. Nevertheless, even at frequencies
as low as 20 kilocycles, beams of ultrasonic waves are well enough
defined to be used in submarine detection.

The intensity of radiation being defined as the energy passing through a unit area per unit time, it is apparent that the concentration of ultrasonic radiation into a cone makes it possible to produce beams of very high intensity. In the 1940's ultrasonic sources were made to generate as much as 50 watts per square centimeter, and beams of radiation have been focused to yield intensities as high as 5,000 watts per square centimeter. These magnitudes became impressive when compared with the intensities of familiar audible sounds. At a distance of 2 meters from a trumpeter the sound intensity is about one-millionth of a watt per square centimeter. If all the sound energy generated by a full symphony orchestra could be concentrated in a point source, at a distance of 2 meters the intensity would be about one ten-thousandth of a watt per square centimeter which is the threshold of pain for the human ear. If all the residents of New York City (population about 7 million) were to speak at the same time, the total power they would generate would be just about enough to light a 60-watt lamp. Obviously, the intensities attainable with ultrasonic waves are enormous in comparison with those in the audible range. The phenomena discovered in the field of ultrasonics are the direct result of the short wavelength and the concomitant high intensity of ultrasonic waves.

EARLY GENERATORS

The first manmade generator of sustained ultrasonic waves was designed as long ago as 1883, when a forced-air whistle reached the frequency of 25 kilocycles. Nature, however, anticipated the work of man by endowing the bat with an ultrasonic generator of its own. Using the vocal cords in its larynx, the bat generates and emits sound waves in pulses of 2-milliseconds duration at a rate of about 30 per second. The frequency in each pulse ranges from about 30 to 100 kilocycles. Reflections received by the bat's ears indicate the location of obstacles, and, in this radarlike manner, ultrasonic radiation is used by the bat to guide itself in flight.

Following the forced-air whistle, a tuning fork with tines only several millimeters in length was developed near the end of the last century, with a frequency ranging as high as 90 kilocycles. Both the

ILLUS. 35—*Ultrasonic waves, coming from the tiny whistle on the end of the J-shaped tube, are reflected onto the table by the concave metal disk. The ridges, formed in talcum powder, show the standing waves formed by reflections from the tabletop and beaker. (Courtesy General Electric Co.)*

whistle and the fork, however, yielded frequencies which could not be controlled accurately and output powers which were relatively small. There was but little further progress in the development of ultrasonic generators until World War I when Prof. Paul Langevin, director of the School of Physics and Chemistry in Paris, was requested by the French government to devise some method of detecting submarines to combat the U-boat menace.

A few years earlier, following the *Titanic* disaster, an Englishman named L. F. Richardson suggested that a hydraulic whistle be used to locate underwater navigational hazards such as icebergs through the echo of a narrow beam of ultrasonic waves, but experiment proved his apparatus to be ineffective. Then, in 1915, a Russian engineer named Chilowski proposed that ultrasonic vibrations be excited in a mica condenser by a Poulsen arc and that the radiation from the vibrating condenser be used for underwater detection. Prof. Langevin tested and then developed Chilowski's idea to such an extent that a transmission range of 2,000 yards in the Seine River was attained early in 1916, despite the fact that the frequency stability and power output of the generator still left much to be desired. Shortly thereafter, two unrelated scientific discoveries were combined by Langevin to provide for the first time a dependable source of ultrasonic waves of controllable frequency and intensity. To replace the inherently unstable Poulsen arc, Langevin chose the newly developed and far more stable vacuum-tube oscillator. To replace the mica condenser he chose a piezoelectric crystal.

Previously, the piezoelectric effect had had no practical application. A French apothecary, Pierre de la Seignette, of La Rochelle, in 1672 discovered the crystal known as Rochelle salt. In 1880, Pierre and Jacques Curie found that mechanical stresses produced electric charges on the faces of a Rochelle-salt crystal. The inverse of this piezoelectric (pressure electricity) effect was theoretically predicted by Lippmann in 1881 and experimentally verified by the Curies the following year — a voltage applied across the crystal produced a change in the thickness of the crystal. Although it was later discovered that many other crystals, including quartz, had this same property, the piezoelectric effect remained nothing more than a scientific curiosity until 1917. In that year Langevin, who became acquainted with the effect while a student in the laboratory of the Curie brothers, applied the output of a vacuum-tube oscillator across a quartz crystal to produce the first stable, powerful generator of ultrasonic waves.

Today Langevin's generator, with relatively minor improvements, remains the best source of ultrasonic radiation of precisely controllable frequency and intensity. The high-frequency voltage output of a vacuum-tube oscillator is applied to electrodes on opposite faces of a properly cut crystal. When the oscillator frequency is adjusted to the natural resonant frequency of the crystal, powerful mechanical vibrations result, and a beam of ultrasonic waves is radiated through the medium surrounding the crystal. In addition to quartz and Rochelle salt, a number of other neutral and synthetic crystals may be employed to serve particular applications.

LATER GENERATORS

During the decade following World War I, progress in ultrasonics again slowed to a snail's pace except for certain classified military developments in underwater signaling and the development of the magnetostriction oscillator in 1925 by G. W. Pierce. Pierce used a ferrous-metal rod as the core of a solenoid which was energized by an alternating current. As the result of magnetostriction, the ferrous rod periodically changed its length in the alternating magnetic field and a beam of ultrasonic waves was radiated from the end of the vibrating rod. This magnetostriction generator is widely used today, but is limited in the range of frequencies it can generate. For high frequencies the length of the ferrous rod required for resonance becomes too short for practical use, limiting the output of this generator to a maximum frequency of about 60 kilocycles. For higher frequencies the piezoelectric generator has no contender.

It was not until 1930 that nonmilitary ultrasonic research received its first real impetus as the result of the work of R. W. Wood and A. L. Loomis. Wood, who attributed his interest in the subject to the demonstrations he witnessed in Langevin's laboratory at Toulon, imbued Loomis with his own enthusiasm. Alfred Loomis, a wealthy amateur (in the French sense of the word) in the physical sciences, helped Wood set up an elaborate laboratory at Tuxedo Park, N. Y., where they undertook the first serious, comprehensive study of the physical and biological effects of ultrasonic radiation.

Their apparatus consisted of a disk of quartz resting upon a lead plate at the bottom of a shallow dish filled with transformer oil. The upper surface of the quartz was covered by a thin metal foil, and the foil and the lead plate were connected to the output of a 2-kilo-watt vacuum-tube oscillator. The oscillator was an imposing affair indeed! Consisting of two huge Pliotron tubes, a huge bank of oil condensers, a variable condenser 6 feet high and 2 feet in diameter, and an induction coil, it delivered upward of 50,000 alternating volts to the quartz transducer.

When the quartz was excited near its resonant frequency, a mound of oil was raised several centimeters above the oil level in the dish and appeared to be in violent agitation. A thermometer immersed in the oil showed only a moderate rise in temperature, but a finger immersed in the oil experienced a scalding pain of considerable severity. When a test tube containing paraffin and water was held in the oil bath, a rapid dispersion of the paraffin in the water took place, yielding a suspension of unusual permanence. Blood corpuscles and other cells of animal or vegetable tissues immersed in a bath in contact with the oil were violently disrupted, and frogs and small fish were quickly killed. A tapering glass rod, half a millimeter in diameter at the tip, with its butt immersed in the oil, transmitted ultrasonic vibrations of such intensity that a chip of wood smoked and emitted sparks when pressed against the tip, the rod burning its way rapidly through the wood. If a glass plate was substituted for the wood, the rod drilled its way through the plate throwing out the displaced material in the form of a fine powder or minute fused globules of glass. The heating occurred only at the point of contact, the remainder of the glass rod being quite cold. These and a host of other new and interesting effects discovered by Wood and Loomis pointed out the path which has since led into fields of the most surprising variety, interest, and practical importance.

A TOOL FOR RESEARCH

A discovery of particular importance was made in 1932 at the Massachusetts Institute of Technology. During the course of a lecture, Prof. Peter Debye discussed Brillouin's theory of the disper-

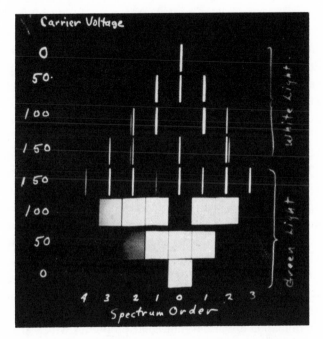

ILLUS. 36—*The Debye-Sears light-diffraction effect. Parallel light is beamed at right angles through a cell containing a liquid in which standing ultrasonic waves have been formed by a vibrating crystal. The alternate regions of compression and expansion form a kind of diffraction grating, but the extent to which light is passed to each of the various orders depends on the amplitude of the standing waves and hence on the voltage applied to the crystal. This photograph shows the diffraction spectra produced by ten-megacycle waves in water. The upper narrow-line spectra are obtained by using a narrow-slit aperture for the light which crosses the cell. The lower broad spectra are made with a very wide slit which is used in light valving. Note that at 100 volts little or no light is left in the center (or zero) order. (Courtesy Bell Laboratories Record.)*

sion of light and X-rays by heat motion treated as a system of elastic waves at which Bragg reflections take place. Debye predicted that the periodic variations in density in a liquid traversed by ultrasonic waves would give rise to the diffraction of light traversing the ultrasonic field. Prof. F. W. Sears, who happened to be in the audience, immediately thereafter set up the experiment. He immersed a quartz plate with metallic electrodes in a glass trough, of rectangular cross section, filled with carbon tetrachloride, and applied a radio-frequency voltage to the crystal, thus sending a train of ultrasonic waves down the trough. A source of monochromatic light, a slit, and a lens were so arranged that a parallel beam of light was sent through the liquid perpendicular to the path of the sound waves. After passage through the trough the light was gathered by another lens and, true to the prediction of Debye, formed, instead of a single image of the slit, a beautiful series of its diffraction images. Thus was born the Debye-Sears effect.

The ultrasonic waves in the liquid set up regions of strong compression and rarefaction with different indices of refraction of light. These regions act like a phase grating (echelon) to produce the various diffraction images. From the spacing of the images and the wavelength of the light the sound wavelength can be determined, which, together with the frequency of the sound, permits the determination of the velocity of the sound in the liquid. The measurement of the velocity of ultrasonic waves in a given medium by this method, and by interferometric and pulse methods, permits the determination of various molecular properties which are of interest to both the physicist and the chemist. For example, these measurements permit the determination of the adiabatic compressibility, which, in turn, permits the computation of the specific heat at constant volume, otherwise calculable only by means of complicated thermodynamic relations. From such measurements the relation between the compressiblity and the concentration of solutions was determined, permitting the test of a number of interesting questions in the modern theory of electrolytes. Theory predicted that the molar compressibility of electrolytes should vary as the square root of the molar concentration, a prediction that was confirmed by these ultrasonic methods. The measured variation of the velocity of sound with frequency, not predicted by classical theory, leads to a determination, via quantum statistics, of the lifetimes of the excited vibrational states of various atoms and the collision efficiency for excitation.

Ultrasonic waves are also used to set up space transmission gratings in transparent solids, which then scatter light in the way that crystal atoms scatter X-rays, resulting in diffraction patterns similar to those of X-ray Laue patterns. Measurements made on these patterns permit the evaluation of the longitudinal and shear velocities of sound in the solid, and hence of the elastic constants of the medium. Similar measurements permit the determination of the photoelastic constants of the material with greater precision and far less work than was entailed in the older interferometric methods. It should be clear from the foregoing that ultrasonic research can be expected to be of use to the molecular physicist, who ordinarily relies upon light or intense electric and magnetic fields to produce disturbances which he can measure. In ultrasonics he has a new agent, a mechanical one, with which to work.

As the intensity of the ultrasonic waves in the liquid-diffraction cell is increased, more and more light is forced from the zero order into the diffracted images, and at a certain sound intensity all the light is removed from the zero order. If a slit is used to permit only the zero order light to pass, the amount of light passing through the slit can be controlled by the intensity of the ultrasonic waves. Ultrasonic cells, thus acting as light valves, have been used as the light-modulating element in sound-on-film recording systems and in the British Scophony system of television. Furthermore, if stationary ultrasonic waves are set up in the cell by reflection, the diffraction effect is intermittent, with double the frequency of the sound, the sound-wave grating being created and destroyed twice each cycle. Light passing through the exit slit is then modulated with this frequency and can be used to give stroboscopic illumination with considerably better light output, simpler construction, and lower electrical losses than the widely used Kerr cell. A drawback, however, is the fact that the modulation frequency depends upon the resonant frequency of the particular crystal used and hence is not continuously variable. Still another slight change in the optical system, the addition of a lens to focus the central plane of the cell on a screen, permits the actual shape of the sound beam to be made visible. Very clear photographs of the reflection, refraction, and interference of ultrasonic waves can thus be obtained.

A FEW APPLICATIONS

Since the pioneer work of Wood and Loomis, each year has seen new progress in ultrasonics. University and industrial laboratories investigated the potentialities of the new field from various directions. Navy interest in sonar also stimulated ultrasonic research, and both the Navy and the Army Signal Corps sponsored investigations of the properties and effects of high-frequency sound. The results of these investigations indicate the unusually wide applicability of ultrasonics.

A pulse technique has been developed for the location of flaws in metals and other solid materials. A crystal is used to send a short pulse of ultrasonic waves into the object to be tested. The same crystal is used (through the direct piezoelectric effect) to receive reflections of the primary pulse. The amplified electrical output of the crystal, portrayed on the screen of a cathode-ray oscilloscope, depicts the primary pulse and all reflected pulses. Reflections caused by flaws permit the presence and location of imperfections to be detected. This technique possesses advantages over X-ray testing in that the equipment is portable, and far greater depths of material can be penetrated. Masses of raw materials can be tested to avoid the machining of defective material, and periodic fatigue checks can easily be made on parts which are under strain as they work without the dismantling of the machinery. One major rubber company tests its entire output of tires by such ultrasonic methods.

The violent agitation produced by high-intensity sound waves has a marked dispersive effect on the solids and liquids, producing true colloidal solutions and fine emulsions. By means of ultrasonic irradiation while in the molten state, alloys can be produced of metals such as iron and lead which are ordinarily not miscible in the liquid state. New bearing materials have been made in this way. By such means it has also been possible to produce photographic emulsions of improved homogeneity, stability, and sensitivity. The homogenization of milk through ultrasonic irradiation is today an

ILLUS. 37—a. *Five solid glass marbles suspended in space by sound waves from a high-intensity ultrasonic siren which are beamed against a reflecting board. (Courtesy Harold K. Schilling, Pennsylvania State College.)*
b. *Transmission of a wide ultrasonic beam through aluminum wedges of increasing taper. Transmission occurs only where the wedge is such as to give internal resonance. (Courtesy Bell Laboratories Record.)*

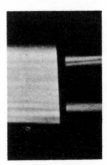  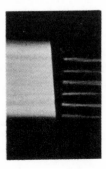

industrial process. The coarse crystals of sulfathiazole have been broken down by ultrasonics to form a creamy emulsion which can be injected through fine hypodermic needles, a technique which was previously impossible.

In spite of the fact that ultrasonic waves have this strong dispersive effect on hydrosols, their effect on aerosols is exactly the opposite — namely, coagulation. Irradiation by intense high-frequency sound causes almost immediate agglomeration and precipitation of the solid and liquid particles in mist and smoke. At an installation in Kingsmill, Tex., this technique is used to recover carbon black from a smokestack. At the Naval Landing Aids Experiment Station, Arcata, Calif., intense sound has been used in this way to turn heavy fog to rain.

Chemical reactions can also be influenced by ultrasonic irradiation. Certain reactions are accelerated, and even depolymerization can be brought about. The chain molecule of starch has been broken down into several fragments to produce dextrine, and gum arabic and gelatine have been decomposed. The aging of whiskey by ultrasonics has been proposed, inasmuch as in the aging process there is a gradual change in the structure of complex molecules, a change which perhaps could be accomplished much more rapidly by sound irradiation.

The biological effects of ultrasonic waves are of particular interest. In several cases the radiation has produced marked diminution in the virulence of bacteria. Yeast cells lose their power of reproduction, luminous bacteria lose their luminosity, and the mosaic virus of tobacco is powerfully deactivated. However, the growth of colon bacilli cannot be influenced even by long exposure to high-intensity sound. The bacteria in milk can be destroyed, permitting pasteurization at low temperatures. Experiments undertaken by sugar refiners show that the enzymes in sugar syrup can be destroyed to retard the inversion of sucrose into glucose. Food decay has been halted for as much as several weeks, indicating the possibility of sterilization of canned foods through ultrasonics. The time required for the germination of seeds has been changed, genes have been made to mature at abnormally fast rates, and in some cases genes have been altered to yield unusual mutations.

At the Pennsylvania State College Acoustical Laboratory an

ultrasiren was used to kill roaches, mosquitoes, and mice. Laboratory workers who were exposed to the sound reported unusual fatigue, occasional loss of equilibrium even when wearing ear protectors, and a disagreeable tickling sensation in the mouth and nose. At another university, an attempt is being made to focus ultrasonic waves inside living tissue in order to produce the destruction of cells in localized regions. The treatment of deep-seated tumors with X-rays irradiates not only the tumor but the intervening tissues as well. Focused ultrasonic radiation may possibly avoid the over-all destructiveness of X-rays. Only further research can show whether this technique is feasible.

Whereas the field of ultrasonics is a logical extension of low-frequency acoustics, the higher-frequency range provides a new tool which can bring new aspects of nature into view. It is rare for a physical phenomenon to have found within a few decades such wide application in science and industry. In a broad survey such as the foregoing, it is manifestly impossible to portray the great variety of detail which has been developed in ultrasonic research, and only a few of the interesting problems and applications have been mentioned. Nonmilitary research in this field is still in its infancy, and many of the observed effects have as yet no adequate explanation. Ultrasonics today, a broad and beckoning field for research, holds forth the promise of exciting new discoveries just beyond the horizon.

SUPPLEMENTARY NOTE

During the past 15 years ultrasonics has, as predicted, found new and important applications. In industry, ultrasonic energy is being used in the welding of metals, the bonding of plastics, the cleaning of intricate parts, the nondestructive detection of internal flaws in a wide variety of items including large structures such as the Apollo manned-spacecraft capsule and the 33-foot-diameter Saturn second stage, the measurement of the thickness of road pavement and plastic sheets and cattle fat, the processing of information in radars and computers by means of delay lines, and the atomization of gasoline and oil fuels to provide more complete burning and minimize the production of smog. Still another industrial application is in the machining of delicate and Lilliputian parts, often from highly intractable materials; ultrasonic machining with ever-increasing accuracy is being used in semiconductor wafers, carbide dies, ceramics, hardened tool steels and even refractory metals.

A flat-faced, solid-state television screen may result from current studies involving both ultrasonics and electroluminescence. Transducers mounted on adjoining edges of a ceramic slab send plane orthogonal ultrasonic pulses through the slab. Since the ceramic is piezoelectric, electric charges accompany the ultrasonic pulses as they move across the slab. At the moving point of intersection of the orthogonal waves the total charge is sufficient to excite the phosphor in an overlying luminescent screen, thus yielding a moving spot of light whose position is determined by the timing of the ultrasonic pulses and the speed of the ultrasonic waves in the ceramic slab. Success in this development may one day provide the ideal television screen, requiring no vacuum containment and thin enough to hang on the wall. Another application of ultrasonics to optical devices is found in the new field of lasers. Traveling ultrasonic waves in a Debye-Sears diffraction cell are being used as a shutter in the feedback path of a ruby laser to gate or amplitude-modulate the output of coherent laser light.

Sonar, as used by the U.S. Navy, has undergone extensive development into surprisingly sophisticated systems which are used both for navigation and for antisubmarine warfare. Civilian modifications of such systems are widely used in oceanographic investigations, since sound is the only form of energy which is useful for obtaining information over great distances in the sea. These systems make it possible to survey rapidly large areas of the ocean floor. An underwater towed transducer is being used by an American company to survey the surface contours and subsurface geological structure (to a depth of 600 feet in waters 200 feet deep) of 160 square miles of the floor of the English Channel between Dover and Calais. (The work is being done under contract to the Channel Tunnel Study Group, a British-French-U.S. consortium which proposes to complete, by 1971, a 32-mile tunnel to link England and France, as first proposed by Napoleon's engineers.)

By coupling piezoelectric or magnetostrictive materials to the rapidly alternating electromagnetic field in a microwave cavity, the frequency range of ultrasonic waves has now been extended into the range of gigacycles (10^9 cps). These acoustic waves, with very short wavelengths approximately equal to those of visible light, are providing a powerful research tool for the study of matter. The lattice vibrations produced by thermal or acoustic energy in a solid may be treated as waves passing through the lattice, or their quantized nature may be emphasized by treating them quantum-mechanically as particlelike "phonons," which are to vibrational waves what protons are to light waves. Since gigacycle phonons interact with thermal phonons, with electron spins, and with nuclear spins, the study of solid-state physics has been greatly enhanced by the use of ultrasonics. Ultrasonic methods are being employed to map the topology of the Fermi surface in solids, to study the super-conducting state, and to explore the properties of semiconductors. The interaction between gigacycle phonons and electrons in certain piezoelectric semiconductors such as cadmium sulfide has been harnessed to amplify ultrasonic waves by transferring energy from the conduction electrons to the acoustic waves; it is anticipated that a 10-gigacycle acoustic wave may be amplified by a factor of a million after traveling only half a millimeter in certain materials. The electron-phonon interaction has also made possible the generation and amplification of acoustic waves in a paramagnetic crystal in much the same way that electromagnetic waves are amplified in a maser. Some of these fairly esoteric effects, only recently discovered, are already being intensively explored with a view to applications.

Finally, the diagnostic, therapeutic, and surgical uses of ultrasonics have become established in the field of medicine. In diagnosis, ultrasonic sonar-type echoes of pulses reveal soft internal tissues which are nearly invisible to X-rays; in addition, the ultrasonic waves do not present the radiation hazard which accompanies X-rays. Thus, ultrasound is being used to view the human foetus in the mother's womb in order to measure its size and position and to determine whether a Caesarean section is needed. Ultrasonic encephalography yields anatomical detail and permits the detection of tumors, cerebral hemorrhages, and concussions in the brain. Ultrasonic cardiography, in which the acoustic waves are reflected by the pulsating organ, reveals heart-value defects and verifies the effectiveness of repairs, and may some day warn of oversized hearts which are ripe for attacks. Cancerous tissue reflects ultrasound differently from normal tissue, and serious study is therefore being given to the detection and diagnosis of cancer by ultrasonics. In some cases, cancer of the breast was diagnosed by ultrasonics and verified by biopsy, at the same time that other methods of detection failed to indicate a tumor. Recently, a young woman had a rapidly growing mass in her abdomen which could have been a pregnancy (tests were inconclusive) or a tumor. Ultrasonics revealed the head of a foetus a few weeks old as well as two abdominal tumors. (Surgeons were able to remove the tumors and leave the pregnancy undisturbed.) In another case, at Walter Reed General Hospital, an eye of a nine-year-old boy was saved which surely would have been lost but for ultrasonics. A three-pronged chip of brass was lodged in his eye by the explosion of a rifle cartridge. Ultrasonic forceps (resembling tweezers with a tiny built-in source of ultrasonic waves) were used to successfully home on and remove the brass fragment without damaging the retina. Ultrasonic therapy is a frequently prescribed pain reliever for people suffering from spinal arthritis and bursitis, and was used a few years ago on the late President Kennedy when he was having trouble with his back. Focused high-power ultrasonics is being used in human neurosurgery deep within the brain structure to selectively destroy tissue and produce lesions in small localized regions in order to block conducting nerve pathways and provide dramatic cures of, for example, the uncontrollable tremors in Parkinson's disease. Similarly, neuroreceptor cells in the semicircular canals of the inner ear have been successfully destroyed with ultrasonics to relieve the vertigo, nausea, and progressive deafness of Ménière's disease.

This brief review of the current status of ultrasonics reveals that significant progress has indeed been achieved, and it may confidently be expected that the future will see a further expansion in the domain of ultrasonics and its impact on research and applications.

E. M. McCORMICK

Digital Computers: Their History, Operation, and Use

[FROM THE SMITHSONIAN REPORT FOR 1960[1]]

DEVELOPMENTS *in science and technology have come so fast in recent years that new marvels are soon taken for granted and we have almost lost our sense of wonder. An example in point is the digital computer, which has become so widely used as to be commonplace, yet the first electronic computer was built as recently as 1946. Thousands of computers in some form are now in everyday use in solving almost instantaneously difficult mathematical problems that formerly required months of arduous manual calculations, in the quick and accurate processing of vast amounts of data for banks and many other types of businesses, and even for guiding missiles and space vehicles. Their seeming ability to think and make decisions have caused them to be looked upon as mechanical brains. The author of this article, E. M. McCormick, now associated with the National Science Foundation where he is concerned with the application of computers to technical information systems, has been successively a radar instructor for the Army Air Corps, electronic engineer with Goodyear Aircraft Corporation, and head of the Digital Computer Applications Group, U.S. Naval Ordnance Laboratory at Corona, Calif. He reviews the brief his-*

[1] Revised as of March 1965.

tory of computers, tells how they work, and gives detailed ex-amples of the way in which they go about solving problems. If a reader who is unfamiliar with computers will conscientiously fol-low through these examples, he will understand the strange ways of an electronic computer in solving complex problems formerly attempted only by the human brain.

INTRODUCTION

In the past 20 years digital computers have emerged as an interesting and extremely useful tool not only for scientists but for workers in many other fields of human endeavor. Their use has been so widespread as to suggest that they may be the basis for another revolution comparable in significance to the industrial revolution. Their appeal and usefulness are due largely to the fact that they perform tasks which heretofore have required "intellec-tual" effort for their accomplishment. Much has been said about the ability of computers to perform in relatively short periods of time tasks which otherwise might require the brainpower of many humans working over long periods of time. Since computers do work which man normally does mentally, in contrast to doing jobs which require musclepower, there is some confusion and mis-conception about digital computers and their use. Man does not know nearly as much about intellectual activities as he does about physical. Further, he is less able to judge them by measures which are commonly understood.

First impressions of digital computers are impressive and per-haps confusing. Computers are expensive devices costing thou-sands or even millions of dollars. They consist of hundreds of thou-sands of electronic components interconnected in what appears to be a very complicated manner. Some of the equipment for putting information into or taking information out of computers is perhaps familiar, since commonly used electric typewriters and business accounting machines have been adapted for this purpose. How-ever, much of the rest of the equipment is unfamiliar.

Digital computers are information-processing devices. The information is generally represented by numbers and the processing involves the performing of simple arithmetic operations such as adding, subtracting, multiplying, and dividing. Scientists use digital computers for solving very complicated mathematical problems, and businessmen use them for the clerical operations associated with the processing of their data.

HISTORY

Mechanical aids to computation go back to the abacus, an ancient device still widely used in many parts of the world. The number representation system of a form of the abacus, with two beads above a bar and five below for each decimal digit, has been used in an electronic equivalent form, *biquinary*, in modern computers. The adding machine was invented in 1642 by Blaise Pascal. This type of calculator was developed especially in the last century and is now widely used. Automatic multiplication and division by calculators was invented in 1902.

The man who had the original concept of what is now known as a digital computer was Charles Babbage, 1792-1871. Babbage was a professor of mathematics at Cambridge University but engaged in many activities outside the field of mathematics[2]. Babbage first conceived of a "difference engine" in 1822. This mechanical device would permit the automatic production of mathematical tables such as logarithms, sine, cosine, and other numerical functions. However, before he had completed this project he conceived of a much more general computing device called an "analytical engine." It contained most of the concepts now considered to be essential in a digital computer. He drew up elaborate detailed drawings for the device. However, it was mechanical and required skills not then available. Only part of the machine was built; it is now in the British Science Museum.

[2] As indicated in Bowden (see bibliography), Babbage invented the cowcatcher, the speedometer, suggested a fixed fee for posting letters, made an operations research analysis of the pin industry, was the first to sail across a railroad viaduct in a handcar, among other interesting activities.

Despite the fact that it was never built, the significance and implications of such a device were understood by a number of people at that time. Lady Ada Augustus Lovelace, 1815-52, daughter of Lord Byron, was quite familiar with the analytical engine and its potentialities. Much of what we know about the device is due to her writings on the subject.

About 100 years after Babbage, circumstances made it possible to build a digital computer. During World War II techniques were developed which were used for building the first electromechanical computers using electrical relays. Mark I was built at Harvard in 1944. Electronic techniques, however, permitted much higher rates of operation. The first electronic computer, ENIAC, was built at the University of Pennsylvania in 1946. It used 18,000 tubes, and with the unreliability of tubes at that time it was easy to "prove" that tubes would fail faster than they could be replaced. Nevertheless, this and many other problems were solved, and many thousands of computers have been built since then. It was 1950 before the first digital computer was built with all the characteristics now considered to be essential.

Interestingly, many of the devices adapted for use in computers have been available for some time. The basic bistable electronic circuit (the *flip-flop*) was invented in 1919. The equipment for input to and output from digital computers is adapted from communication and business-accounting devices. Punched paper tape was used by Samuel F. B. Morse, inventor of the telegraph. The familiar punched card was used by Jacquard in 1801 and is still in use to control weaving looms for making designs in cloth. (Babbage had intended to use punched cards in his analytical engine.) Hollerith adapted punched cards for the 1890 census, and many other uses have been made of them since then. And, finally, the mathematics needed for the logical design of digital computers was developed by another English mathematician of the last century, George Boole, 1815-64.

COMPUTERS VERSUS CALCULATORS

The solving of mathematical problems and processing of business data have been accomplished for some time by the use of manual calculators. How are computers different from calculators, which also do arithmetic operations? To answer this we must realize that doing the arithmetic operations is only part of the process of solving a problem when using a calculator. Deciding what numbers to put into the calculator, putting them into it, and after performing the arithmetic, deciding what to do with the numbers resulting from it and then doing it all involve more time than the arithmetic itself.

Computers differ from calculators in that computers do the *complete* job of solving a problem. They contain within themselves all the data pertinent to a problem and all the instructions for solving it, including alternate sets of instructions to be followed on the basis of decisions which the machine itself can make. Thus a digital computer is capable of completely solving a problem at electronic speeds without human intervention during the solution. However, the setting up of a computer to do this is frequently time-consuming and expensive.

But what has a computer really gained over a calculator and its operator except speed? First, we must realize that for many purposes this speed advantage itself is sufficient gain. Being able to do hundreds of thousands or even millions of operations in the time formerly required for one is a tremendous advantage in solving a problem.

Ways for solving problems involving a very large number of operations have been known for many years, but the time and labor required made them impracticable. For example, the value of *pi* can be calculated to any number of decimal places by several different formulas. William Shanks, 1812-82, an English mathematician, spent many years calculating the value of *pi* to 707 places. The results were published in 1854, and 92 years passed before a computer duplicated this remarkable feat[3]. There have been several subsequent calculations of *pi* to many decimal places, including to 3,089 places in 1954 (13 minutes computing time) and 100,000 places in 1961 (8 hours and 43 minutes computing time).

---

[3] Shanks had verified his results to 500 places. The computer solution, however, showed that Shanks had erred so that his figures beyond the 527th place are incorrect.

There are many other problems that can be represented mathematically, the solution of which required a tremendously large number of operations. The solving of a large number of simultaneous linear equations is one example. Others are the "monte carlo" and relaxation methods of solving the intricate mathematics associated with atomic energy studies.

However, to answer the question above, digital computers do have advantages other than speed. They can perform *logical* operations as well as *arithmetic*. This is a very important property, which we will consider further after discussing some of the details of how a computer works and of the particular arithmetic of a computer.

HOW COMPUTERS WORK

Mechanical calculators use a system of motors, wheels, levers, dials, and other mechanical devices to perform the operations required of these calculators. The motor and wheels accomplish various numbers and types of mechanical operations, and the levers convey these operations to the dials for indicating the numbers. Each dial has 10 positions on it for the numbers 0 through 9.

Digital computers, on the other hand, are predominantly electronic rather than mechanical devices, but the electronic operations are analogous to many of the mechanical operations in calculators. Numbers are represented in computers by series of electrical pulses traveling from one part of the computer to another by wires. (These pulses are much like those produced in dialing a telephone.) They occur at such a high speed (hundreds of thousands or millions per second) that mechanical devices cannot be used to produce, control, or count them. Instead, electronic devices called *gates,* which use radio tubes or transistors, are used. Electronic *flip-flop* devices (devices which are in one condition or another, with no intermediate positions) also are widely used for counting pulses in computers. Many thousands of these gates and flip-flops may be used in any one computer.

To obtain the very high speed and extreme reliability required for accurately producing, controlling, and counting pulses, electronic engineers use devices which represent numbers not by a base of 10, but by a base of 2, that is, a binary system using only 0 and 1. Thus numbers are represented by combinations of many individual electronic devices, each of which are either on or off, or by pulses which are either present or absent at any given time. Many of these electronic devices have small neon lamps connected to them so that the lamps either glow or not depending on whether that device is representing a 1 or a 0. These lamps flash on and off quite rapidly as a computer operates and are frequently shown in movies or television views of computers. The binary system of representing numbers will be considered in detail later.

Since the numbers inside a computer are represented by electrical pulses sent from one part of the computer to another, the input and output devices for computers must operate in much the same manner. A common device for input and output for a computer is quite similar to a teletype machine. The numbers are represented by combinations of holes punched in a paper tape. As this tape is moved over a *reading* device, the presence or absence of holes in the tape produces a series of electrical pulses which the computer uses to represent the numbers. Similarly, a series of pulses in a computer can cause an output device to punch a series of holes in a paper tape. These pulses can also cause an electric typewriter to type the numbers in the usual form. This is desirable as the numbers are difficult to read as holes in a tape. Further, the typing of numbers on the keyboard of an input device will produce a punched paper tape suitable for input to the computer.

Many computers use business-accounting type machines for input and output. Numbers are represented by holes in the familiar punched card. However, the basic operation of these devices is essentially the same as considered above.

METHOD OF SOLVING PROBLEMS

An analogy can be used to illustrate the method by which a computer solves problems. Consider a room in which there is a large number of file cabinets, each file drawer marked by a number. Each drawer contains a slip of paper which is either a number or an instruction for some action to be taken. In this room is a clerk who goes to the first drawer and obeys the instruction he finds there. He will then go to the second drawer and obey the instruction there, and so on. The only exception to this sequence is when the instruction in a drawer specifically states that the next instruction is to be taken from some other storage location. The clerk, in obeying most of the instructions, will have to refer to some other specified drawer for the data he needs to follow out the instruction. He also has a pad of paper on which to store temporarily the results of each operation he performs in obeying these instructions. Except for the first drawer, the clerk will not know in advance which drawers contain numbers and which contain instructions.

Yet by following the above procedure, which involves performing very simple operations at each step, it is possible for the clerk to solve a large number of problems including some of the most abstruse mathematical problems. The clerk will not need to know what he is doing or why.

As an example let us consider in detail how this technique can be used to calculate the value of a sum of money subject to compound interest. Assume that we wish to do this for just 20 periods of interest accumulation. Further assume that the file drawers (storage locations) are numbered 000, 001, 002, and so on. The clerk goes first to the first drawer (number 000) and finds there an instruction which says, "Take the number in drawer 020 and write it on the pad." The clerk then goes to drawer marked 020 and in it finds a number representing the initial value of principal. Having written this on the pad, he next goes to drawer 001 and reads the instruction there. It says, "Multiply the number on the pad by the number in drawer 021; leave only the answer on the pad." Since the number in 021 will represent the interest rate, the result of this multiplication would be the amount of interest earned. The clerk now goes to drawer 002, where he is instructed to "Add the number in 020 to the number on the pad." In so doing the new value of principal is computed. He then goes to 003, where the next instruction is, "Store the number on the pad in drawer 020, leaving the pad blank." (This storing of a number in a drawer always means that the number that was previously in that location is erased. However, the process of reading a number in a drawer does not affect that number.)

Now the clerk, upon going to drawer 004 for his next instruction, might find, "Go to storage location 000 for your next instruction." If so, he will again repeat the instructions in 000, 001, 002, 003, and 004 in turn, but this time using the new value of principal. This sequence of operations will be repeated over and over again. Each time this "loop" is repeated the number in 020 will increase, representing the value of principal with the accumulated interest for that number of interest periods. Thus if the initial number in 020 represented $10,000 and the number in 021 represented 5 percent, then the values in 020 would represent $10,500 after the first loop, $11,025 after the second, $11,556.25 after the third, and so on.

However, this process would not solve the problem as originally stated, which specified that the process must stop after 20 calculations. Yet the set of operations resulting from the above instructions would go on indefinitely unless the procedure is modified. The modification would start with changing the instruction in 004 to "Put the number in drawer 022 on the pad." (The number in 022 will be 0 when the problem starts.) Next in 005 the instruction would be, "Add the number on the pad to the number in 023 and leave only the answer on the pad." Since the number in 023 is 1, the sum will be 1. In 006 the instruction is, "Store the number on the pad in location 022, leaving the pad blank." Thus a 1 is stored in 022 in place of the 0 which was there. The number in 022 thus indicates the number of interest calculations that have been made.

To use this to determine when to stop, the instruction in 007 is, "Take the number in 022 and write it on the pad." Then in 008, "Subtract from the number on the pad the number in drawer 024, leaving only the result on the pad." Since the number in 024 is 20, the first time this instruction is obeyed the result will be − 19. Now assume that in 009 there is a decision instruction of this nature: "If the number on the pad is 0 or positive, go to the next instruction in order; if the number is negative, erase it and go to drawer 000." Thus the clerk would in this case go back to 000 and repeat the entire process. However, the next time he came to 022 he would find a 1 in it which would be changed to a 2, leaving − 18 after executing the instruction in 008 the second time. Thus in response to instruction in 009 the process would repeat again. The third time the result would be − 17, and so on. However, after the value of principal plus accumulated interest has been computed for the 20th time, the result of executing the instruction in 008 will be a 0 on the pad. Now when the instruction in 009 is encountered, the result will be that the clerk will go for the first time to 010 for his next instruction. Thus after 20 iterations the program of activity indicated by the instructions in the drawers results in a "branch" to an alternate course of action. The instruction in 010 can be simply "Stop" or it could be the first instruction of a sequence which will solve some other problem.

A digital computer generally solves problems in just this manner. The "storage" of a computer takes the place of the group of file cabinets. Each drawer is an individual storage location containing a "word" which is a sequence of numbers which may be data or an instruction. Each storage location is identified by an "address" much as houses are identified by different addresses. Instead of the pad of paper, a computer has an electronic storage device called an "accumulator." (This corresponds to the row of dials on the top of many manually operated calculators.) The equipment for storage and for performing the duties of the clerk are electronic and operate automatically at high rates of speed.

The speed of a digital computer means the speed at which it can perform arithmetic operations. This may be tens of thousands per second. The size of a computer generally indicates the amount of information that may be contained in its storage, possibly millions of words.

Note that the computer need do only a limited number of operations. In the program given above, the "operation" to be performed in storage locations 000, 002, 004, 005, and 007 are all the same. They differ only in the address of the number to be added to the number already in the accumulator. Thus each instruction consists of two parts, an operation portion and an address, or in other words, what to do and wherefrom to do it.

Numbers can be used to designate operations. Thus the *add* operation in drawers or storage locations 000, 002, 004, 005, and 007 can be arbitrarily designated to the computer as "1," the *subtract* operation in 008 as "2," the *multiply* in 001 as "3," the *store* of 003 and 006 as "5," and the *decision* operation in 009 as "7." If each word of a computer consists of 10 decimal digits with the operation digit in the 6th position and the address digits in the 8th, 9th, and 10th positions, then the above compound-interest problem can be specified to a computer as shown in Table 1. This is a "program" for computer operation; sometimes also called a

TABLE 1. — *Example of a digital computer program to compute compound interest*[4]

Storage location	Instruction or number	Remarks
000........................	0000010020	Take principal.
001........................	0000030021	Multiply by interest rate.
002........................	0000010020	Add principal.
003........................	0000050020	Store new principal.
004........................	0000010022	Take tally.
005........................	0000010023	Add 1.
006........................	0000050022	Store as new tally.
007........................	0000010022	Take new tally.
008........................	0000020024	Subtract 20.
009........................	0000070000	Test for repeat.
•		
•		
•		
020........................	....	Principal.
021........................	....	Interest rate.
022........................	....	Tally.
023........................	0000000001	
024........................	0000000020	

"routine." The first column indicates the storage location of the instructions and the data used in the problem. The column "Instruction or number" indicates the contents of each of these storage locations. The "Remarks" column is given merely to assist humans in understanding what is being done; the computer makes no use of it. A thorough grasp of the sequence of computer operations used in solving the compound-interest problem is essential to the understanding of digital computers.

Table 1 also shows how instructions can have the same form as numbers used as data and hence are interchangeable with data. Thus a computer can do arithmetic operations on its instructions,

[4] Tables 1, 6, 7, and 8 are reprinted by permission from *Digital Computer Primer*, copyright 1959, McGraw-Hill Book Co., Inc.

an interesting and useful characteristic of digital computers.

The above example also illustrates the different manner in which a computer and a human would solve a problem. The most important difference is the extreme detail of the instructions that must be given to the computer, and especially the manner in which these instructions must be stated in order to use the limited number of operations that a computer can perform. Contrast this with the instructions that one would give to a human to do the same job. Even if the calculation of compound interest had to be explained, it would not be necessary to go into such detail to insure that just 20 sets of calculations were made. It will also be noted that many of the operations are concerned with the manipulation of data (going to and from storage, etc.) rather than with the calculations themselves. These "bookkeeping" or "red tape" operations occupy a considerable portion of the program and of the time used in solving the problem. This applies also, however, to the use of a calculator for solving a problem. In a computer it is more obvious, as the instructions for these operations have the same general form as the instructions for doing the arithmetic itself.

THE PARTICULAR ARITHMETIC OF COMPUTERS

Aside from manipulation of data and decision-making, the essential operations of a computer are simple arithmetic. Since we all know how to add, subtract, multiply, and divide, it may be of interest to know how computers perform these functions. Generally their method differs from that of humans not only in the number system, but also in details of all arithmetic operations.

Binary numbers. — Most modern digital computers use a binary number system rather than the familiar decimal system. There are only 2 marks, 0 and 1, instead of 10 different marks, 0 through 9. Each position on either side of the binary point (corresponding to the decimal point) is a power of 2. This is illustrated by Table 2, which shows the binary equivalent of decimal digits 0 through 9. The rightmost binary position indicates the presence (by a 1) or the absence (by a 0) of a 1, the next position the presence or

TABLE 2. − *Table of binary equivalents to decimal numbers*

Decimal	Binary	Decimal	Binary
0	0000	5	0101
1	0001	6	0110
2	0010	7	0111
3	0011	8	1000
4	0100	9	1001

absence of a 2, the next a 4, an 8, and so on. Thus 0111 is $4+2+1$, or 7; 1001 is $8+1$, or 9; 1100010001 would be $512+256+16+1$, or 785; 110.011 would be $4+2+\frac{1}{4}+\frac{1}{8}$, or $6\frac{3}{8}$.

The reason for using a binary notation system is a practical one. Computers consist of devices which must be very fast and extremely reliable. The electronic devices which best meet these requirements are *two-state* (*bistable*) elements. Thus it is possible only to know whether these devices represent one *bit* of information, that is, either a 0 or 1. For example, whether a certain spot on a magnetic tape is magnetized in one direction or in the other direction, whether a vacuum tube is conducting current or not, a hole is punched in a card or it is not, etc.

Binary addition. − Another advantage of the binary number system is that binary arithmetic is quite simple. The binary addition table is given in Table 3. The two numbers A and B can each have values of 0 or 1 so that there are only four possibilities to consider. An example of binary addition which uses all four combinations is given in Table 4. However, binary representation means that about $3\frac{1}{3}$ times as many marks are needed to repre-

TABLE 3. − *The binary addition table*

A	B	Carry	Sum
0	0	0	0
0	1	0	1
1	0	0	1
1	1	1	0

TABLE 4. − *Binary addition and decimal equivalent*

Binary				Decimal	
1	1	0	0	8+4	=12
1	0	1	0	8+2	=10
1 0 1 1 0				16+4+2	=22

sent a number, as with the decimal system. For example, the 3-decimal digit number 785 requires 10 binary bits 1100010001 for its representation. Thus a binary computer would need to do 3⅓ times as many binary operations to be equivalent to decimal arithmetic. However, this is a small price to pay for the advantages gained.

Referring back to Table 3, we note that the conditions under which the *sum* digit is a 1 can be stated in words as, "when A is a 1 *or* B is a 1 *and* both A *and* B are *not* 1." Similarly, the condition for a 1 in the *carry* digit is, "when A is 1 *and* B is 1." The italicized words are important because they show how a binary addition operation can be expressed in words, *and, or,* and *not,* which are terms with logical meaning. The basic ideas of *and, or,* and *not* are familiar to everyone and their use in digital computer adders is the same as in the usually understood concepts of these terms. It is thus possible to draw a *logical* diagram for binary addition as shown in Illustration 38. This figure should be compared with the above word statement on binary addition and with Table 3. They are equivalent ways of expressing the same thing.

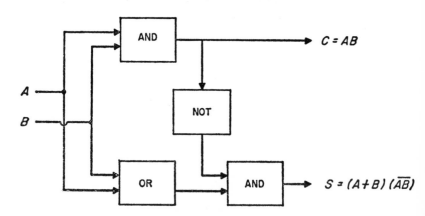

ILLUS. 38—Logical circuit for binary addition.

The exact form of the adder in a digital computer varies from one computer design to another. The *and, or,* and *not* devices may use vacuum tubes, transistors, or magnetic devices. However, the logic, no matter how implemented, is the same.

Obviously, the addition operation must be done for each pair of digits in the two numbers to be added. Furthermore, in general, it is not simply a matter of adding just two digits together; it is necessary also to add the carry digit from the previous less significant addition. Thus a *full-adder* considers all three inputs. The device of Illustration 38 is a *half-adder* since it considers only two inputs. A full-adder can be formed by using two half-adders.

The "logical design" in digital computers extends to much more than the adder. Most of the other operations of the computer, including storage and decision operations, can be expressed in logical terms and hence be composed of the same electronic logical devices. The logical design of a computer is indeed very complicated, and most computers use many thousand logical elements.

So far we have considered only binary arithmetic. However, humans who put data into computers and read its answers are much more familiar with decimal numbers than with binary. Thus it is necessary to convert decimal numbers into some form of binary for input to a computer and to convert binary to decimal for output. The computer itself can do this converting. One way of doing this is to use combinations of binary digits to represent decimal digits in *binary-coded decimal* systems. Table 2 can be considered as an example of such a system. By such methods it is possible to use digital computers as if they were true decimal devices, although in fact they all are binary in some form or another.

Subtraction. — Subtraction can be, and sometimes is, done in a manner comparable to addition, that is, the subtraction table is formed, the logical equivalent determined, and the corresponding electronic circuitry built. However, many computers use the adder to do subtraction by representing negative numbers by a *complement* notation.

To understand this, consider Table 5 where the left column gives the normal sequence of numbers from +5 backward to −5. It includes the concepts of zero and negative numbers. A complement system for representing these numbers is given in the right column. (For convenience, we consider only four digit numbers.)

When the number is negative, the complement representation is the same as if the number were subtracted from 9999. The process of subtracting by adding the complement obviously is dependent on the fact that the complement can be obtained by a process simpler than subtraction, and indeed it can be done electronically.

The sequence of numbers in the right "counter" column is unusual but is as valid as the usual sequence if a set of rules is used for manipulation that differs somewhat from the usual set. Examples are given in Table 6. Note first that results are always obtained by adding. Further, when the sum of the two numbers exceeds the four-digit size assumed, then the carry is added back to the right end of the sum. This last rule is a result of the way the sequence of numbers was defined. It is due to the fact that 0000

TABLE 5. — *Complement representation for negative numbers*

Number	Counter	Number	Counter
5	0005	−1	9998
4	0004	−2	9997
3	0003	−3	9996
2	0002	−4	9995
1	0001	−5	9994
0	9999		

TABLE 6. — *Counter column illustrates how complements can be used for handling negative numbers*

	Number		Counter	
(A)	+5		0005	
	−2		9997	
	——		——	
	+3	1	0002	Before end-around carry
			0003	After end-around carry
(B)	+1		0001	
	−4		9995	
	——		——	
	−3		9996	
(C)	−2		9997	
	−3		9996	
	——		——	
	−5	1	9993	Before
			9994	After

is not given in this sequence and that zero is represented by 9999. Again the reasons for this will not be considered here, but it does simplify the computer design. It is suggested that the reader try other examples using complements, such as adding zero (9999) to other numbers including itself.

Multiplication. — Most computers do not multiply as such, that is, they do not use multiplication tables. They multiply by a process of repeated addition much as calculators do. The product of 3,514 by 7,596 could be obtained by adding 7,596 for a total of 3,514 times, but this would be a tedious process. However, by combining left shift operations (which are the equivalent of multiplying by 10 in a decimal machine or by 2 in a binary machine) with add operations, the number of additions required for multiplication can be considerably reduced.

The details of how such a multiplication could be done are given in Table 7. Assume that the multiplier 3,514 is initially in columns 2 through 5 and that the multiplicand 7,596 is added in columns 6 through 9. Each time the multiplicand is added, the number in column 1 is reduced 1. When the number in column 1 is 0 the whole accumulator is shifted one position to the left and the process repeated. The 18 steps involved in this particular multiplication should be noted in detail. In this example only $3+5+1+4$ or a total of 13 additions would be required.

Division. — Computer division also is generally done in a manner analogous to methods used in calculators. It involves successive subtracting, testing, correcting, and shifting operations. Table 8 shows how 26,693,578 can be divided by 7,596 to obtain 3,514 as the quotient with a remainder of 1,234. After an initial left shift, the process involves subtracting the divisor 7,596 from columns 2 through 5 of the dividend until the remainder is negative. This indicates that one too many subtractions has occurred, so the program adds the divisor back and then shifts the remainder one position to the left. Then the process repeats. Since a 1 is added in column 9 for each subtraction which leaves a positive remainder, the final result is that the quotient (3,514) is in columns 6 through 9 and the remainder (1,234) is in columns 2 through 5.

TABLE 7. — *Steps in process of multiplying 3,514 by 7,596 to get 26,692,344 as a computer might do this multiplication*

Steps		Columns								
		1	2	3	4	5	6	7	8	9
1	Start	0	3	5	1	4	0	0	0	0
2	Shift	3	5	1	4	0	0	0	0	0
3	Add	2	5	1	4	0	7	5	9	6
4	Add	1	5	1	4	1	5	1	9	2
5	Add	0	5	1	4	2	2	7	8	8
6	Shift	5	1	4	2	2	7	8	8	0
7	Add	4	1	4	2	3	5	4	7	6
8	Add	3	1	4	2	4	3	0	7	2
9	Add	2	1	4	2	5	0	6	6	8
10	Add	1	1	4	2	5	8	2	6	4
11	Add	0	1	4	2	6	5	8	6	0
12	Shift	1	4	2	6	5	8	6	0	0
13	Add	0	4	2	6	6	6	1	9	6
14	Shift	4	2	6	6	6	1	9	6	0
15	Add	3	2	6	6	6	9	5	5	6
16	Add	2	2	6	6	7	7	1	5	2
17	Add	1	2	6	6	8	4	7	4	8
18	Add	0	2	6	6	9	2	3	4	4

LOGICAL USES OF COMPUTERS

So far we have considered digital computers only as they are fast equivalents of a clerk with a calculator. The clerk functions were assumed to be quite simple and the routine was spelled out in specific detail. It was over 100 years ago that Lady Lovelace said that a digital computer "has no pretensions to originate anything. It can do whatever we know how to order it to perform." The statement is still true. It can be interpreted to indicate the limitations of computers in that humans must think through in advance everything that a computer might do and tell the computer specifically the course of action in each case. However, it is perhaps more correct to interpret the statement to mean that the limitations encountered in using computers are more of a reflection on our ability as humans to use them than on the computers themselves.

This is particularly true in the increasing use being made of computers as "logical" devices. While many useful human activities involve the use of arithmetic, many others require the solution of

TABLE 8. — *How a computer might divide 26,693,578 by 7,596 to obtain a quotient of 3,514 and a remainder of 1,234*

Steps		Columns								
		1	2	3	4	5	6	7	8	9
1	Start	0	2	6	6	9	3	5	7	8
2	Shift	2	6	6	9	3	5	7	8	0
3	Subtract	1	9	0	9	7	5	7	8	1
4	Subtract	1	1	5	0	1	5	7	8	2
5	Subtract	0	3	9	0	5	5	7	8	3
6	Subtract	−0	3	6	9	0	4	2	1	7
7	Add	0	3	9	0	5	5	7	8	3
8	Shift	3	9	0	5	5	7	8	3	0
9	Subtract	3	1	4	5	9	7	8	3	1
10	Subtract	2	3	8	6	3	7	8	3	2
11	Subtract	1	6	2	6	7	7	8	3	3
12	Subtract	0	8	6	7	1	7	8	3	4
13	Subtract	0	1	0	7	5	7	8	3	5
14	Subtract	−0	6	5	2	0	2	1	6	5
15	Add	0	1	0	7	5	7	8	3	5
16	Shift	1	0	7	5	7	8	3	5	0
17	Subtract	0	3	1	6	1	8	3	5	1
18	Subtract	−0	4	4	3	5	1	6	4	9
19	Add	0	3	1	6	1	8	3	5	1
20	Shift	3	1	6	1	8	3	5	1	0
21	Subtract	2	4	0	2	2	3	5	1	1
22	Subtract	1	6	4	2	6	3	5	1	2
23	Subtract	0	8	8	3	0	3	5	1	3
24	Subtract	0	1	2	3	4	3	5	1	4
25	Subtract	−0	6	3	6	2	6	4	8	5
26	Add	0	1	2	3	4	3	5	1	4

essentially logical problems. An executive managing a business concern, the officer directing a military operation, and a chess player are examples of people who must consider the often complicated situations in which they find themselves and "decide" on an appropriate course of action. There are probably many more practical problems requiring a logical solution than those calling for arithmetic operations. Thus the ability of computers to handle logic is particularly important. This ability may be considered an outgrowth of operations already mentioned. The decision operation, "If the number in the accumulator is zero or positive, go to the next storage location for the next instruction; if it is negative, clear the accumulator and go to the storage location specified for the next instruction," is an example used in the compound-interest problem. Most digital computers can use any of many decision operations.

The binary notation incidentally is convenient for logical operations. The 1 and 0 can represent words — *true* and *false, yes* and *no* — as well as they can represent numbers. Furthermore, we noted that electronic computers use logical elements such as *and, or,* and *not* to do arithmetic, and since logical problems are also generally stated in these terms, obviously the same devices used for arithmetic operations can be used for strictly logical operations.

As an example of a logical problem, let us consider the "logic" of a two-way switch. Assume two switches, A (the upstairs switch) and B (the downstairs switch) where 0 in each case represents the switch in the down position and 1 represents the switch in the up position. Assume further that the hall light is represented by S where 0 is the light being off and 1 is the light being on. Further, we know that "the hall light is on when the upstairs switch is up *and* the downstairs switch is down *or* the upstairs switch is down *and* the downstairs switch is up, but *not* when both switches are up *or* when both switches are down." How can this be represented in terms which have already been considered?

The answer is the A, B, and Sum columns of Table 3. There the A and B represented binary numbers being added, but the logic is the same. When the condition of the hall light being on is restated as "the upstairs switch is up *or* the downstairs switch is up *and* both the upstairs switch *and* the downstairs switch are *not* up" then it is directly analogous to the word statement previously given for the sum digit in binary addition.

Of course, practical logical problems are much more complicated than indicated by this example, the number of different possibilities being enormous. To illustrate, let us consider how computers have been used for a process well recognized as a model of logic, that is, the proving of Euclidean plane geometry theorems.

Plane geometry theorem proving. — The use of a digital computer for proving theorems of plane geometry is illustrated by the example in Illustration 39, in which is given the machine proof that a certain construction involving the midpoints of two sides and two diagonals of a quadrilateral results in a parallelogram.

The general procedure used here for theorem proving is to work backward. Given as its goal to prove that a quadrilateral EFGH is a parallelogram, the computer first selects subgoals which would allow EFGH to meet the definition of a parallelogram. Each subgoal causes further subgoals to be generated, and so on. There

PREMISES

QUAD–LATERAL ABCD
POINT E MIDPOINT SEGMENT AB
POINT F MIDPOINT SEGMENT AC
POINT G MIDPOINT SEGMENT CD
POINT H MIDPOINT SEGMENT BD

TO PROVE

PARALLELOGRAM EFGH

SYNTACTIC SYMMETRIES

BA, AB, DC, CD, EE, HF, GG, FH.
CA, DB, AC, BD, GE, FF, EG, HH.
DA, CB, BC, AD, GE, HF, EG, FH.

PROOF

SEGMENT DG EQUALS SEGMENT GC
    DEFINITION OF MIDPOINT
SEGMENT CF EQUALS SEGMENT FA
    DEFINITION OF MIDPOINT
TRIANGLE DCA
    ASSUMPTION BASED ON DIAGRAM
PRECEDES DGC
    DEFINITION OF MIDPOINT
PRECEDES CFA
    DEFINITION OF MIDPOINT
SEGMENT GF OF PARALLEL SEGMENT AD
    SEGMENT JOINING MIDPOINTS OF SIDES OF TRIANGLE IS PARALLEL TO BASE
SEGMENT HE PARALLEL SEGMENT AD
    SYNTACTIC CONJUGATE
SEGMENT GF PARALLEL SEGMENT EH
    SEGMENTS PARALLEL TO THE SAME SEGMENT ARE PARALLEL
SEGMENT HG PARALLEL SEGMENT FE
    SYNTACTIC CONJUGATE
QUAD–LATERAL HGFE
    ASSUMPTION BASED ON DIAGRAM
PARALLELOGRAM EFGH
    QUADRILATERAL WITH OPPOSITE SIDES PARALLEL IS A PARALLELOGRAM

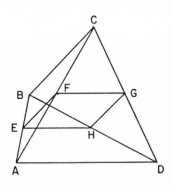

ILLUS. 39—Example of use of computer for logical process of proving a plane geometry theorem.

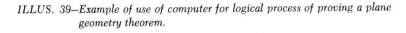

may be several levels of such goals. The computer examines various possibilities until a certain sequence of subgoals has been found that proves the theorem. It is necessary to keep the number of subgoals investigated at each level as small as possible. If there were 10 subgoals generated for each goal or subgoal for a total of 6 levels, there would be over a million possibilities to consider[6]. The limiting of the number of pertinent subgoals in this case is done by checking each subgoal to see if it is consistent with the diagram. If it is consistent, it is kept as a possible step in the proof; otherwise it is rejected.

In the example of Illustration 39 the theorem was proved by demonstrating that it was reducible to the definition, "a quadrilateral with opposite sides parallel is a parallelogram." Intermediate steps in the proof used the theorems that "segments parallel to the same segment are parallel" and "segment joining midpoints of the sides of a triangle is parallel to (its) base." Otherwise, the proof involves the definition of a midpoint and on assumptions based on the diagram.

It will be noted that the information must be specified to the computer in a degree of detail that may not be required in a human proof of theorems. In this example, the term "precedes DGC" means that points D, G, and C are collinear in that order. This may appear to be obvious, but it is needed for the proof. Similarly, much of what is given as "syntactic symmetries" appears to be "obviously" implied by the diagram. The usual proof of this theorem assumes these symmetries but does not necessarily consider them as formally as the machine must.

This example is a relatively simple one; much more complicated theorems have been proved. Furthermore, the brief description given here does justice neither to the magnitude nor the significance of the work being done in using computers to "prove" as well as compute. Obviously, the ability to prove geometrical or other theorems is not significant in itself; the important investigation is to show how these significant intellectual endeavors can be performed in terms of the simple operations which a computer can perform. Knowing this, it may be possible to extend these techniques to more useful intellectual activities.

---

[6] A very significant recent development in computer application involves *heuristic programing* wherein the computer is instructed with regard to techniques that drastically limit the amount of search required for solution of complex problems. This is necessary since even the largest, fastest feasible computer could probably not search all possible solutions in plane geometry and certainly could not in checker or chess playing.

FUTURE OF COMPUTERS

It is apparent that computers are acquiring much faster operating speeds and that their storage capacity is increasing while at the same time their physical size is decreasing. The cost per operation is going down, and it is certain that computers are going to be much more widely used than they are now. Many more thousands of people in the next few years will find that digital computers will play an essential part in their activities.

While computers will be increasingly used for arithmetic problems, it is also to be expected that they will find more and more uses of a logical nature. The proving of geometry theorems is only a step in the direction of using computers for nonarithmetic operations. It does illustrate the use of computers in situations in which the programer cannot possibly anticipate all the possible courses of action. The computer is given very general instructions for determining its sequence of operations and will be able to adapt or "learn" as necessary to solve the problem presented to it. This should open new vistas for application of computers, and it has even been suggested that this use of computers has significant sociological implications.

Digital computers by their nature will also produce other indirect benefits. Lacking a tool that would permit doing a large number of operations to solve a problem, man has characteristically developed techniques using relatively few but necessarily complex operations. This is especially true in the fields outside the exact sciences. However, scientists are now engaged in analyzing many operations in simple, fundamental terms suitable for use by computers. This has the desirable side result of increasing knowledge over and above that which can be fed to computers.

The limited number of operations that computers can perform compels all who use them to employ a common means of expression. The computer does not know whether the sequence of instructions which it performs were written by an accountant, linguist, philosopher, librarian, theologian, social scientist, physical scientist, engineer, or mathematician. Furthermore, its operations are independent of the natural language (English, French, or any other) of the person writing the program for the computer. At least at this level the activities in all sciences and of all nationalities are in a sense unified. This is especially interesting in an age when many fields of human endeavor are becoming more and more specialized and the problems of communicating between disciplines more difficult.

REFERENCES

BOWDEN, B. V., ed. 1953. Faster than thought. Pitman Publishing Corp., New York.

FEIGENBAUM, E. A., and FELDMAN, J., eds. 1963. Computers and thought. McGraw-Hill Book Co., Inc., New York.

GREENBERGER, M., ed. 1962. Computers and the world of the future. The M.I.T. Press, Cambridge.

LEDLEY, R. 1962. Programing and utilizing digital computers. McGraw-Hill Book Co., Inc., New York.

McCORMICK, E. M. 1959. Digital computer primer. McGraw-Hill Book Co., Inc., New York.

PHILIPSON, M., ed. 1962. Automation: implications for the future. Vintage Books, New York.

GEORGE A. W. BOEHM

The New Uses of the Abstract

[FROM THE SMITHSONIAN REPORT FOR 1959]

MATHEMATICS *can hardly be called a new science — in fact, it is undoubtedly one of the oldest. Yet within the past decade it has been put to so many new uses that it can legitimately find a place in an anthology of 20th century science. For example, the abstract branch known as celestial mechanics, long used to predict the positions of planets and comets, has within the past few years been given the task of calculating earth-satellite orbits. Biologists and sociologists are just beginning to utilize mathematical and statistical theory in their fields of investigation. Among the various aspects of abstract mathematics that are finding strictly utilitarian applications, says the author, George A. W. Boehm, are probability, multidimensional geometry, nonparametric inference, and nonlinear differential equations. Russian emphasis on the last-named branch of abstract mathematics may explain their success with long-range missiles. The increasing demand for trained men in these fields is resulting in a shortage of mathematical manpower in America, and the author reviews the attempts being made in educational institutions to remedy the situation.*

N EVER BEFORE have so many people applied such abstract mathematics to so great a variety of problems. To meet the
demands of industry, technology, and other sciences, mathematicians have had to invent new branches of mathematics and expand
old ones. They have built a superstructure of fresh ideas that people trained in the classical branches of the subject would hardly
recognize as mathematics at all.

Applied mathematicians have been grappling successfully with
the world's problems at a time, curiously enough, when pure mathematics seems almost to have lost touch with the real world.
Mathematics has always been abstract, but pure mathematicians
are pushing abstraction to new limits. To them mathematics is an
art they pursue for art's sake, and they do not much care whether
it will ever have any practical use.

Yet the very abstractness of mathematics makes it useful. By
applying its concepts to worldly problems the mathematician can
often brush away the obscuring details and reveal simple patterns.
Celestial mechanics, for example, enables astronomers to calculate
the positions of the planets at any time in the past or future and
to predict the comings and goings of comets. Now this ancient and
abstruse branch of mathematics has suddenly become impressively
practical for calculating orbits of earth satellites.

Even mathematical puzzles may have important applications.
Mathematicians are still trying to find a general rule for calculating the number of ways a particle can travel from one corner of a
rectangular net to another corner without crossing its own path.
When they solve this seemingly simple problem, they will be able
to tell chemists something about the buildup of the long-chain
molecules of polymers.

Mathematicians who are interested in down-to-earth problems
have learned to solve many that were beyond the scope of mathematics only a decade or two ago. They have developed new statistical methods for controlling quality in high-speed industrial mass
production. They have laid foundations for Operations Research

techniques that businessmen use to schedule production and distribution. They have created an elaborate theory of "information" that enables communications engineers to evaluate precisely telephone, radio, and television circuits. They have grappled with the complexities of human behavior through game theory, which applies to military and business strategy alike. They have analyzed the design of automatic controls for such complicated systems as factory production lines and supersonic aircraft. Now they are ready to solve many problems of space travel, from guidance and navigation to flight dynamics of missiles beyond the earth's atmosphere.

Mathematicians have barely begun to turn their attention to the biological and social sciences, yet these once purely descriptive sciences are already taking on a new flavor of mathematical precision. Biologists are starting to apply information theory to inheritance. Sociologists are using sophisticated modern statistics to control their sampling. The bond between mathematics and the life sciences has been strengthened by the emergence of a whole group of applied mathematics specialties, such as biometrics, psychometrics, and econometrics.

Now that they have electronic computers, mathematicians are solving problems they would not have dared tackle a few years ago. In a matter of minutes they can get an answer that previously would have required months or even years of calculation. In designing computers and programing them to carry out instructions, furthermore, mathematicians have had to develop new techniques. While computers have as yet contributed little to pure mathematical theory, they have been used to test certain relationships among numbers. It now seems possible that a computer someday will discover and prove a brand-new mathematical theorem.

The unprecedented growth of U.S. mathematics, pure and applied, has caused an acute shortage of good mathematicians. Supplying this demand is a knotty problem. Mathematicians need more training than ever before; yet they cannot afford to spend more years in school, for mathematicians are generally most creative when very young. A whole new concept of mathematical education, starting as early as the ninth grade, may offer the only escape from this dilemma.

CONVENIENCE OF THE OUTLANDISH

The applied mathematician must be a creative man. For applied mathematics is more than mere problem solving. Its primary goal is finding new mathematical approaches applicable to a wide range of problems. The same differential equation, for example, may describe the scattering of neutrons by atomic nuclei and the propagation of radio waves through the ionosphere. The same topological network may be a mathematical model of wires carrying current in an electric circuit and of gossips spreading rumors at a tea party. Because applied mathematics is inextricably tied to the problems it solves, the applied mathematician must be familiar with at least one other field — e.g., aerodynamics, electronics, or genetics.

The pure mathematician judges his work largely by esthetic standards; the applied mathematician is a pragmatist. His job is to make abstract mathematical models of the real world, and if they work, he is satisfied. Often his abstractions are outlandishly farfetched. He may, for example, consider the sun as a mass concentrated at a point of zero volume, or he may treat it as a perfectly round and homogeneous sphere. Either model is acceptable if it leads to predictions that jibe with experiment and observation.

This matter-of-fact attitude helps to explain the radical changes in the long-established field of probability theory. Italian and French mathematicians broached the subject about three centuries ago to analyze betting odds for dice. Since then philosophers interested in mathematics have been seriously concerned about the nature of a mysterious "agency of chance." Working mathematicians, however, do not worry about the philosophic notion of chance. They consider probability as an abstract and undefined property — much as physicists consider mass or energy. In so doing, mathematicians have extended the techniques of probability theory to many problems that do not obviously involve the element of chance.

Probability today is almost like a branch of geometry. Each outcome of a particular experiment is treated as the location of a point on a line. And each repetition of the experiment is the coordinate of the point in another dimension. The probability of an outcome is a measure very much like the geometric measure of volume. Many problems in probability boil down to a geometric analysis of points scattered throughout a space of many dimensions.

One of the most fertile topics of modern probability theory is the so-called "random walk." A simple illustration is the gambler's ruin problem, in which two men play a game until one of them is bankrupt. If one starts with $100 and the other with $200 and they play for $1.00 a game, the progress of their gambling can be graphed as a point on a line 300 units (i.e., dollars) long. The point jumps one unit, right or left, each time the game is played, and when it reaches either end of the line, one gambler is broke. The problem is to calculate how long the game is likely to last and what chance each gambler has of winning.

Mathematicians have recently discovered some surprising facts about such games. When both players have unlimited capital and the game can go on indefinitely, the lead tends not to change hands nearly so often as most people would guess. In a game where both players have an equal chance of winning — such as matching pennies — after 20,000 plays it is about 88 times as likely that the winner has led all the time as that the two players have shared the lead equally. No matter how long the game lasts, it is more likely that one player has led from the beginning than that the lead has changed hands any given number of times.

The random-walk abstraction is applicable to a great many physical situations. Some clearly involve chance — e.g., diffusion of gases, flow of automobile traffic, spread of rumors, progress of epidemic disease. The technique has even been applied to show that after the last glacial period seed-carrying birds must have helped reestablish the oak forests in the northern parts of the British Isles. But some modern random-walk problems have no obvious connection with chance. In a complicated electrical network, for example, if the voltages at the terminals are fixed, the voltages at various points inside the circuit can be calculated by treating the whole circuit as a sort of two-dimensional gambler's ruin game.

RISK VERSUS GAIN

Mathematical statistics, the principal offshoot of probability theory, is changing just as radically as probability theory itself. Classical statistics has acted mainly as a tribunal, warning users against drawing risky conclusions. The judgments as handed down are always somewhat equivocal, such as: "It is 98 percent certain that drug A is at least twice as potent as drug B." But what if drug A is actually only half as potent? Classical statistics admits this possibility, but does not evaluate the consequences. Modern statisticians have gone a step farther with a new set of ideas known collectively as decision theory. "We now try to provide a guide to actions that must be taken under conditions of uncertainty," explains Herbert Robbins of Columbia. "The aim is to minimize the loss due to our ignorance of the true state of nature. In fact, from the viewpoint of game theory, statistical inference becomes the best strategy for playing the game called science."

The new approach is illustrated by the following example. A philanthropist offers to flip a coin once and let you call "heads" or "tails." If you guess right, he will pay you $100. You notice the coin is so badly bent and battered that it is much more likely to land on one side than the other. But you cannot decide which side the coin favors. The philanthropist is willing to let you test the coin with trial flips, but he insists you pay him $1.00 for each experiment. How many trial flips should you buy before you make up your mind? The answer, of course, depends on how the trials turn out. If the coin lands heads up the first five times, you might conclude that it is almost certainly biased in favor of heads. But if you get three heads and two tails, you would certainly ask to experiment further.

Industry faces this kind of problem regularly. A manufacturer with a new product tests it before deciding whether to put it on the market. The more he tests, the surer he will be that his decision will be right. But tests cost money, and they take time. Now modern statistics can help him balance risk against gain and decide how long to continue testing. It can also help him design and carry out experiments. New methods involving a great deal of multi-dimensional geometry can point out how products and industrial processes can be improved. A statistician can often apply these methods to tune up a full-scale industrial plant without interrupting production. (For an example, see the diagrams, Illustrations 40 and 41.)

Classical statistics has been extended in another way. One of the latest developments is "nonparametric inference," a way of drawing conclusions about things that can be sorted according to size, longevity, dollar value, or any other graduated quality. What matters is the size of the statistical sample and the ranking of any particular object in that sample. It is not actually necessary to measure any of the objects, so long as they can be compared. It is possible to say, for instance, that if the sample consists of 473 objects, it is 99 percent certain that only 1 percent of all objects of this sort will be larger than the largest object in the sample. It makes no difference what the objects are — people, automobiles, ears of corn, or numbers drawn out of a hat. And the statement is still true if instead of largeness you consider smallness, intelligence, cruising speed, or any other relevant quality.

In practical application, nonparametric inference is being used to test batches of light bulbs. By burning a sample of 63 bulbs, for example, the manufacturer can conclude that 90 percent of all the bulbs in the batch will almost certainly (99 chances out of 100) have a longer life than the second bulb to burn out during the test.

One of the most fascinating recent developments in applied mathematics is game theory, another offshoot of probability theory (see "A Theory of Strategy," *Fortune*, June 1949). From a mathematical viewpoint, game theory is not particularly abstruse; many mathematicians, indeed, consider it shallow. But it is exciting because it has given mathematicians an analytic approach to human behavior.

Game theory is basically a mathematical description of competition among people or such groups of people as armies, corporations, or bridge partnerships. In theory, the players know all the possible outcomes of the competition and have a firm idea of what each outcome is worth to them. They are aware of all their possible strategies and those of their opponents. And invariably they behave "rationally" (though mathematicians are not sure just how to define "rational" behavior). Obviously, game theory represents

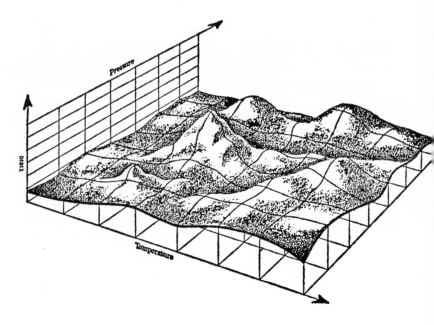

ILLUS. 40 and 41—Geometry helps statisticians improve industrial products
and processes, such as the hypothetical chemical process shown
in the diagram in Illus. 40. Like a great many processes, it is hard
to perfect because it responds in a very irregular way to changes
in temperature and pressure. The statistician doesn't have to know
any chemical theory to find out what temperature and pressure
settings give the maximum yield—represented by the highest point
on the "response surface." Rather, he approaches the problem like
a blind man trying to find the highest peak in an unfamiliar country. The drawing in Illus. 41 illustrates his procedure. He starts
with arbitrary settings and varies them slightly so that he can

a high degree of abstraction; people are never so purposeful and
well informed, even in as circumscribed a competition as a game
of chess. Yet the abstraction of man is valid to the extent that game
theory is proving useful in analyzing business and military situations.

When it was first developed in the twenties, chiefly by Émile
Borel in France and John von Neumann in Germany, game theory
was limited to the simplest forms of competition. As late as 1944
the definitive book on the subject (*Theory of Games and Economic
Behavior,* by Von Neumann and Princeton economist Oskar Mor-
genstern) drew many of its illustrative examples from a form of

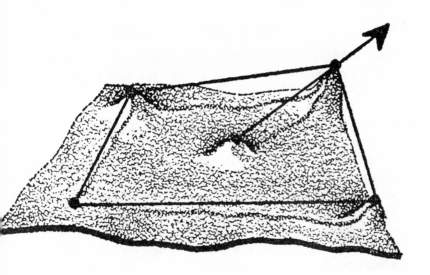

determine yields at the corners of a small square on the surface. If one corner is significantly higher than the others, he starts over again at that point and varies the settings to explore another small square. Successive steps lead him higher and higher. As the diagram in Illus. 40 makes evident, he could be misled by several topographic features—e.g., the small peak in the foreground, the ridge at the right, or the crest of the pass between the twin peaks in the rear. Such a response surface could just as well represent engine performance as fuel and carburetor adjustment vary, or any other measurable quantity. When there are many variables to consider, the geometry becomes more complicated, because the surface has as many dimensions as there are independent variables.

---

one-card poker with limited betting between two people. Now, however, the strategies of two-person, zero-sum games (in which one player gains what his opponent loses) have been quite thoroughly analyzed. And game theorists have pushed on to more complex types of competition, which are generally more true to life.

Early game theory left much to be desired when it assumed that every plan should be designed for play against an allwise opponent who would find out the strategy and adopt his own most effective counterstrategy. In military terms, this amounted to the assumption that the enemy's intelligence service was infallible. The game-theory solution was a randomly mixed strategy — one in which each move would be dictated by chance, say the roll of dice, so that the enemy could not possibly anticipate it. (For much the same reason the United States Armed Forces teach intelligence officers to estimate the enemy's capabilities rather than his intentions.) Many mathematicians have felt that this approach is unrealistically cautious. Recently game theorists have worked out strategies that will take advantage of a careless or inexpert opponent without risking anything if he happens to play shrewdly. (For a relatively simple example, see diagram, Illustration 42.)

The most difficult games to analyze mathematically are those in which the players are not strictly competing with one another. An example is a labor-management negotiation; both sides lose unless they reach an agreement. Another complicating factor is collusion among players — e.g., an agreement between two buyers not to bid against each other. Still another is payment of money outside the framework of the "game," as when a large company holds a distributor in line by subsidizing him.

WHO GETS HOW MUCH?

The biggest problem in analyzing such complex situations has been to find a mathematical procedure for distributing profits in such a way that "rational" players will be satisfied. One formula has been developed by Lloyd Shapley of the Rand Corp. An outside arbitrator must decide the payments. The formula tells him how to give the players payments appropriate to the strength of their bargaining powers, and it also maximizes the total payment. There are obvious practical difficulties in applying Shapley's "arbitration value." In the first place, the payment, or value, each player receives can seldom be measured simply in dollars. Thus the arbitrator would have a hard time deciding on the proper distribution if the players were to lie about what they wanted to get from the game and how much they valued it.

While game theory has already contributed a great deal to decision theory in modern statistics, practical applications to complex human situations have not been strikingly successful. The chief

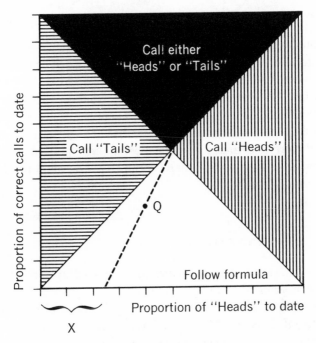

ILLUS. 42—*How to play smarter than safe. Early workers in game theory designed strategies that were safe to use against infallible opponents, but mathematicians now know ways to take advantage of a careless opponent without risking anything. The diagram dictates the best strategy for guessing whether your opponent has placed a concealed coin heads up or tails up. If he were wise, he would mix heads and tails randomly, simply by flipping the coin each time. In that case, you could do no better than break even in the long run. But if he tries to anticipate your guesses, the strategy in the diagram enables you to win whenever he follows any regular pattern; and in any event you will do no worse than break even in the long run.*

As the game progresses, you keep track of the proportion of times your opponent has placed the coin heads up and the proportion of times you have won. This determines the point Q. When Q is in the black or gray triangles, you follow the pure strategies shown in the diagram. But when Q is in the white triangle, you must adopt a mixed strategy, which you calculate as follows: Draw a line connecting the center of the diagram with Q and extending to the base line. The length X determines your strategy. Since X is in this case ¼, you should adopt some random way of calling heads or tails that makes it three times as likely that you will call tails. (You might put four slips of paper in a hat—three of them marked tails—and draw one.) This method takes advantage of your opponent's apparent tendency to place the coin tails up, yet it keeps him from guessing your strategy. If you follow this plan, the point Q should ultimately end up in the black triangle, which represents a profit for you.

troubles seem to be that there are no objective mathematical ways to formulate "rational" behavior or to measure the value of a given outcome to a particular player. At the very least, however, game theory has got mathematicians interested in analyzing human affairs and has stimulated more economists and social scientists to study higher mathematics. Game theory may be a forerunner of still more penetrating mathematical approaches that will someday help man to interpret more accurately what he observes about human behavior.

UNIVERSAL TOOL

The backbone of mathematics, pure as well as applied, is a conglomeration of techniques known as "analysis." Analysis used to be virtually synonymous with the applications of differential and integral calculus. Modern analysts, however, use theorems and techniques from almost every other branch of mathematics, including topology, the theory of numbers, and abstract algebra.

In the last 20 or 30 years mathematical analysts have made rapid progress with differential equations, which serve as mathematical models for almost every physical phenomenon involving any sort of change. Today mathematicians know relatively simple routines for solving many types of differential equations on computers. But there are still no straightforward methods for solving most nonlinear differential equations — the kind that usually crop up when large or abrupt changes occur. Typical are the equations that describe the aerodynamic shock waves produced when an airplane accelerates through the speed of sound.

Russian mathematicians have concentrated enormous effort on the theory of nonlinear differential equations. One consequence is that the Russians are now (1959) ahead of the rest of the world in the study of automatic control, and this may account for much of their success with missiles.

It is in the field of analysis that electronic computers have made perhaps their most important contributions to applied mathematics. It still takes a skillful mathematician to set up a differential equation and interpret the solution. But in the final stages he can usually reduce the work to a numerical procedure — long and tedious, perhaps, but straightforward enough for a computer to carry out in a few minutes or at most a few hours. The very fact that computers are available makes it feasible to analyze mathematically a great many problems that used to be handled by various rules of thumb, and less accurately.

MATHEMATICS OF LOGIC

Computers have also had some effects on pure mathematics. Faced with the problems of instructing computers what to do and how to do it, mathematicians have reopened an old and partly dormant field: Boolean algebra. This branch of mathematics reduces the rules of formal logic to algebraic form. Two of its axioms are startlingly different from the axioms of ordinary high-school algebra. In Boolean algebra $a+a=a$, and $a \times a=a$. The reason becomes clear when a is interpreted as a statement, the plus sign as "or," and the multiplication sign as "and." Thus, for example, the addition axiom can be illustrated by: "(this dress is red) or (this dress is red) means (this dress is red)."

Numerical analysis, a main part of the study of approximations, is another field that mathematicians have revived to program problems for computers. There is still a great deal of pure and fundamental mathematical research to be done on numerical errors that may arise through rounding off numbers. Computers are particularly liable to commit such errors, for there is a limit to the size of the numbers they can manipulate. If a machine gets a very long number, it has to drop the digits at the end and work with an approximation. While the approximation may be extremely close, the error may grow to be enormous if the number is multiplied by a large factor at a later stage of the problem. It is generally safe to assume that rounding off tends to even out in long arithmetic examples. In adding a long column of figures, for instance, you probably won't go far wrong if you consider 44.23 simply as 44, and 517.61 as 518. But it is sheer superstition to suppose that rounding off cannot possibly build up a serious accumulation of errors. (It obviously would if all the numbers happened to end in .499.)

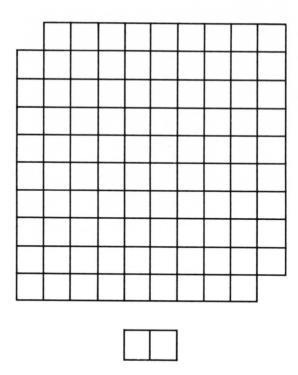

ILLUS. 43—How to make the difficult simple. Problem: Given as many of the small rectangles as you want, can you arrange them to cover completely the large figure? None of the small rectangles must overlap or jut beyond the margins of the large figure. As it happens, the feat is impossible, but the difficult thing is to prove conclusively that it is impossible. (For a mathematical solution, see Illus. 44.)

There are subtler pitfalls in certain more elaborate kinds of computation. In some typical computer problems involving matrices that are used to solve simultaneous equations, John Todd of the California Institute of Technology has constructed seemingly simple numerical problems that a computer simply cannot cope with. In some cases the computer gets grossly inaccurate results; in others it cannot produce any answer at all. It is a challenge to numerical analysts to find ways to foresee this sort of trouble and then avoid it.

PATTERNS IN PRIMES

Computers have as yet made few direct contributions to pure mathematics except in the field of number theory. Here the results have been inconclusive but interesting. D. H. Lehmer of the University of California has had a computer draw up a list of all the prime numbers less than 46,000,000. (A prime is a number that is exactly divisible only by itself or 1 — e.g., 2, 3, 17, 61, 1,021.) A study of the list confirms that prime numbers, at least up to 46,000,000 are distributed among other whole numbers according to a "law" worked out theoretically about a century ago. The law states that the number of primes less than any given large number, X, is approximately equal to X divided by the natural logarithm of X. (Actually, the approximation is consistently a little on the low side.) Lehmer's list also tends to confirm conjectures about the distribution of twin primes — i.e., pairs of consecutive odd numbers both of which are primes, like 29 and 31, or 101 and 103. The number of twin primes less than X is roughly equal to X divided by the *square* of the natural logarithm of X.

Lehmer and H. S. Vandiver of the University of Texas have also used a computer to test a famous theorem that mathematicians the world over are still trying either to prove or disprove. Three hundred years ago the French mathematician Fermat stated that it is impossible to satisfy the following equation by substituting whole numbers (except zero) for all the letters if n is greater than 2:

$$a^n + b^n = c^n$$

Lehmer and Vandiver have sought to find a single exception. If they could, the theorem would be disproved. Fortunately they have not had to test every conceivable combination of numbers; it is sufficient to try substituting all prime numbers for n. And there are further shortcuts. The number n, for example, must not divide any of a certain set of so-called "Bernoulli numbers"; otherwise it cannot satisfy the equation. (The Bernoulli numbers are irregular. The 1st is 1/6; the 3d, 1/30; the 11th, 691/2,730; the 13th, 7/6; the 17th, 43,867/798; the 19th, 1,222,277/2,310. Numbers later in the series are enormous.)

Lehmer and Vandiver have tested the Fermat theorem for all prime n's up to 4,000, but they seem to be coming to a dead end.

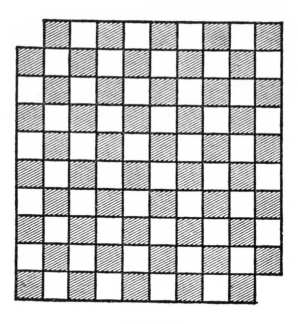

ILLUS. 44—Solution to problem in Illus. 43. The key to the solution is to imagine that adjacent squares have different colors, as on a chessboard. Then it becomes obvious that each rectangle has to cover precisely one black square and one white square. Since the large figure contains unequal numbers of black and white squares, there can be no way to cover it with rectangles. The solution represents a conclusive negative proof, a logical feat that is peculiar to mathematics; in other sciences negative conclusions are invariably risky. The postulation of color is a relatively easy abstraction, but it is characteristic of some of the more complex abstractions that mathematicians use to simplify problems and theorems.

The Bernoulli numbers at this stage are nearly 10,000 digits long, and even a fast computer takes a full hour to test each n. The fact that a machine has failed to find an exception does not, of course, prove the Fermat theorem, although it does perhaps add a measure of assurance that the theorem is true.

But it is possible for a computer to produce a mathematical proof. Allen Newell of Rand Corp. and Herbert A. Simon of Carnegie Tech have worked out a program of instructions that tells a high-speed computer how to work out proofs of some elementary theorems in mathematical logic contained in *Principia Mathematica*, a three-volume treatise by Alfred North Whitehead and Bertrand Russell.

The Newell and Simon program is based on heuristic thinking — the kind of hunch-and-analogy approach that a creative human mind uses to simplify complicated problems. The computer is supplied with some basic axioms, and it stores away all theorems it has previously proved. When it is told to prove an unfamiliar theorem, it first tries to draw analogies and comparisons with the theorems it already knows. In many cases the computer produces a logical proof within a few minutes; in others it fails to produce any proof at all. It would conceivably be possible to program a computer to solve theorems with an algorithmic approach, a sure-fire, methodical procedure for exhausting all possibilities. But such a program might take years for the fastest computer to carry out.

Although most mathematicians scoff at the idea, Newell and Simon are confident that heuristic programing will soon enable computers to do truly creative mathematical work. They guess that within 10 years a computer will discover and prove an important mathematical theorem that never occurred to any human mathematician.

HELP WANTED

But computers are not going to put mathematicians out of work. Quite to the contrary, computers have opened up so many new applications for mathematics that industrial job opportunities for mathematicians have more than doubled in the last five years. About one-fourth of the 250 people who are getting Ph.D.'s in mathematics this year are going into industry — chiefly the aircraft, electronics, communications, and petroleum companies. In 1946 only about one in nine Ph.D.'s took jobs in industry.

While most companies prefer mathematicians who have also had considerable background in physics or engineering, many companies are also eager to hire men who have concentrated on pure mathematics. Starting pay for a good young mathematician with a fresh Ph.D. now averages close to $10,000 a year in the aircraft industry, about double that of 1950 (and about double today's starting pay in universities).

Still, a great deal of industrial mathematics is done by physicists and engineers who have switched to mathematics after graduation. And there is also room for people with bachelor's and master's degrees, particularly in programing computers to perform calculations.

Different companies use mathematicians in different ways. Some incorporate them in research teams along with engineers, physicists, metallurgists, and other scientists. But a growing number have set up special mathematics groups, which carry out their own research projects and also do a strictly limited amount of problem solving for other scientific departments.

The oldest and most illustrious industrial mathematics department was set up in 1930 by Bell Telephone Laboratories. It started with six or eight professional mathematicians and grew slowly until after the war. Then in 10 years it doubled in size. Today the department has about 30 professional mathematicians, half of them with Ph.D.'s in mathematics, the rest with Ph.D.'s in other sciences. The department has made outstanding contributions to mathematics. Notable is information theory, which was developed during and after the war by Claude Shannon as a mathematical model for language and its communication.

CRISIS IN EDUCATION

The demand for mathematicians of every sort is rapidly outstripping the capacity of the U.S. educational system. Swelling enrollments in mathematics courses are already beginning to tax college and university mathematics departments. At Princeton, for example, the mathematics majors have for years numbered only five to 10, but 19 members of the 1958 junior class elected to major in mathematics. To complicate matters further, the good college and university departments no longer require their professors to teach 12 to 15 hours a week. So that the teachers can also do research, the average classroom time has been reduced to 9 hours in most schools, and to less than 6 in some of the best universities. Yet the serious mathematics student now needs more training than ever before. If he wants a good job in industry or in a top university, he must have a doctor's degree; and if he wants to excel in research, he should have a year or two of postdoctoral study.

There is a great deal to be mastered in modern mathematics, but surprisingly it is relatively easier to learn than most of the mathematics traditionally taught in high school and college, despite its abstractness and complexity. One change that would obviously help would be to start teaching the important modern concepts and techniques earlier. The way mathematics is taught now, complains John G. Kemeny of Dartmouth, "it is the only subject you can study for 14 years [i.e., through sophomore calculus] without learning anything that's been done since the year 1800."

THE DARTMOUTH PLAN

Some colleges are now making progress in modernizing their mathematics curricula. Several no longer require a special course in trigonometry. "We really don't have to train everybody to be a surveyor," explains one department head. Under the leadership of Kemeny, Dartmouth in the last five years has almost completely revised its undergraduate course. There are now (1959) three separate courses of study in mathematics: one for mathematics majors, another for engineers and others who must have mathematical training, and a third for the liberal-arts students who want to make mathematics part of their cultural background.

The courses are amazingly popular. Ninety percent of all Dartmouth students take at least one semester of mathematics, and more than 60 percent finish a year of it (mathematics is an elective for most of them). Kemeny and two associates have written for one of their courses a remarkable textbook entitled *Introduction to Finite Mathematics*. Within a year after its publication in January 1957, it was being used by about 100 colleges, in some cases just for mathematics courses especially designed for social-science majors. And several New York high schools have adopted the book for special sections of exceptional students.

MATHEMATICS FOR CHILDREN

The movement to teach more mathematics and teach it sooner has filtered down to the secondary-school level. The College Entrance Examination Board, through its commission on mathematics, has drawn up a program for modernizing secondary-school mathematics courses. The chief aim of the commission, according to its executive director, Albert E. Meder, is to give students an appreciation of the true meaning of mathematics and some idea of modern developments. Algebra, he points out, is no longer a "disconnected mass of memorized tricks but a study of mathematical structure: geometry no longer a body of theorems arranged in a precise order that can be memorized without understanding."

The College Board has the support of most leading mathematicians. About 20 of them are meeting with 20 high-school mathematics teachers this summer at Yale to write outlines of sample textbooks based partly on the College Board's recommendations. This group, headed by E. G. Begle of Yale, plans to write the actual books within the next year so that teachers and commercial publishers will know how mathematicians think mathematics ought to be taught in high school.

Perhaps the most radical step in U.S. mathematical education has been taken by the University of Illinois' experimental high school. There, under the guidance of a member of the university's mathematics department, a professor of education, Max Beberman, has introduced a completely new mathematics curriculum. It starts with an informal axiomatic approach to arithmetic and algebra and proceeds through aspects of probability theory, set theory, number theory, complex numbers, mathematical induction, and analytic geometry. The approach reflects the rigor, abstractness, and generality of modern mathematics. To make room for some of the new concepts, Beberman and his advisers have had to reduce the amount of time spent drilling on such techniques as factoring algebraic expressions.

So far the experiment has been very stimulating to students — partly, of course, because of the very fact that the course is an experiment. In the college entrance examinations of 1957, the first group of students to complete four years of the Illinois course made some of the highest scores in the nation.

While 12 other high schools have now experimentally adopted the Illinois mathematics curriculum, it is not likely to be widely used for some time. The reason is that most high-school teachers have to be completely retrained to teach it. With Carnegie Foundation support, the University of Illinois has begun to train high-school teachers from many States to teach the new curriculum.

For many years it has been hard for a would-be teacher to learn what mathematics he needs to teach any serious high-school course. Prof. George Polya of Stanford explains: "The mathematics department [of a university] offers them tough steak they cannot chew, and the school of education vapid soup with no meat in it." The National Science Foundation has helped more than 50 colleges and universities set up institutes where high-school teachers can study mathematics for a summer or even a full academic year.

OPPORTUNITY AHEAD

However many mathematicians there may be, there will always be a need for more first-rate minds to create new mathematics. This will be true of applied mathematics as well as pure mathematics. For applied mathematics now presents enough of an intellectual challenge to attract even academic men who pride themselves on creating mathematics for its own sake. One young assistant professor, recently offered $16,000 by industry, is seriously thinking of abandoning his university career. He explains: "I think that the problems in applied mathematics would offer me just as much stimulation as more basic research."

Whole new fields of mathematics are needed to cope with problems in other sciences and human affairs. Transportation engineers, for example, still lack a mathematical method to analyze the turbulence of four-lane highway traffic; and it may be years before they can apply precise mathematical reasoning to three-dimensional air traffic. Biologists have used almost no mathematics aside from statistics, but now some of them are seriously 'thinking of applying topology. This branch of mathematics, which deals with generalized shapes and disregards size, may be the most appropriate way to describe living cells with their enormous variations in size and shape. Neurophysiologists are looking for a new kind of algebra to represent thinking processes, which are by no means random, yet not entirely methodical.

There are still some remarkably simple questions that are teasing mathematicians. They have not yet found, for example, a general solution to the following problem: Given a road map of N folds, how many ways can you refold it? And when this is solved, there will be another puzzle, and another.

SIR ALEXANDER TODD

Organic Chemistry: A View and a Prospect

[FROM THE SMITHSONIAN REPORT FOR 1961]

ALTHOUGH chemistry in some form is, like mathematics, one of the oldest of the sciences, the branch known as organic chemistry had its beginnings only a century ago. The author, Sir Alexander Todd, professor of organic chemistry at the University of Cambridge, England, points out that the chemistry of living matter has come to the fore only in the present century, for the understandable reason that the constituents of living matter are the most complex of all substances. At the same time, they are obviously of the greatest interest and importance to the human race because they include the deoxyribonucleic acids (DNA) which form the material of the genes that control heredity. The nucleic acids also are the basic constituents of viruses, the cause of so many intractable human diseases. Work in these phases of organic chemistry is steadily increasing in intensity, and spectacular results of vital significance to mankind may confidently be expected in the future. The author also reviews the great impact on industry of research in organic chemistry through the production of such synthetic materials as plastics, fibers, rubber, drugs, and vitamins.

217

ORGANIC chemistry is as old as chemistry itself, but it was first recognized as a separate division at the end of the 18th century. Its growth to become not only the largest part of chemistry, but one of the largest of all the sciences in its factual content and in the number of its adherents, has occurred essentially during the past hundred years — since indeed it acquired its necessary theoretical basis through the work of Frankland, Couper, Kekulé, van't Hoff, and Le Bel, to mention only the major names associated with the basic structural theory of carbon compounds. Today its rate of growth is as fast as ever and the output of original work is prodigious. Some idea of that output is given by the calculation made a few years ago that, assuming an organic chemist were to read for 8 hours each day, it would take him about 18 months to read all the literature in his own subject produced during one year and published in the standard European and American journals.

Parallel with the phenomenal growth of the science, there has been an equally phenomenal growth of organic chemical industry until today it is a vital factor in the economy of Britain as well as of all other industrial countries. During the six years ending in 1960, when chemical industry as a whole showed an annual growth rate of 6.5 percent (as against an over-all rate of 3.1 percent for industry as a whole), the annual rate of growth for certain of the main organic sectors was even higher (plastics 15 percent, general organic chemicals 13 percent, pharmaceuticals 8.4 percent). These figures reflect the constantly growing impact of organic chemistry on nearly every aspect of our material civilization, for many products of the industry based on it such as plastics, synthetic fibers, dyes, detergents, adhesives, coatings, etc., are absorbed by and form a vital part of a variety of industries not themselves ordinarily regarded as chemical. In these circumstances it is interesting, at the end of about a century's growth — for the science of organic chemistry and the organic chemical industry have grown side by side in close association with one another — to look at the present position of the science and to see whether future trends are discernible. This involves not only consideration of the most recent advances, but also a brief glance at the course of development in past years; for development patterns tend to repeat themselves in science as elsewhere.

NATURAL PRODUCTS

Organic chemistry is usually defined as the chemistry of the carbon compounds, but its original definition given by Berzelius just over 150 years ago was "the chemistry of substances found in living matter." Although Berzelius's definition is inadequate insofar as a very large number of carbon compounds are known which do not occur in living matter, the older definition is worth remembering because it was interest in the chemistry of living matter that initiated the science. It is, moreover, fair to say that study of substances found in living matter has provided most of the stimuli to the advance of organic chemistry throughout its history, and there is little reason to doubt that this will continue to be the case. But the direct study of substances present in living matter — broadly described as natural products — which is now one of the dominant features of organic chemistry has only become so during the 20th century. This is not, however, surprising. Many of the products of living matter are of extreme complexity, and they were for the most part far beyond the reach of the early organic chemists. Even when the basic theory essential for modern developments was laid down about a hundred years ago the practical techniques available were too feeble to do more than permit the study of some relatively simple examples, and the second half of the 19th century was the period in which structural and synthetic organic chemistry grew to the point at which a return to the study of complex natural substances became practicable. It was during this initial intensive phase of development that the organic chemical industry also grew to be of major importance. Modern organic chemical industry had its origin in the dyestuffs industry which began just a hundred years ago in this country with W. H. Perkin's accidental discovery of mauveine in the course of an abortive attempt to synthesize quinine in the laboratory, and was spurred on by work such as that of Graebe and Liebermann on the dyestuff of madder root which led to the synthesis of alizarin. It was thus born of academic research and as it grew and prospered, so did the science of organic chemistry. From those early days up to the present time the industry and the science have been closely associated; this has been greatly to the advantage of both and may help to explain their extraordinarily rapid growth. No industry stands closer to its parent science than does the organic chemical industry and in no industry is the gap between scientific discovery and industrial development smaller.

SYNTHESIS AND THEORY

Synthetic organic chemistry, which was well established by the beginning of this century, was and remains the backbone of the organic chemical industry and it still continues as one of the main-streams of research in the science. Natural-product chemistry has been, however, dominant in the academic field for close on 50 years; essentially concerned with structural elucidation, it has also had a considerable influence on synthetic chemistry, since total synthesis of a natural product is commonly regarded as the final proof of structure. Many natural products are of such complexity that novel synthetic procedures have had to be devised for them, enriching the general arsenal of synthetic methods at the chemist's command. Natural-product chemistry has, of course, also influenced the course of industry by giving it new leads to the production of materials with desirable properties in one direction or another; this has been particularly marked in the pharmaceutical industry in the fields of hormones, hormone substitutes, and synthetic drugs. But it is also noticeable in other branches — the connection between natural coloring matters and the dyestuffs industry has already been mentioned, and the plastic and polymer field owes much to work such as that of the German chemist Harries on natural rubber; many other examples could be given.

There is, however, a third important line of advance in organic chemistry which has come into special prominence during the past 20 years or so. This concerns theoretical aspects of the subject. It is true to say that organic chemistry at the beginning of this century was in danger of stagnation since its theoretical basis, although essentially sound, was relatively undeveloped, and the science, with its enormous factual content, was distinctly topheavy. Fortunately, ideas stemming from the new atomic physics were soon brought to its aid through the young science of physical chemistry, and these have led over the years to a much deeper and more precise understanding of organic structures and of the mechanism of organic chemical reactions. These theoretical advances have greatly influenced recent developments in all branches of the subject, although they have presented a number of knotty problems to the universities since they have entailed a lot of re-thinking of teaching methods; it is doubtful whether a wholly satisfactory solution to these problems has yet been found.

These three, admittedly somewhat arbitrary, divisions of organic chemistry represent the main lines of advance which, by their progress and interplay, have brought organic chemistry to its present level in the academic and industrial fields.

NEW TECHNIQUES

One final point regarding their development should, however, be made. All three divisions have owed much to the successive introduction of new techniques and indeed without the development of microanalytical methods, chromatography — paper, ion-exchange, and more recently vapor-phase — and the introduction of physical methods of analysis and identification using spectroscopy in its various forms as well as X-ray crystallography, none of them could have reached its present position. What has been achieved and how far can one estimate from the answer to that question the outlook for the future?

Carbon compounds both natural and synthetic fall into two great groups. The first comprises those substances whose molecules can be regarded as units in themselves; these are of relatively low molecular weight varying from methane (CH_4) with a molecular weight of 16 to vitamin B_{12} ($C_{63}H_{88}N_{14}O_{14}PCo$) with one of 1354. The second group is that of the so-called macromolecules which includes inter alia the polysaccharides, proteins, nucleic acids, and rubber among natural products, and the synthetic polymers and plastics among synthetic materials. These substances have very large molecules, and their molecular weight may run into millions, as in the case of nucleic acids. It is characteristic of them that they are made up of a very large number of small unit molecules all joined together in a more or less regular manner by process of polymerization or polycondensation. Since substances of the second group cannot normally be purified by the traditional methods of crystallization or distillation it is not surprising that most of the progress in organic chemistry has hitherto been in the field of the relatively small "unit" molecules.

There indeed it has been spectacular. The structures of a very large number of complex natural products have been worked out — vitamins, hormones, antibiotics, alkaloids, steroids, coenzymes, etc. — and most of them have been synthesized; many, indeed, are today manufactured by synthesis on a commercial scale. The power of modern organic synthesis has been amply demonstrated in recent years by such achievements as the total synthesis of steroids, such as cholesterol and cortisone, of chlorophyll, of cozymase, and of alkaloids such as strychnine. Synthetic methods have indeed reached such a level of perfection that very few structures would seem beyond their grasp. Structural determination, which in natural-product chemistry usually precedes synthesis, has in the past 10 years or so made enormous strides by the introduction of new physical methods based on ultraviolet, infrared, and nuclear magnetic resonance spectroscopy, and on X-ray crystallography. The power of the last-named analytical tool is amply demonstrated in the brilliant work of Prof. D. Crowfoot Hodgkin on the structure of vitamin B_{12}. Such techniques have already rendered obsolescent many of the older degradative methods of the organic chemist — in which the structure of a complex molecule was arrived at by a study of the breakdown products formed from it in different conditions — and further advances in the same direction may be expected from the newer applications of mass spectroscopy which enables a mixture of molecules to be separated on the basis of their respective masses. The flowering of structural and synthetic chemistry is reflected in the triumphs of the allied industry — the stream of synthetic drugs which have given for the first time cures rather than palliatives for many diseases, pesticides and herbicides, new dyes of vastly improved performance, as well as detergents and a host of other materials now regarded as normal features in our daily life. Moreover, the spectacular development of catalytic methods of synthesis and degradation in the field of petroleum chemistry has led not only to the appearance of a wealth of new intermediates for the chemical industry, but also to a gradual ousting of coal in favor of petroleum as its raw material.

MACROMOLECULES

Progress in the study of macromolecular substances was, until comparatively recently, very slow, largely because of the absence of experimental techniques for dealing with them. But with the appearance of the newer physical techniques of separation, study of the natural macromolecules both by degradation and synthesis has begun to grow very rapidly. Among the more spectacular developments have been the structural elucidation of a number of protein or polypeptide hormones including insulin and the total synthesis of a number of the smaller members of the group such as vasopressin. Substantial progress is now being made in determining the structure of the larger natural proteins, a striking example being provided by the very recent work on myoglobin structure using X-ray methods as a primary tool. The outlook in protein chemistry, which 15 years ago was still rather bleak, is now full of promise and offers new vistas in biology and medicine. Equally spectacular have been developments in the nucleic-acid field. Since the establishment of the general structure of the nucleic acids by chemical means 10 years ago and the consequent establishment of the physical nature of the deoxyribonucleic acids which form the genic material in living cells, there has been an astonishing flowering of chemical and biological work in this field. Occupying as they do a central position in the cellular economy by controlling the transmission of hereditary characteristics and by guiding the synthesis of cellular proteins, the nucleic acids form a group of compounds whose importance in life processes can hardly be overestimated. They are also key constituents of viruses, and the relevance of their study to research on cancer is being increasingly recognized. Much remains to be done chemically, before anything approaching a full understanding of the structure and function of individual nucleic acids will be realized, but the increasing attention being paid to them certainly holds out considerable hope for the future.

The production of synthetic macromolecular materials — plastics, synthetic fibers, resins, and rubbers — is one of the fastest growing sectors of organic chemical industry. It had its beginnings in the production of synthetic resins like bakelite and in the efforts made, notably in Germany, to produce satisfactory substitutes for natural rubber by polymerizing butadiene and other conjugated dienes, and it has since undergone enormous development. The reason for this development is easily understood, since by applying polymerization or polycondensation methods to a variety of small organic molecules one can obtain materials analogously constituted to the great classes of natural macromolecules and so produce fibers, elastomers, and plastic materials which may in many cases be more suited to a particular use than naturally occurring materials (cf., for example, nylon, wool, and silk). In this field the most striking recent advances have been perhaps in the field of olefine polymerization (notably, ethylene and propylene) at low pressures with organometallic catalysts, and the production of isotactic polymers in which the monomer units are arranged in a stereochemically regular manner. This regularity, which is always found in the natural macromolecules, opens the way to synthetic polymers with properties markedly different from the randomly arranged polymers produced by older processes.

POINTERS TO FUTURE

In these various fields there are visible a number of trends which, I believe, point to likely directions of future research and industrial development. On the academic side natural-product chemistry has been slowly changing in emphasis in recent years. Methods of analysis and synthesis have been brought to a high stage of perfection and, partly because of this, since the mid-thirties interest has been turning slowly from molecular structure as such to the study of structure in relation to function and to the mechanism of biosynthesis of natural products — an area of research which has received major stimulus from the availability of radioactive isotopes with which biosynthetic intermediates can be "labeled" and their ultimate location in the final products determined. A brilliant contribution in the field of biosynthesis has been the elucidation of the method used by living organisms to make steroids, terpenoids, and carotenoids, the raw material in every case being acetic acid. Examples of work in which structure and function are related are to be found in the study of chemical reactions in living systems where transfer of energy and oxidation are simultaneously effected using organic phosphates, and on the joining together of complex molecules by oxidation. These trends suggest that organic chemistry is likely to move deeper into the biological field and that academically its main growing points are likely to be in the study of the course of biochemical processes and in the investigation of the natural macromolecules and their functions in the cell. It seems likely, too, that theoretical organic chemistry will turn also in the direction of biological processes and so make a major contribution in the same general fields of advance. This is likely to be the case not only in the study of reaction mechanisms but also in the further development of dynamic stereochemistry which has sprung into prominence in many important fields of research — for example, in the search for new drugs related to cortisone.

All this does not mean that the broad field which I earlier described as synthetic organic chemistry is likely to wither. On the contrary, since it is an essential component of progress in organic chemical industry, it is likely to continue in vigorous growth searching for new and more economical methods of production, and for an ever-increasing array of new products each with some special property or combination of properties. On the industrial side the way ahead for the pharmaceutical industry is clear but it may find itself devoting more of its synthetic effort to the macromolecular substances as virus diseases become an increasing preoccupation. For the rest, plastics and polymers are likely to continue as a major growing point. Here, as indeed also in general synthetic chemistry, the trend to the study of compounds containing, in addition to carbon, other elements such as fluorine, silicon, and boron is likely to become increasingly evident.

Already polymers based on tetrafluoroethylene are being marketed and silicon-containing polymers (silicones) are well known. The introduction of other elements into carbon compounds opens up new fields of endeavor, since the products so formed often have quite different properties (such as thermal stability, behavior under extremes of temperature and pressure) from those met with in ordinary organic chemicals. It is likely, too, that synthetic polymers and polycondensates will find increasing use as structural materials in their own right. This will not only stimulate increased research in the field but it will lead to enormously greater production and to a number of plastics still regarded as "chemicals" becoming everyday structural materials and being used like wood and steel; such a change may considerably influence the structure of the industry producing them.

It is, of course, impossible to review adequately the present situation of organic chemistry either in the academic or industrial field within the compass of a short article. Developments in recent years have been so rapid and so multifarious that it is difficult to single out the really important advances or to see the whole in perspective. For this reason it is rash to prophesy; all that one can do is to make a personal estimate of current trends and where they may lead. But one thing is certain — organic chemistry is still in a period of vigorous growth and in the future the industry based on it will be an increasingly important factor in the national economy.

K. E. BULLEN

Earthquakes and Related Sources of Evidence on the Earth's Internal Structure

[FROM THE SMITHSONIAN REPORT FOR 1958]

It is understandable that we have but little certain knowledge regarding the structure of other planets in the solar system, but it seems strange on reflection that what we know about the interior of our own planet earth rests almost entirely on seismographic evidence, except for a very few miles below the surface. The author of this article, Prof. K. E. Bullen, of the University of Sydney, Australia, among many other honors, has been president of the International Association of Seismology and Physics of the Interior of the Earth, and chairman of the Australian National Committee of the International Geophysical Year. He is the author of books and many scientific papers on seismology and related subjects. He here presents what knowledge we have of the earth's internal structure, information deduced from earthquake waves that proceed through the earth and can be recorded and studied. It may be surprising to learn that each year a hundred thousand earthquakes are strong enough to be felt by human beings. Fortunately an average of only 10 a year are strong enough to constitute real *disasters. Prof. Bullen explains the methods used to deduce earth structure by the variation in records received of quakes that have passed through all layers of the earth's interior. It is made clearly evident that there is great variety in structure and composition as the waves proceed through the mantle, including crust and sub-crust, and through the outer core and inner core.*

EARTHQUAKE ENERGY

W HEN THE SUBJECT of earthquakes is mentioned the nonseismologist commonly thinks of death and destruction: every year there are a number of earthquakes in various parts of the world which command newspaper headlines because of the great damage done. Perhaps the greatest recent earthquake is the one that occurred in Assam on August 15, 1950, causing utter devastation over some thousands of square miles, and felt over an area in excess of a million square miles.

During the past 200 years or so there has been a steady accumulation of systematic knowledge of earthquake occurrence and effects. For example, it is now well known that earthquakes originate largely in two main belts. Eighty percent of all earthquake energy comes from a belt that passes around the Pacific Ocean and affects countries with coastlines bordering on this ocean — for example, New Zealand, New Guinea, Japan, the Aleutian Islands, Alaska, California, Colombia, Ecuador, and Chile. A second belt passes through the Mediterranean region eastward across Asia, and joins the first belt in the East Indies. The energy released in the second belt amounts to 15 percent of the total, leaving only 5 percent for the whole of the rest of the world.

It is also known that 85 percent of the energy comes from centers or "foci" within 50 miles or less of the surface, the remaining 15 percent coming from foci down to a depth of 450 miles. During the present century, i.e., over the whole period of accurate recording of earthquakes, there has, in fact, been no earthquake with a focal depth exceeding 450 miles. Moreover, all but one of the earthquakes which originated near this extreme depth have been confined to the circumpacific belt. The exceptional earthquake originated at a depth of nearly 400 miles below Spain in 1954.

The total number of earthquakes is very great. On an average there are 10 earthquakes each year which are regarded as national disasters. Another 100, classed as destructive earthquakes, do considerable damage, while 1,000 do at least some damage. Ten thousand others are strong enough to cause alarm, and 100,000 are felt by human beings every year. In addition to that, a great many more earthquakes are instrumentally detected.

The energy released in an extreme earthquake is more than one (American) billion times that in the smallest generally felt earthquake. In the extreme earthquake the energy is about the same as that in a major hurricane; but whereas the latter energy takes some hours or more to spend itself and covers a great area, the energy in an earthquake issues in the space of a few seconds at most from a confined region below the earth's surface whose linear dimensions do not ordinarily exceed a few miles. The energy in the extreme earthquake is nearly 100,000 times that in a normal atom bomb explosion, and perhaps 10 to 100 times that in a typical hydrogen bomb explosion.

Seismologists, who study earthquakes by physical means, have long realized that any real understanding of the forces that bring about earthquakes must be preceded by a thorough detailed study of the structure of the earth below the surface. And it happens that earthquakes themselves provide the principal means of unraveling this structure. The greater part of seismologists' efforts is, in fact, devoted to analyzing physical data on earthquakes with a view to charting out the earth's interior to the highest precision possible.

When an earthquake occurs, it sends waves down into the earth's interior, and the shapes and speeds of the waves are influenced by the nether regions they traverse. The waves, on emerging again at the surface, are recorded by seismographs in the 1,000 or so seismological observatories that are spread over the globe in nearly all countries. Every year there are many earthquakes large enough to send sizable waves right through the earth's interior, including the center. In deciphering the "seismograms," i.e., the records of the waves taken at the surface, the seismologist is in effect X-raying the earth, for seismic waves, mathematically speaking, are very similar to light waves.

The immediate cause of the larger earthquakes is known to be the release of elastic strain energy which has accumulated in sizable volumes of material in the earth below the surface, sometimes over a long period beforehand. There comes a stage when the material is strained to breaking point, and the place where fracture starts becomes the focus of an earthquake. The point of the earth's surface above the focus is called the epicenter; it is usually in the vicinity of the epicenter that the main damage is done. If the epicenter is at sea, then, depending on the characteristics of the fracture at the focus, there may be formed great seismic sea waves, or tsunami, which can cause havoc along low-lying shores of adjacent U- and V-shaped bays. There is as yet no universally accepted explanation of the primary causes that give rise to this accumulation of strain energy in the earth's interior, although nearly all theories relate the development of strain to the earth's thermal history.

TYPES OF EARTHQUAKE WAVES

When a seismogram is scrutinized, it is found, on the first level of examination, to show the presence of three broad classes of seismic waves. The first identification of these waves was made by Oldham in England in 1897, nearly 70 years after the relevant mathematical wave theory had been formulated.

One of the three classes consists of waves that travel over the earth's surface and do not penetrate to great depths. On seismograms taken at considerable epicentral distances, these waves appear as the largest (except when the depth of focus is appreciable); this is because the surface waves, which spread out in only two dimensions, diminish more slowly with distance than the other waves which spread out through the three dimensions of the earth's interior. The surface waves are dispersed as they travel (the speed of any one group of surface waves depends on the wavelength) and the degree of dispersion for a given epicentral distance throws important light on the structure of the outermost 25 miles or so of the earth. The present article, however, will be mainly concerned with the other classes of waves, called bodily waves, for these are the ones which supply information on the earth's deeper interior.

The two classes of bodily seismic waves are called the primary or P waves, and the secondary or S waves, respectively. Both P and S waves travel faster than the surface waves, and they contribute to the earlier part of the record on the seismogram. The P waves are longitudinal like waves in sound, while the S waves cause the particles of the earth to move transversely to the direction of wave advance. For points not too close to the focus and epicenter, earthquake energy can for many purposes be regarded as traveling outward along seismic rays, analogous to rays of light. For most of their length both P and S rays are curved, with their concavity upward, although a limited number of surfaces of discontinuity inside the earth exist at which the rays are bent suddenly downward. Thus rays which start off downward at the focus, but not too steeply, emerge at relatively short distances from the epicenter, while the steeper rays emerge at great distances, even as far away as the antipodal point, or anticenter.

The P waves travel through solid parts of the earth about 1½ times as fast as S waves. In fluid regions, the S waves are not transmitted. Thus the detection of S in addition to P waves in a part of the earth is positive evidence of solidity (in a sense to be defined a little later). Likewise, failure to detect S waves is negative evidence of fluidity. Near the outer surface of the earth, P waves travel at a speed of about 3 miles per second. The greatest speed, 8½ miles per second, is reached at a depth of 1,800 miles below the surface.

One of the great labors of seismologists over the first 40 years of this century was to evolve, by successive approximation from crude beginnings, seismic travel-time tables which give the travel times along seismic rays in terms of the angular distances subtended by the rays at the earth's center. The accuracy of the Jeffreys-Bullen tables, which are the ones used in compiling the International Seismological Summary, is of the order of 1 or 2 seconds in travel times of the order of 20 minutes, in the best instances. (Twenty minutes is the time taken for a seismic P pulse to go straight through the earth from one side to the other.)

REGIONS OF THE EARTH'S INTERIOR

From the travel-time tables, it is possible by a mathematical process to estimate the speeds of P and S waves at points throughout a large part of the earth's interior. In the case of P waves, the speeds are moderately well known throughout nearly the whole interior, while for S waves this knowledge is available down to a depth of 1,800 miles. On the basis of the calculations, it has become possible to divide the interior into a number of concentric regions. The boundaries between these regions are indicated by the levels at which the P and S velocities, or their gradients with respect to depth, change abruptly with increase of depth.

In continental regions, there is a fairly marked jump in the P and S velocities some 25 miles below the surface. The first evidence for this was obtained by the seismologist Mohorovičić in investigating local features of a Balkan earthquake in 1909, though he thought the change occurred rather deeper than 25 miles. Later work by others showed the change of property to be worldwide, and the boundary where the change occurs has come to be called the Mohorovičić discontinuity. In oceanic regions, work to date indicates that the depth of the discontinuity is of the order of only 5 miles below the ocean floor. The region which lies above the discontinuity is sometimes called the earth's crust, though it is well to realize that the term has only a conventional meaning nowadays. For more than 1,000 miles below the crust, the earth is solid, with increasing rigidity. Above the crust, the velocities of the P and S waves vary rather erratically and can vary in the horizontal as well as the vertical direction. In contrast, the velocities below the crust depend very largely on the depth alone, and the variation with depth is much more steady.

An early triumph in seismology was the revelation that the earth has a large core sharply separated from the part outside, called the mantle. The existence of a central core had been suspected for the last century, but was not established until Oldham supplied the necessary evidence from seismology in 1906. In 1913, Gutenberg (then in Göttingen, later in California) made a famous calculation which gave the depth of the core boundary as 1,800 miles, a figure that Jeffreys with the use of statistical theory showed in 1939 to be accurate within 3 miles or so.

The discovery of the existence of the central core came about this way. Consider P waves issuing from a large hypothetical earthquake with focus at the South Pole. Then it transpires that the waves would be strongly recorded at all stations in the Southern Hemisphere, and, as well, in the Northern Hemisphere as far north as latitude 15°, i.e., up to the latitude of Guatemala. But between the latitudes of Guatemala (15° N.) and Winnipeg (52° N.), there would be a "shadow zone" in which the regular P waves would be much less prominent. Then at the latitude of Winnipeg, the P waves would come in strongly again and be well recorded from there to the North Pole. The whole of the United States would thus be inside the shadow zone for the particular earthquake. Similar shadow zones occur with all earthquakes large enough to be recorded on the opposite side of the earth, the location of the shadow zone depending, of course, on the location of the focus.

On examination it was seen that the only possible explanation of the shadow is the presence of a central core. The regular P rays which emerge at epicentral distances up to 105° lie entirely in the mantle. Rays which emerge at 105° just graze the boundary of the core. Slightly steeper P rays strike the boundary at an angle and the shadow is produced through these rays being bent or "refracted" sharply downward at the boundary, with the result that they do not emerge at the surface until at distances beyond 142°. The phenomenon is similar to the refraction of light rays at the boundary which separates a water surface from the air and which causes a straight stick partly immersed in the water to be apparently bent at the surface.

No S waves have ever been detected in the earth's central core. This is part of the evidence that shows the central core, for most of its volume, to be in a fluid or molten state. The complete evidence for this conclusion includes measurements of tidal deformation of the solid earth, and astronomical observations that enable movements of the earth's poles to be determined. These measurements, together with seismic data on the earth's mantle, make it possible, by a difficult mathematical calculation, to set limits on the extent to which the earth's central core can deviate from the fluid state. Recent important calculations of the Japanese Takeuchi and the Russian Molodenski indicate that the outer part (at least) of the central core is very close to the fluid state.

On the other hand, both S and P waves are detected throughout the whole of the mantle. This shows that, apart from the oceans and isolated pockets of molten material near volcanoes, the earth is essentially solid down to a depth of 1,800 miles.

It is well at this point that some indication should be given of the terms "solid" and "fluid." The elastic properties of an ordinary material in a laboratory are specified by the values of two coefficients which together describe how the material will be deformed under any given applied stress. The two coefficients are commonly taken as the "incompressibility," which specifies the resistance of the material to change of density under pressure, and the "rigidity," which specifies the resistance to distortion of shape. For ordinary materials, values of the coefficients are determined by fairly direct laboratory measurements. For materials of the earth's deep interior the values are inferred from observations of seismic waves themselves; seismology shows that, in spite of the great pressures that occur, the stress-strain relations for materials deep down in the earth have, to good approximation, the same mathematical form as for materials at ordinary pressures.

Materials, both at the earth's surface and in the deep interior, are called solid when the coefficients which represent the incompressibility and rigidity are both appreciable, and fluid when the rigidity is very small compared with the incompressibility.

The seismic data show that the rigidity and the incompressibility both increase steadily with depth throughout the mantle. Inside the core, the rigidity falls to a small fraction of the mantle value while the incompressibility maintains a high value.

It needs to be remarked that the discrimination here made between solid and fluid relates only to the behavior under stresses of short duration such as those involved in the transmission of seismic waves, i.e., stresses that have periods of the order of a few seconds or so. A material that is solid in the sense here defined might nevertheless be subject to internal convection currents taking place over long periods of time. Whether such convection currents or other long-sustained forms of flow do take place in the earth's mantle is a matter of current controversy which the data of seismology cannot at present resolve.

So far, we have seen that seismic data enable us to make a broad division of the earth into a solid mantle, including crust and sub-crust, and a central core which is largely fluid or molten.

The behavior of P and S waves in the mantle reveals further that there is some measure of inhomogeneity in the mantle below the crust. In the outermost 700 miles of the subcrust the velocity gradients are too great to be compatible with a uniform chemical and physical state. The precise location of these changes is complicated by the fact that the steep velocity gradients cause the travel-time curves to bend back on themselves, and this makes for difficulty in identifying the corresponding pulses on seismograms. The evidence shows that these changes of property may set in at a level as high as 100 miles below the surface, and that they are complete at a depth of 700 miles or less. The changes may be due to variation in chemical composition or to a physical change of state brought about by the considerable pressure.

From a depth of 700 miles to within 100 miles or so of the core, the P and S velocity gradients are very steady, and it is likely that the chemical composition is nearly uniform in this part of the earth. In the lowest 100 miles of the mantle the velocity gradients fall to nearly zero and suggest some departure from uniformity.

Prior to 1936, the central core was thought to consist of nearly homogeneous molten iron and nickel. Then in 1936, a Danish seismologist, Miss I. Lehmann, looked more closely at records of two New Zealand earthquakes in the "shadow zone." It was already known that the shadow zone is not a complete shadow — that there are relatively small observations of P waves in the zone. Before 1936, these observations had been attributed to various diffraction effects — to deviations from the ray theory in waves refracted by the core boundary. Similar diffraction effects are well known in the transmission of light. Miss Lehmann proposed, as an alternative explanation, that some of the waves observed in the shadow zone are really associated with rays that have passed into an *inner* core, inside the central core, the P velocity in the inner core being great enough to bend sharply upward certain of the rays which penetrate into it.

Gutenberg and Richter showed that the travel-time data available by 1938 fitted Miss Lehmann's hypothesis, and in 1939 the existence of the inner core came to be well established when Jeffreys showed that the competing hypothesis of diffraction could not explain the size of some of the observed waves in the shadow zone. Small though the waves were, some of them were too large to be accounted for by diffraction. Recently, Burke-Gaffney and I have been able, from a study of several hydrogen-bomb explosions of 1954, to show the separate existence both of Miss Lehmann's waves, and of diffracted waves, on the same seismograms; this adds a further link to the chain of evidence for the existence of the central core.

Thus the earth is further divided into what, for want of a better name, is called the outer core extending between depths of 1,800 and nearly 3,200 miles, and the inner core occupying the remaining 800 miles to the earth's center. As will be shown later it is probable that the inner core is solid. In between these two parts of the central core there may exist a transition region about 100 miles thick. Jeffreys has found evidence of such a region, though not all seismologists as yet support the finding. It is difficult at the present stage to draw sharp conclusions on this part of the earth, and more evidence is desirable.

The following table summarizes in broad terms the division of the earth into regions according to the evidence from seismology.

TABLE 1. — *Division of the earth into regions according to the evidence from seismology*

Region	Range of depth	Description
A	0–10 miles (oceanic) ...... 0–25 miles (continental) ..	The earth's ocean and "outer layers." Very variable in composition.
B, C	25–700 miles	The upper mantle, in which there is some variation of composition not yet precisely located.
D' ...... D"	700–1,700 miles .... 1,700–1,800 miles	The lower mantle; D' appears to be nearly uniform in composition; in D" there is probably some accumulation of somewhat dense material.
E	1,800–3,100 miles	The outer core. Fluid, and probably uniform in composition.

Table continued:

F	3,100–3,200 miles........	Somewhat uncertain transition region between outer and inner core.
G	3,200–3,960 miles........	The inner core, probably solid.

DENSITY, PRESSURE, GRAVITY, AND ELASTICITY IN THE EARTH'S DEEP INTERIOR

To a good approximation, the velocities of seismic waves at any point inside the earth depend on just three properties, namely the incompressibility k, the rigidity μ, and the density ρ. The previous section shows that values of the P and S velocities are known down to the base of the layer E. (Inside E, the S velocity is taken to be zero because of the evidence for fluidity.) This knowledge supplies two equations connecting the three items k, μ, and ρ. If only a third independent source of information were available, it would be a matter of simple algebra to calculate the values of all three of k, μ, and ρ down to a depth of more than 3,000 miles, and so obtain good knowledge of the variation of density and elasticity in the earth.

In practice, no such third source of information is directly available, and the problem has to be attacked indirectly. Use is made first of the fact that in parts of the earth where the composition is uniform, the density changes due to increasing pressure are related to the incompressibility, so that seismic data can be further brought to bear to determine density gradients in these parts of the earth. Second, restrictions on the possible density variations are provided from knowledge of the mass and moment of inertia of the earth. (The moment of inertia, which contains information on the degree of central condensation of matter in the earth, is found from the dynamics of the earth-moon system in conjunction with measurements of the shape of the earth.) Third, by matching P and S velocities in the outer part of the earth against the results of laboratory experiments on rocks, an estimate can be made of the density just below the crust.

Calculations that I carried out some years ago on these lines gave density values ranging from 3.3 gm./cm.^{3} just below the crust to about 5½ gm./cm.³ at the bottom of the mantle. The value jumps suddenly to 9½ gm./cm.³ at the top of the outer core, and is between 11 and 12 gm./cm.³ at the bottom of the outer core. At the earth's center, the density probably lies between 14½ and 18 gm./cm.³. The uncertainty on the central value cannot be resolved until more is known about the character of the transition region F.

This work also enabled a number of other properties of the deep interior to be deduced. Atmospheric pressure at sea level is referred to as 1 atmosphere (15 pounds weight per square inch). In a steam locomotive the pressure may be about 30 atmospheres. At the bottom of the Pacific Ocean, the pressure can reach 800 atmospheres. In special high-pressure laboratories, values between 100,000 and 300,000 atmospheres have been reached. Inside the earth, however, the pressures become still greater. At the bottom of the mantle, the immense value of 1⅓ million atmospheres is reached, while at the earth's center the figure lies between 3½ and 4 million atmospheres.

Another section of the results relates to the acceleration g due to gravity in the earth. It is remarkable that, down to a depth of 1,500 miles, g keeps within 2 percent of its surface value of 32 ft./sec.². The maximum value, 34 ft./sec.², is reached at the bottom of the mantle. Inside the core the value of g steadily diminishes, becoming zero at the center.

The calculations showed further that the rigidity steadily increases with depth throughout the entire mantle until at the bottom the value is about four times that for steel at atmospheric pressure. The value then drops suddenly across the core boundary, and remains close to zero throughout the outer core, in keeping with the evidence that the outer core is fluid or molten.

But perhaps the most important fruits in this series of calculations were the results for the incompressibility k. Whereas the outer core boundary is characterized by sudden large changes in the values of the density and rigidity, the figures for k showed a change of only 5 percent, a change which, moreover, is inside the margin of uncertainty on which the calculations rest. Further, the gradient of k with respect to pressure was not detectably different on the two sides of the boundary.

This led me to suggest that, for the materials of the earth's deep interior, k changes fairly smoothly with the increasing pressure everywhere between a depth of 700 miles and the earth's center, a suggestion that has since received support from theoretical work on the variation of k with pressure beyond 10 million atmospheres.

This hypothesis of the smooth variation of k in the earth's central core led me further to the inference that the inner core is solid in the sense earlier defined, this being the natural interpretation of the jump in the P velocity which Miss Lehmann found between the outer and inner core. The seismic wave velocity equations show that either k or the rigidity μ must jump to account for the jump in the P velocity, and the available evidence all points to the conclusion that the jump is in μ. The jump is from zero rigidity in the outer core to a rigidity in the inner core two to four times that of steel.

It would be desirable to have the solidity of the inner core tested by direct detection of S waves in the inner core. The difficulty here is to excite S waves in the inner core from waves incident through the outer core from above; the latter waves, because of the fluidity of the outer core, must necessarily be P waves. A calculation that I have made on the expected amplitudes of S waves in the inner core shows that they are at best on the border of observability with present seismic resolving power, even with the mightiest earthquakes. The problem is illustrated by the fact that when atom bombs have been exploded underwater, and thus in a fluid region analogous to the earth's molten outer core, detectable S waves are only rarely excited in the mantle below the ocean even when P waves are quite well observed.

These various details show that, while much remains to be done, seismology has already given a good insight into the principal mechanical properties of the earth's interior.

THE EARTH'S COMPOSITION

In now venturing a few remarks on the earth's composition, I need to say that this subject is much more conjectural than the subject of the earth's mechanical properties. The numerical results that emerge from seismology lead, however, to a few interesting suggestions on composition, even though much uncertainty remains.

Ideas on the composition of the mantle come from matching numerical values of the density, the incompressibility, and their gradients with respect to pressure, against results derived in high-pressure experiments on rocks made by Adams, Williamson, Bridgman, Birch, and others. This work indicates that the outer mantle probably consists of ultrabasic rock, an olivine composition being commonly assumed; other possibilities that have been considered are that the rocks are eclogite or peridotite. Birch has suggested that the lower mantle may consist of phases including silica, magnesia, and iron oxide. It is possible than an appreciable quantity of free iron also occurs in the mantle. It is not yet certain whether the changes in the outer mantle are essentially progressive composition changes or are due to change of crystal type or other physical transformation. There is as yet no widely accepted explanation of the character of the changes inside the lowest 100 miles of the mantle.

The question of the composition of the central core has lately become interesting. Until a few years ago, it was widely accepted that the whole core consists predominantly of iron and nickel. This conclusion was based on observations of meteorite composition, and on the known relatively high density in the core.

Then in 1941 two European geophysicists put forward the radically different theory that the core consists of compressed hydrogen. Overwhelming arguments against this theory were quickly stated, but the theory led to an important calculation in 1946 which showed that, at 700,000 atmospheres (a pressure reached inside the earth's lower mantle), the density of hydrogen would suddenly jump from about 0.4 to 0.8 gm./cm.^{3}. This led to the idea, first advanced by W. H. Ramsey of Great Britain, that perhaps at the huge pressure of 1⅓ million atmospheres reached at the outer core boundary, the material there existing might suddenly jump in density from 5½ to 9½ gm./cm.^{3} as a direct consequence of the high pressure and not as a change of composition from rock to iron. Such modification of the rock (or other material) of the lower mantle would incidentally have all the physical properties of a metal and be electrically conducting. Thus theories which attribute the earth's magnetism to currents in the outer core would not be affected.

An interesting point is that, on the new theory, the density in the earth's interior would be largely determined by pressure alone, which would not be the case if the mantle and core were of distinct chemical composition. Hence, knowing the pressure-density relation for the earth, it becomes possible on the new theory, given the mass of a planet of identical composition, to compute its diameter. Starting from the known masses of Venus and Mars, calculations made in this way give in fact fair agreement with the observed diameters of the two planets, and also with the observed ellipticity of figure of Mars. In contrast, Jeffreys has shown that Venus, the Earth, and Mars must have considerably different over-all compositions if the earth's mantle and core are chemically distinct. Hence the Ramsey theory is closely linked with the question of a common composition of the three planets. The planet Mercury in its present state has too high a mean density to fit this common composition, but there is a possibility that the present Mercury through its proximity to the sun and consequent temperature may be appreciably denser than the primitive Mercury.

The question of the composition of the outer core continues to be controversial, and as yet it has not been possible to devise a crucial experimental or theoretical test to discriminate between the old and the new theories.

Although the regions E and F of the earth may not be composed predominantly of iron and nickel, several arguments all show that these two metals must predominate in the inner core. The course of the P velocity variations further suggests that there is some progressive change of composition inside the inner core, perhaps due to the presence of some additional denser materials.

EARTHQUAKES AND NUCLEAR EXPLOSIONS

Atom and hydrogen bombs resemble earthquakes in that they can send seismic waves down into the earth's interior. Although, as pointed out earlier in this article, the available energy in them is less than that in the waves produced by large natural earthquakes, there is a great compensating advantage to seismic research in that the source and location of artificial explosions can be known in advance.

In spite of the knowledge so far gained from natural earthquakes, we are much troubled in our inferences from this data because of our initial total ignorance of conditions at the source. On the other hand, a nuclear explosion can in effect be regarded as a "controlled earthquake" in which the time and place of origin can be precisely known, so that there is the possibility of inferring the internal structure of the earth much more accurately. For this reason, seismologists have been greatly interested in the possibility of using nuclear explosions to help them in their studies. Chemical explosions have already been employed with much success in unraveling the structure of the earth's crust. But larger sources are needed to send waves deep into the interior.

The very first atom bomb, exploded in New Mexico in 1945, was seismically recorded. A noteworthy feature of that explosion is that, whereas the origin time recorded at the source was uncertain by 15 seconds, the origin time is known to within 2 seconds from seismic records.

There was no mistake at the source in recording the Bikini underwater explosion of July 1946. The origin time of that explosion was officially released to two decimal places of a second! The resulting seismic waves were recorded at eight observatories in the United States at epicentral distances as great as 5,000 miles. Even though so few observatories recorded the waves, the results are seismically valuable, and have supplied important corrections to the travel-time tables.

From 1947 until 1957 there was no general release of source data on nuclear explosions in any country, although in some cases individual seismologists have been given access to data. For example, Dr. B. Gutenberg and Dr. D. S. Carder have been able to make important inferences from records of a number of explosions carried out by the United States. In Australia, a group of seismologists was given advance knowledge, and subsequently the relevant source data, on four nuclear tests carried out in central Australia. This information has been invaluable in leading to our first reliable knowledge of the broad structure down to a depth of 30 miles or so in a part of Australia.

The United States hydrogen-bomb explosions of 1954 have proved to be of great interest, and have been the subject of special studies by T. N. Burke-Gaffney, Director of the Riverview Observatory (Sydney), and myself.

About the middle of March 1954 news that a hydrogen bomb had been exploded was made public. Following this, information from Japanese fishermen indicated that the explosion had taken place near Bikini Atoll slightly before dawn on March 1, local time. This news made it feasible for a search to be made on a sufficiently limited stretch of the Riverview seismograms, and it transpired that there was indeed an isolated sharp movement near the expected time. The routine summary of seismic wave onsets recorded at Brisbane, 600 miles from Sydney, also reported a sharp movement in agreement with the Riverview reading.

This was enough to warrant an inspection of overseas seismological bulletins as they came in. It soon became evident that seismic waves from four of the 1954 hydrogen-bomb explosions had been distinctly recorded in at least 12 countries. Strangely enough, several of the observatories concerned had not realized that certain of their routine readings related to these explosions.

When all the data were put together, we diagnosed what we felt to be the pattern of the explosions, and made estimates of the origin times. A release by the United States Atomic Energy Commission shows that our estimates were correct within 0.0, 0.1, 0.4, and 0.7 second, respectively. The results have proved to have been of importance to geophysics in shedding further light on the earth's inner core, and have supplied additional useful corrections to the travel-time tables.

Further work on hydrogen-bomb explosions has been carried out by Gutenberg, Carder, Burke-Gaffney, and Rothé.

In 1957 there was an interesting development following my presidential address to the International Association of Seismology and the Physics of the Earth's Interior on the subject of "Seismology in Our Atomic Age." Three days later a cable from Dr. W. F. Libby of the United States Atomic Energy Commission gave advance source details of an underground explosion that was carried out in Nevada on September 19. This advance news greatly excited the seismologists gathered at Toronto who made hurried endeavors to have the seismic waves from the explosion as well recorded as possible.

Actually, the waves that went into the ground from the explosion turned out to be relatively small, and, generally speaking, were recorded only in Western United States at distances up to about 700 miles. There were, however, recordings by special field instruments which had been set up for the purpose in Mexico at a distance of 1,400 miles, and by a very sensitive seismograph in Alaska, 2,300 miles away. Doubt remains as to whether the more distant recordings would have been identified as waves from a nuclear explosion if the source data had not been released. From the seismic point of view, the explosion was principally useful in supplying further information on crustal structure in Western United States.

Seismologists hope to utilize nuclear explosions to sharpen many of their inferences on the earth's interior. At the same time, seismologists appreciate that all such controlled experiments that are carried out at their instigation must be subject to total scrutiny on the score of human welfare, genetical and otherwise.

Earthquakes and atom bombs both have great potentialities as destructive agents. But both can, nevertheless, be turned to great advantage in enabling us to understand the properties of our planet earth.

REFERENCES

BATES, D. R., ed. 1957. The planet Earth. London. (Includes discussions, written for the lay reader, on various aspects of the earth's interior.)

BULLEN, K. E. 1953. Introduction to the theory of seismology. 2d ed. Cambridge University Press. (Contains a mathematical discussion of seismic waves in relation to the earth's interior.)

1954. Seismology. London. (A briefer and less advanced account of seismic waves and the earth's interior.)

JEFFREYS, SIR H. 1950. Earthquakes and mountains. London. (An account written for the layman.)

1952. The earth. 3d ed. Cambridge University Press. (An advanced account of the problems of the earth's interior.)

PHILIP B. YEAGER[1]

The New Age of the Sea

[FROM THE SMITHSONIAN REPORT FOR 1961]

Although the sea has for centuries been of vital importance to mankind for both trade and warfare, yet only in the 20th century has it become apparent that the solution of many of man's social and economic problems may come from the world's oceans. The author of this revealing article, Philip B. Yeager, is a member of the professional staff of the Committee on Science and Astronautics of the U.S. House of Representatives. During committee activities on legislation and studies coming within its purview, time and time again the testimony has seemed to point to a fuller knowledge of the sea as the answer to many problems. The author here categorizes under seven headings the areas in which the oceans seem to hold needed answers: security, living room, water, climate, resources, industry, and deeper knowledge itself. The present-day greatly increased research directed toward the various phases of oceanography seems to foreshadow a "new age of the sea."

[1] The opinions or assertions in this article are the author's personal ones and are not to be construed as official or as the views of the House Committee on Science and Astronautics.

IF, IN the past few years, there has been doubt that the world is plunging into unprecedented social and technological revolutions, the doubt is swiftly fading. Too much is happening too fast in both areas. It is almost as if someone had pulled keystones from a mountainside and started twin avalanches — one a rapid acceleration of social problems (including economic, political, and military ones), and the other a tumbling series of brilliant technological advances.

But there is a curious phenomenon connected with all this. It is a phenomenon growing more pronounced with each passing day. It consists of the fact that insofar as the world's rising social difficulties may find their answer in science, each is likely to do so by a route leading directly through the sea. That is, nearly all the major challenges of the future which are now discernible seem to point like magnetized needles toward the oceans — indicating that an important part of their respective solutions lies somehow in deep water.

It is doubtful if there is any parallel for this situation in the history of mankind. Of course the sea has been a powerful influence on the affairs of men for thousands of years, particularly since the age of discovery and exploration spanning the 15th, 16th, and 17th centuries. Most of us are accustomed to the thought that the sea came into its own when venturesome, visionary men like Magellan, Cabot, Columbus, and Vespucci proved its utility as a medium of global transport. Some of us would set the date as early as the time of Eric the Red and his son Leif, or of the Mediterranean fleets of Carthage and Rome.

When the naval frigate and the 80-gun ship-of-the-line materialized, to be followed quickly by the American clipper and the steam voyage of *Savannah*, the age of the sea appeared to have reached full maturity; it had become a primary area for both commerce and conflict. And such, magnified many times, it remains. Yet a careful look ahead shows that, influential as it has been in the past and is today, the true significance of the sea for civilization is only beginning to become apparent.

Those who have heard the scientific testimony presented to the committees of Congress in recent years are especially conscious of this. The inquiries of these groups have ranged from biological warfare to the political issues of exploring outer space, from the need for language computers to the potential uses of rocket engines, from geodetic myths and fallacies to the shifting curricula of American education. Through these and other technological surveys, there has been revealed not only the capabilities, wants, and expectations of the scientific fraternity, including anthropologists, but also those of the economist, the industrialist, the conservationist, the engineer, the government official, the teacher, the student, the soldier, and the sailor.

In addition to providing a factual base for current legislation, the inquiries have been designed to give public officials a preview of the issues they will be called upon to face in the decades ahead — issues so sweeping in scope that they must be anticipated and planned for well in advance if they are to be met at all.

It is from the analysis of the vast amount of information poured into Congress by the country's most knowledgeable men and women that the image of the sea has emerged, almost startlingly, as a potent force which spreads across the entire spectrum of future human affairs.

The direction in which we turn seems to make little difference. Regardless of the social complex or problem under study, if we trace its predictable convolutions far enough ahead, we discover that sooner or later the trail encounters some aspect of the expanding influence of the oceans.

The most competent forecasts available today indicate strongly that the remainder of the 20th century will find Americans — and, indeed, people everywhere — forced to concentrate upon seven great quests. These are: the search for security, for living room, for water, for climate, for resources, for industry, and for knowledge itself.

In every one of these areas, the sea is proving a crucial element — so crucial that it is difficult to escape the conclusion that the new age into which we are moving is not only the age of the atom, the electron, and space: it is also a new age of the sea.

ILLUS. 45—Launching solid propellant rockets from the sea. Handling and logistics requirements for such rockets are simple and inexpensive, and mobility is unlimited over the surfaces of the oceans. Furthermore, the launching-pad environment costs nothing, cannot be destroyed, and hides the missile-firing apparatus from would-be attackers.

THE SEARCH FOR SECURITY

Nuclear weapons, the rising tide of nationalism throughout the world, and the rapidly growing East-West battle for the mind of man are putting an unprecedented premium on national security. At the same time, it is apparent that today, more than ever, strength is crucial from a psychological as well as from a physical standpoint.

Since the channel to security through international comity and negotiation cannot be depended upon, either now or in the foreseeable future, a strong military posture is the alternative. There is very little disagreement about this. What is strange is the fact that our technological revolution, while introducing radical new concepts of weapons and weapon systems, actually tends to accentuate the ancient role of the sea as a theater of military activity.

One does not need to be a military expert to see that this is so. In fact, not being an expert has its advantages. For if one is not, it is possible to evaluate the meaning of our new technology without being overly influenced by tradition, pride, ambition, or economic security.

To the nonmilitary expert, who is, however, familiar with the various military and civilian views concerning the employment of modern science in national defense, it is clear that current technology is underlining the necessity for mobility and secrecy of operational bases. And this is where the finger of logic points squarely to the sea.

No doubt it is true, as many of our military men assert, that we are moving inevitably into a time of astropower. But it is equally true that for many years to come the most efficient operational bases for asserting such power will be located on earth. And even when bases in space become possible, their vulnerability from the standpoint of mobility and secrecy will scarcely be less than bases functioning on or below the surface of the sea. Paradoxically, the missile-space era itself seems destined to emphasize this salt-water utility.

Since the refinement of the missile, target accuracy has become uncomfortably high. With the addition of the nuclear warhead, its threat obviously is a devastating one. As soon as geodetic surveys have been perfected and geographical locations are precisely known, as soon as missile production and servicing become simplified and reliable, the risks we face will prove less and less tolerable and land bases more and more vulnerable. Even the so-called "hard" launching sites — those constructed underground — may find their effectiveness partially canceled, particularly if the enemy is capable of contaminating the surrounding area with a hovering lid of deadly radiation or destructive chemical or biological agents.

Mobility and secrecy, at this point in time, will cease to be marginal necessities. They will be absolute ones. They may be obtainable on land by such schemes as the mobile-transport Minuteman. They will also be easily and efficiently attained at sea.

It appears likely, then, that an increasing percentage of U.S. deterrent power will shift to the sea. This may include more than the submarine-Polaris-missile concept, which, for all its virtues, has certain limitations as to communications, timing, and attack potential. It will almost certainly have to include a new concept of an extremely fast surface fleet capable of firing missiles accurately, shifting its base materially at a moment's notice, and capable of utilizing any patch of water as a launching site for any type of missile needed. The idea, which conceives of firing the missile from the surface of the water itself, requires pinpoint navigation and new missile technology rather than radical approaches to naval shipbuilding. In other words, it is new weapon handling technique that will be essential, not revolutionary types of ships.

When viewed through political and economic eyes, this extra reliance on the sea assumes doubled import. Government officials and others well versed in international affairs and the economic facts of life are aware that the United States is not likely to keep military bases throughout the world forever. At the same time, such bases are an added liability (in the sense of being targets) when placed on American soil.

They may be kept partially in the air or, someday, in space. But the sea is also looming as a likely locale, since it will have virtually all the advantages of foreign or sky-based launch sites, few of the disadvantages, and seems to offer a more practical and generally cheaper way of doing the job.

Thus it appears that the role of the Navy in the security picture, far from diminishing with the revolutions of our times, may become more comprehensive and conclusive than it has ever been — despite the many innovations and changes in seagoing missions, methods, and machines.

THE SEARCH FOR LIVING ROOM

Recognition of the growing population problem is now fairly widespread. During the 1950's, its warning was sounded frequently enough and the evidence became concrete enough to initiate serious thinking on the consequences of overpopulation.

Still, and in spite of dire warnings from the sociologists, most of us tend to toss off the matter as something we cannot do anything about. Or else we persist in treating it as too remote to warrant doing something about right now.

ILLUS. 46—Will future island dwellers commute in hydrofoils? These speedy craft would make living in presently isolated insular regions feasible. With a cheap local supply of power and fresh water, islands would become highly desirable residential areas.

Both attitudes seem fallacious. Certainly the second one is. To determine how much so, one need only glance at the United States. It required 300 years for the American population to reach the 1910 level of 90 million persons. Yet in the past 50 years that number has doubled. It will double again before the turn of the century, unless the birth rate slackens or some disaster wipes out great segments of the population.

One of the most important aspects of the population explosion is the problem of living space — of sufficient room to move around in with some semblance of freedom and privacy.

Interestingly enough, the evidence is that long before food or housing shortages become really serious, the difficulties arising from cramped living will have reached a critical peak, a peak demanding dramatic measures for a solution.

We have already begun to see the signs which are at once physical and psychological. Witness the mushrooming suburbs with their postage-stamp lots; the crowded expressways; the new traffic bottlenecks that materialize faster than old ones are dissolved; the smog blights; the polluted rivers; the disappearing trees and forest lands; the crowded classrooms; the accelerating noise level; the increasing crime rates; the high incidence of mental illness; the diminishing art of neighborliness; the self-enforced isolation of apartment dwellers; the periodic adult fetish for "getting away from it all"; the year-round emphasis on keeping children organized; the climbing divorce statistics; the courtroom dockets that are jammed with petty civil suits; and so on.

All these symptoms, in one way or another, stem at least in part from too many people living too close together. At the moment, the pressures creating the symptoms may not be sufficient to cause boiling. But imagine a doubling of the pressures. What then?

The social scientists believe that if our heterogeneous civilization is to remain reasonably healthy, in body, mind, and spirit, it cannot afford to let itself be forced to live like ants. Men need space. This means that the population must somehow spread out as it grows instead of concentrating more and more.

When a national park is forced to close its gates to 7,000 would-be campers during a single holiday weekend, when Congress must consider legislation to prohibit commercialization of the remaining 2 percent of American wilderness land in order to preserve at least a small part of the country in its natural state — the imminence of the problem begins to sink in.

Serious as is the situation, however, scientists do not believe solutions are impossible. They are depending on the sea and sea-related techniques to help find them.

The prognosticated picture is for gradually accelerating migration from heavily populated countries to lightly populated ones. The influx will be toward Australia, New Zealand, Canada, Alaska, and South America. In fact, the move has already begun. And it is receiving its greatest push, at the moment, from nations whose people historically have been strongly attached to their native lands—the English, the Dutch, the Danes, the French, the Belgians, even Americans. Despite political obstacles to free migration, it is believed that such trends will quadruple before the turn of the century. Our shrinking globe and the resultant style of international living, marrying, and working is bound to create a reciprocity of movement which would be quite unbelievable to the citizen of 1920 or even 1950. If Western culture should rub off on the Soviets faster than the reverse, so that Russian barriers to general intercourse are lowered, this trend may also find its way into northern Eurasia.

An equal, and perhaps earlier, phenomenon arising from the press of population along the world's seaboards may be the jump to island living. Presently there are thousands of coastal islands which are deserted or only sparsely inhabited. They offer an attractive alternative to crowded mainland living, and the forecasters are convinced that in the decades ahead these islands will turn into much sought-after real estate.

A third result of the spreading out of the population is expected to be a migration into land areas within the boundaries of the homeland which at present are only marginally desirable or convenient. This movement should be made feasible by technological innovations already in process and on the verge of practical utilization.

The effect of these trends on sea-related activities, and vice versa, will be marked.

With the swift surge toward world travel which is expected to be crucial within 25 years, comes the need for additional sources of rapid, long-range transportation. Air travel has expanded to meet this requirement, but air lanes are by no means likely to be able to handle the needs of the future. Relatively speaking, the air is already more crowded than the sea and its problems of adequate termini are more difficult.

This means a much revitalized demand for ocean travel and for new types of fast, oceangoing transports, and there is little doubt that when the demand is great enough such craft will be made available. We cannot see exactly how tomorrow's sailors will navigate, but we can guess that the naval architects and oceanographers will have hydrofoil craft sailing accurately predicted currents at speeds heretofore reserved for land vehicles. As the techniques grow, they will, in turn, stimulate their own use.

Potential island dwellers who are currently discouraged by the inaccessibility of remote coastal areas will find that smaller versions of these same craft would make an island home feasible and commuting easy. Or the air-cushion vehicle, which rides a few inches or feet above the surface of the water, may be used. Some of the latter are presently in ferry service between English Channel ports. With refinement and simplification, this vehicle, too, has significance for extensive salt-water transportation, especially to and from coastal islands or bay and inlet areas, and upon the world's rivers.

In company with the fast-developing fuel cell, which may permit a reliable source of localized, domestic power, and with the conversion of salt water to fresh water, these oncoming sea-transport methods will make island living not only reasonable but highly desirable.

The need for removing large parts of the presently urbanized population into the hinterlands likewise depends upon independent power sources, fresh water, and a transportation system which does not require expensive (and soil destructive) highways. Here again the sea promises a large part of the solution — the fresh-water, and a land adaptation of the hovercraft, or ground-effect machine, evolved from techniques developed through use on ocean areas.

The search for living room thus conjures up a future network of ocean-current corridors, seagoing traffic, and sea-dependent facets of living which the most confirmed old sea dogs of yesterday could scarcely have visualized.

THE SEARCH FOR WATER

The years 1954-57 were particularly notable as hurricane years for the east and gulf coasts of the United States. There were many such disturbances, and the American public was presented with distressing facts and figures based on damage caused by such wayward whirlwinds as Hurricanes Connie, Hazel, and Carol.

Notwithstanding the tragedy and damage caused by these and similar storms, they were accompanied by a completely unpublicized but highly valuable asset — namely, relieving the water crisis of a large and parched section of the nation.

This is one blessing, at least, inherent in the hurricane during earth's current dry cycle, 1951-62. As far as the United States is concerned, the torrential rains produced by the hurricane which moves inland have recently rescued more crops than they have destroyed and, while in the process of tearing down beach resorts and causing floods, they have nonetheless granted reprieves to thirsty agricultural industries and well-dry communities from Miami to Bangor.

The situation illustrates the growing fresh-water shortage which, in a few short years, promises to become acute not only in traditionally arid lands but also in such water-blessed areas as the United States, Europe, and western Russia.

More than 200 major communities of the United States face water shortages, and all but a handful of states are experiencing a serious water problem in one form or another. The Middle East, Holland, Spain, Italy, South Africa, Israel, the West Indies, and a number of South American countries are worse off.

Thus the stage is set for an acute shortage of man's most precious commodity. The precariousness of the situation is being augmented, of course, by the increasing population, the many new domestic uses to which water is being put, the rising use of irrigation and industrial water, the pollution of fresh-water streams and rivers, and a general failure to conserve water.

Very likely the world will get by the present 11-year dry cycle, which is scheduled to merge into a wet decade this year (1961), without too much suffering. And since wet cycles often run as much as 7 to 12 percent above normal rainfall, the evolution of fresh-water problems from 1962 to 1973 may be somewhat retarded. But assuming a new dry cycle in 1973, when the needs of a much larger population will have to be met, the availability and use of fresh water is expected to take its place among the world's crucial issues — or so the water engineers predict — unless substantial new sources of fresh water are uncovered.

Education of water users, conservation, and rigidly enforced anti-pollution laws will aid a great deal in alleviating the situation. Assuming, however, that standards of living will not be allowed to slip and that the population will continue to increase, the experts prophesy that nothing offers a permanent solution to future shortages except large new sources of water. This means the conversion of sea water to fresh water.

Conversion, of course, is nothing new to sailormen who have been doing it aboard ship for many decades. (Large aircraft carriers today convert salt water at a rate of 200,000 gallons per day.) But it is quite another matter to convert salt water to fresh water when the method used must be made to serve the world's millions.

Progress is being made by a number of methods, mainly through a variety of distillation techniques, solar energy, electrodialysis, and freezing, chemical, and electrical conversion. At present the largest plants converting saline water are located in South Africa, the Persian Gulf, the West Indies, Venezuela, Argentina, Ecuador, Greenland, Italy, and, in the United States, California and Pennsylvania. They convert anywhere from 100,000 gallons per day to 3.5 million gallons per day, at a cost of from $1.74 to $4.00 per thousand gallons. This compares with American municipal water rates which range from 25 to 40 cents per thousand gallons — but which do not reflect the rising costs of developing *new* sources of fresh water by conventional means.

When conversion costs drop to around 35 cents per thousand gallons, ocean or bay water will become a major source of the world's fresh-water supply. The Dutch are already operating elec-

ILLUS. 47—a. Pilot plant for converting sea water to fresh. Assembled for
        sea-site testing at Wrightsville Beach, N. C., this plant uses the
        vacuum-freezing method. Its capacity is 15,000 gallons per day.
    b. Progress in oceanography has been made; it must be increased.
        The bathyscaphe Trieste is shown preparing a dive off the
        Island of Panza in the Tyrrhenian Sea. She was purchased by
        the U.S. Navy, and made a record dive of 35,800 feet off Guam
        in 1960.

trodialysis-membrane plants which come close to 50 cents when brackish water (less than a third the salinity of sea water) is used. It is interesting that this is the price paid by Dallas, Tex., residents for a single gallon of extra fresh water during the drought of 1957 — twice what they paid for gasoline.

The U.S. government, through the Interior Department's Office of Saline Water, is subsidizing research in this area at a rate of between $1 and $3 million a year. Seven states — California, New Mexico, Arizona, Texas, Florida, North Carolina, and South Dakota — are also spending tax money for the purpose. Compared to other government endeavors, however, the total amount is negligible — so far.

The average American family uses 550 gallons of fresh water a day, the average apartment building 50,000 gallons a day, hospitals 50,000 to 100,000 gallons per day, large office buildings 120,000 gallons and up. Total water use in the United States has increased from 40 billion gallons a day in 1900 to 323 billion gallons in 1960, and will go to 597 billion gallons by 1980. Moreover, when we consider that the maximum dependable supply of natural fresh water in the United States, if it were all captured, is 515 billion gallons daily — then we begin to see the urgent need for new water resources.

As the water engineers point out, we must look once again to the sea.

THE SEARCH FOR CLIMATE

The slight knowledge which humans have of weather forces can be seen from the fact that at present we do not even know exactly how rain begins. Learning to predict weather with great accuracy and to modify it is something which geological forecasters take to be a "must" in the years ahead. In this way we may be able to slow down the soil erosion of arable land — that "geological inevitability which man can only hasten or postpone." Like the fresh-water situation, increased human demands upon the soil are creating real difficulties.

The Russian steppes of Kazakhstan are providing the world with a great contemporary dust bowl, reminiscent of that of the middle 1930's, when dust from the Great Plains stretched from Texas to Saskatchewan. Poor land-cultivation policies, drought, and strong easterly winds have combined to produce the trials of southern Russia. So great is the extent of this disturbance that the dust cloud has been identified in photographs taken by American weather satellites at altitudes of 400 miles.

Of course, wind erosion is only one of the processes whereby the earth's arable land is diminishing and the deserts increasing; erosion by water also sweeps away the soil. But insofar as the dust bowl of the Soviet steppes has diminished food resources at a time when the number of mouths to feed is increasing rapidly, it is a rather ominous indication of more serious troubles to come.

How long, the geologists inquire, can the world afford floods and dust bowls? The answer, obviously, is not much longer. Not, at least, if we expect to avoid famine, pestilence, and the threat of an exhausted soil at a time when we can least afford it.

Doing something about understanding and controlling (to a degree) the climate is apt to prove a far more difficult task than easing the shortage of fresh water. It will involve a tremendous amount of research. But again that research apparently begins and ends with the sea.

Meteorologists know that the sea is the breeding ground for the two great forces which contribute most to soil erosion — wind and rainfall. But they do not yet have enough understanding of the interplay of all the various elements contributing to weather to know why the earth's climate is as it is — or even to predict the long-range trends our climate may be taking. Until they do have a very good understanding of how and why the forces of climate behave, man seems destined to remain relatively ineffective in his efforts to slow down the present all too rapid erosion of his fertile world.

No doubt there is much that can be done with the land itself. The development of contour farming, for instance, has proved greatly beneficial. Crop rotation, soil chemistry, reforestation, flood control and the like are all highly useful practices. But even they have limitations for the long haul and can scarcely be compared to the benefits which might arise from an ability to create or to modify climate.

While some scientists have grave doubts that such ability will ever exist, others who combine meteorology with oceanography are now inclined to believe that these doubts themselves stem from an insufficient concept of how much information remains to be uncovered — how little we really know of the character and forces of the sea and how inclusive the influence of the sea is upon climate. They believe that the two sciences cannot be separated and that the true understanding of climate must wait upon a true understanding of the sea, which handles the greater part of earth's total "heat budget."

Research into the mysteries of the ocean and its operation is by no means proceeding fast enough to suit the world's oceanographers, but it has picked up startingly in the past few years and gives promise of accelerating still more. The United States has some 1,600 scientists now pursuing this endeavor, and its annual Federal expenditures of about $25 million are expected to be stepped up to $85 million during the 1960's. Other countries, notably England, Norway, Italy, Denmark, and the Soviet Union, are similarly increasing their sea study efforts.

Not all of this effort, nor even the major part of it, is being undertaken with the benefits of climatology in mind. Nevertheless, those benefits may be the greatest by far to come out of the sea-going laboratories now plying the oceans of the world.

THE SEARCH FOR RESOURCES

Running parallel with the patent needs for fresh water and productive soil is the less obvious but worldwide demand for new supplies of all resources. Among the most needed for the future, according to conservation engineers, are biological, mineral, and energy resources. In each category the sea offers particular hope for efficient capture and use. Moreover, the sea has as yet hardly been tapped as a supplier.

Biologically, the sea could be made to yield a limitless amount of protein enrichment for the human diet. Dr. Edward Wenk, a marine scientist who serves as executive secretary to the Federal Council for Science and Technology, points out that the sea "is filled with rich fauna and flora drifting at the surface, or in layers at intermediate depths; there are meadows of plants and swarms of large and small animals grazing or preying upon one another." He adds that only a very few of the 20,000 species of fish are caught and fewer still used, that little is actually known about fishing stocks, rhythmical seasonal changes and their sporadic fluctuation, but that the advent of such information will put a new face upon fishing. Fishing will then lose its hunting characteristics and assume those of cultivation. Development of important plants with life-stimulating properties may be handled the same way.

As far as minerals are concerned, the ocean floors have recently been found to contain high concentrations of manganese, cobalt, nickel, iron, and copper. But the potentially greater source of mineral supply rests in the sea water itself. Ordinary sea water is now known to contain 41 elements. Many of these (aside from chlorine and sodium) are in relatively large quantities — such as magnesium, sulfur, calcium, potassium, bromine, boron, carbon, strontium, silicon, and fluorine. Others, far less abundant, nevertheless are minerals which are becoming critical for modern scientific purposes — cesium (for plasma engines), uranium (for atomic energy), molybdenum (for heat-resistant alloys), and the like.

To date we have learned to extract only bromine and magnesium from sea water on a practical basis. But we know that plants extract potassium from the sea and animals like the octopus extract a copper compound for use in their blood as an oxygen carrier. So the processes for "mining" the sea undoubtedly exist. When they are uncovered, the world should have an unexcelled new natural supply of vital mineral resources.

Perhaps the most attractive side of the sea from a resources standpoint, however, is its potential as a source of energy — energy which can be tapped without depleting some limited type of fuel resource such as coal or oil.

A July 1, 1960, report of the House Committee on Science and Astronautics states:

> The greatest source of energy in the sea lies in the water itself. Hydrogen, one of the elements in water and thus in enormous abundance in the oceans, may be considered the fuel from which energy may be someday derived, imitating the natural process of nuclear fusion that occurs on the sun. Should current research efforts succeed, man would have a virtually inexhaustible store of energy, but the quest is long and arduous.
>
> Still another possible source of energy from the sea has been proposed by taking advantage of the difference in surface and bottom temperature. It has been said that almost 35,000 times the existing annual energy consumption of the world is delivered annually to the earth in the form of solar radiation and since most of the earth's surface is covered by ocean, a major portion of solar energy is absorbed by the sea. The temperature at depths below which sunlight does not penetrate, on the order of 1,200 feet, is ordinarily around 40° F. In the tropics, surface temperatures of 80° to 90° are common. Theoretically, this temperature difference could be utilized to drive a properly designed turbine, but it would operate at low thermal efficiency because the temperature differences are low. Quite obviously the amounts of energy so extracted are unlimited. The major question is whether such systems are economically attractive.
>
> Finally, there is the possibility of extraction of power from the twice daily rise and fall of the tides — such as has been proposed many years ago for Passamaquoddy. It is natural that man should look for means of harnessing some of the power of the tides for his own benefit, and small tide mills have been operated in a few suitable localities for centuries. Many plans for tidal power stations such as the Severn Barrage scheme have been drawn up, but only one project has so far reached the construction stage. This is the French scheme for the Rance Estuary in the Bay of St. Malo which is designed to have a capacity of 340 megawatts and is due to be completed in 1960. The main difficulty in the development of tidal power is that, even with large tidal ranges, the hydraulic head available is comparatively small and large areas of tidal water would have to be enclosed at high capital cost.

While it should be noted that each possibility is accompanied by some reservation, it should also be noted that technological problems just about as difficult and expensive have been solved cleanly in the past 10 or 15 years. When the need becomes great enough — and that time is not far away — there seems little doubt that ways will be found to pull out and transmit the sea's restless, endless energy in the form of useful work.

THE SEARCH FOR INDUSTRY

For the American system of private enterprise, the need for new industry in the years ahead assumes marked importance, not only in order to maintain a high level of consumer goods and a growing economy, but as a means of employment for the rising population.

Exploitation of the oceans rates far up on the list of genuine new industrial possibilities. A recent issue of *Dun's Review,* for example, has cited the oceans as "industry's next frontier" and comments:

> As flights into space become routine in the next decade, the nation may turn in another direction for the next great research frontier — and new multi-billion-dollar marketing opportunities. Close at hand, but still largely out of reach, the depths of earth's oceans are in many ways more a mystery than outer space. The coming drive to plumb the ocean's secrets will mean a great new source of profits for industry. As the navies of the world slowly submerge, demand for equipment that can function under water will burgeon. As the industrial nations exhaust many of the natural resources of the land surface, submarine miners will increasingly exploit the incredible mineral wealth of the oceans, and as the world's population expands beyond the capacity of arable land to feed it, the sea will become a critically important source of edible flora and fauna. . . . Although the objective of the oceanographers is more scientific knowledge of the ocean and the ocean floor, commercial benefits are sure to follow. Here is one example: leading oceanographers are convinced that underwater telephone cable breaks are the result of ocean bottom landslides. If and when oceanographers are able to predict where such displacements of bottom soil will take place, the telephone companies will be able to avoid multi-million-dollar repair bills by laying cables elsewhere or by other methods. . . . When all the current activity connected with the oceans is evaluated, the dimensions of present and potential market opportunities look really impressive.

But the industrial outlook for the sea encompasses far more territory than that suggested above. Besides a trend to improved and more efficient cable laying, a series of other submarine activities are beginning to take place — undersea pipelines, such as the projected crossing of the Mediterranean from North Africa to Spain for pumping gas and oil; undersea tunnels, such as the 32-mile Dover-to-Calais project beneath the English Channel; off-shore mining, such as the new sulfur operations in the Gulf of Mexico; the development of robot equipment for undersea operations, such as the Remote Underwater Manipulator which can act as the hand of man on the ocean floor through a 5-mile coaxial cable.

Then there is the ultimate usefulness of the oceans and coastal areas as places of storage. The seas have been used for generations, of course, as a dumping ground for continental wastes. But the storage demands of the future will be far more sophisticated. One already showing urgency is the storage of unwanted radioactive byproducts of atomic energy. Low-level wastes are presently being dispersed in the sea. High-level wastes cannot be stored there, at least not until much more is known about the inner workings of the sea itself and ways are found to contain the material in a manner which permits radioactive dissipation over long periods of time without contaminating the water.

These very developments, however, as they crystallize, promise a revolutionary shift to sea storage for other commodities and purposes — especially for those which need to be maintained in cool, stable temperatures and/or unexposed to oxygen. As land becomes ever more scarce and the costs of using it for storage less feasible, it will not be surprising if government and commerce alike begin charting off segments of ocean area for this purpose.

Other potential industrial uses allied to the sea can be identified even now. Hydroponic farming — growing plants and vegetables in water containing the essential mineral nutrient salts, rather than in soil — is in its infancy. But there are those who foresee that this endeavor will necessarily become a very large one and that research into the qualitative transformation and manipulation of sea water will make it possible. Another important industry is evolving, based on supplying equipment needed by the world's one million skin divers, plus that of the salvage industry which has been tremendously stimulated by new skin-diving techniques. This, too, is a trend likely to accelerate on both business and pleasure bases.

Of one thing we can be sure. As research into the sea and sea-related activities increases, industrial uses will be found for it which today we cannot visualize. And new professions, unconjectured as of now, are bound to grow with these new industries.

THE SEARCH FOR KNOWLEDGE

When the United States inaugurated its space exploration program in March 1958, the President's science advisers issued a statement in which they observed:

> Scientific research has never been amenable to rigorous cost accounting in advance. Nor, for that matter, has exploration of any sort. But if we have learned one lesson, it is that research and exploration have a remarkable way of paying off — quite apart from the fact that they demonstrate that man is alive and insatiably curious. And we all feel richer for knowing what explorers and scientists have learned about the universe in which we live.

Moreover, as technology continues to take over and the hours of the world's working day shorten, people must have purposeful and creative things to do. The burgeoning quest for knowledge is expected to fill a large part of this inchoate vacuum.

Perhaps the most immediate target of the knowledge seekers will be earth itself, about which so much remains to be learned. A true understanding of our own planet, its origin, composition, and what makes it tick, will be one of the first big steps toward understanding the universe. This, at least, is the allegation of the scientists, who add that the key to better information about the earth very probably lies with the sea.

"Yet the sea," says the House Committee on Science and Astronautics, "which represents 71 percent of the earth's surface, is mostly unexplored. Scientific information is meager concerning the physical and chemical properties of oceans and their currents, the biological and mineral resources of, in, and under the sea, the relationship of the oceans to weather and climate. Even knowledge about the origins of the oceans themselves, their evolution and the changes which may be expected are little known and understood."

A long-held desire of geologists all over the world has been access to earth's interior — to that area below the crust. The U.S.-proposed Project Mohole,[2] which contemplates ocean drilling, may provide it. This program gets its name from the Mohorovičić discontinuity which represents the interface between the familiar crust and the as yet unseen mantle. Because what lies beneath the earth's crust, 7 to 15 miles from the surface, is of such vital importance to the understanding of the origin and geophysical processes of the earth, Project Mohole is designed to drill through the crust into the mantle.

The reason for the approach through the sea is simple. Thus far the deepest successful drilling [for oil] has been limited to about 26,000 feet, far short of the 100,000 feet at which discontinuity is estimated to lie below the surface of continental masses. In the oceans, however, the discontinuity rises to within 15,000 feet of the ocean bed. It is thus proposed to undertake the drilling at sea so as to reduce by a significant amount the depth of hole required.

The answers to come from these and other phases of the growing drive toward ocean sciences will possibly provide us with the first basically accurate understanding of the globe on which we live. What such understanding will mean in terms of material and economic effect, or in terms of mental and physical effect, can only be surmised. It will not be insignificant.

Each of the searches discussed in the foregoing contributes to the others and each, in some degree, is dependent on the others. Taken as a group, however, and in light of their common denominator, they would seem to herald a coming Age of the Sea second to none in earth's history.

---

[2] See the following article in this volume. — EDITOR.

WILLIAM E. BENSON

Drilling Beneath the Deep Sea

[FROM THE SMITHSONIAN REPORT FOR 1961[1]]

IF SPACE EXPLORATION *is the greatest scientific adventure of modern times, as stated in the editorial introduction to a previous article, surely the spectacular research described in the present article must be rated not far below it. William E. Benson, who is the Head of the Earth Sciences Section of the National Science Foundation, gives a graphic picture of one of the strangest scientific undertakings ever envisioned. For the project consists of drilling a hole 3 miles deep under 2 or 3 miles of ocean water. The object is to drill completely through the earth's crust and into the so-called mantle layer beneath the crust, of which we now know only what can be inferred from seismic studies. Why not drill the hole on land? Because the boundary between the earth's crust and the denser interior mantle is 20 miles below the surface of continents and only some 3 to 5 miles below the ocean floor. The author describes some of the incredible difficulties to be overcome in drilling through 2 miles of pipe hanging from an unmoored vessel sometimes in high winds and rough seas. He further tells of the many things that may be learned from this exciting and challenging 20th century scientific adventure.*

---

[1] Revised as of February 1965 by the addition of a supplementary note at end of article.

Two miles below the surface of the Pacific Ocean off the west coast of Mexico, a drill bit studded with diamonds was gently eased inch by inch into the bottom ooze. Jets of water coming down the drill pipe then began to wash the bit farther into the mud. One of the most notable modern experiments in oceanography and geophysics was underway.

The experiment, part of Project Mohole, achieved important results through a combination of two factors — a scientific impetus bordering on the visionary, and imaginative engineering concepts that pushed to its limits today's technology.

Attached to 11,700 feet of pipe dangling from a drilling derrick mounted on a ship, the bit was the tip of an 85-ton probe wielded by scientists intent on unlocking some of the history that is recorded in the sediment that has been collecting on the bottom of the oceans for millions of years.

At the base of the steel tower, scientists and veteran petroleum drillers anxiously watched gages and recording pens trace the shakes and twists of the pipe as, in high winds and heavy seas, the drilling ship *CUSS I* held its position with steering motors.

For the scientists, the drilling operation was part of the first attempt to retrieve samples of the earth's crust at appreciable depths beneath the floor of the ocean basin. Their success has added a completely new technique to the study of the oceans of the world.

For the engineers and drilling personnel who had assembled the longest drilling pipe ever suspended from a ship, the operation was the world's first deep-sea drilling expedition. Furthermore, a drilling crew was working for the first time aboard an unmoored ship, and in water 40 times deeper than in the usual offshore operation.

As they watched the uncoiling ink lines and the quivering gages, the drillers were learning what takes place when more than 2 miles of pipe is hung in water, what effects the ship's pitch and roll produce, and how much vibration is set up by ocean currents and pipe rotation. As one remarked, "This is like hanging a piece of spaghetti from a 12th-floor window to the sidewalk, and then trying to drill a hole with it."

The drilling was the first at-sea experiment for Project Mohole, a 5- to 10-year nationally funded effort to drill through the earth's crust to sample its interior, the largest and least-known area on earth. Mohole is supported by the National Science Foundation and is a combined effort of the nation's leading scientists and engineers working through the AMSOC Committee, organized in 1958, and the National Academy of Sciences-National Research Council.

The project takes its name from Andrija Mohorovičić, a seismologist born in Croatia in 1857, who determined from earthquake waves the existence of a seismic discontinuity. This discontinuity was later shown to be worldwide and has been accepted by most geologists as the boundary between the crust of the earth and its denser interior mantle. The discontinuity was named after its discoverer and, as is the wont of Americans, is commonly abbreviated to "Moho."

Drilling in the deep ocean long was regarded as impossible because of the fundamental limitations of existing methods and materials. It was only with the comparatively recent development and use of drilling ships by the petroleum industry, in coastal waters off California, that deep-water drilling could be considered seriously.

Of all ships developed for offshore work, the most suitable to the purposes of deep-water experimental drilling was the *CUSS I,* a 260-foot converted Navy freight barge, owned by the Global Marine Exploration Co., Los Angeles. Deriving its name from its original joint owners, the Continental, Union, Superior, and Shell oil companies, the ship represented a multimillion dollar technological development by the petroleum industry.

The three-year theoretical work of the AMSOC Committee on the problem of deep-sea drilling represented a bold attack. By late 1960, the work had reached the point at which it was necessary to test their concepts at sea. These concepts were based on existing drilling technology but depended upon the solution of new problems such as keeping an unanchored vessel stationary over the drill site, enabling the ship's pilot to determine accurately the ship's position in relation to the hole, and drilling with an extremely long drill string without casing.

The first problem, that of positioning the ship, was solved by employing four outboard motors, powered by 200-horsepower diesel engines, and capable of delivering thrust in any direction. These units, known as "Harbormasters," were mounted fore and aft and on both sides of the ship. The amount and direction of thrust of each engine were controlled at the pilot's console with a single lever resembling an aircraft joystick. The engines and steering system proved capable of holding the ship within its own length of a position in 12-foot waves and a 25-knot wind.

The second problem, that of determining the ship's position relative to the hole, was overcome by using a unique taut-line, deep-moored buoy system, together with sonar and radar, and a Sperry Mark 14 Gyro-Compass.

The AMSOC staff evolved the design of the 6-foot aluminum buoys in the shape of an oblate spheroid (elliptical viewed from the side, round viewed from above). These were placed about the drill site, anchored to the bottom, with the buoys about 100 feet below the surface of the water. Their special shape reduced their resistance to ocean currents and enabled them to remain moored almost directly over their anchors. Mounted on the buoys were sonar transponders that, when triggered on another frequency from the ship, sent back a signal, giving a sonar screen picture of the buoy pattern relative to the ship. Radar also scanned surface buoys that were secured to the deep-moored buoys. These devices, together with visual sightings of the surface buoys, gave the pilot his relative bearings. The ship's heading was maintained by reference to the Sperry Gyro-Compass repeaters on the bridge.

The third problem, that of the forces at work on the drill pipe, was worked out on paper for a variety of conditions by using a model. On the basis of the calculations, two sets of specially tapered drill pipes were ordered. One was a spare in the event that the other was dropped, or, if the doubters proved to be right, the pipe wound itself up like a corkscrew and snapped. In the course of the actual operation, the drill string proved to be the least troublesome component of the system.

TAUT-LINE BUOY SYSTEM FOR EXPERIMENTAL DRILLING PROGRAM

RADAR REFLECTOR

SURFACE BUOY (fiberglass covered innertube)

ELASTIC SHOCK CORDS (3)

1/16" GALVANIZED STEEL STRAND
(to raise and lower transponder)

7/32" GALVANIZED STEEL STRAND
(min. B. S. 7,000 lbs., 19 strands)

200 to 400 FEET

SONAR TRANSPONDER (sonar system)

DEEP BUOY (aluminum elliptical
dished heads, wt. in air 630 lbs.)

THREELEG BRIDLE

ABOUT 2½ MILES

7/32" GALVANIZED STEEL STRAND

CHAFING CHAIN (6' length)

ANCHOR (cast concrete; about 3' × 3' × 2',
wt. in air 4,150 lbs.)

OCEAN BOTTOM

ILLUS. 48—Taut-line buoy system for experimental drilling program.

WHY MOHOLE?

With all the attendant problems, why drill a Mohole at sea? The answer is simple.

Beneath continents, the average depth to the Moho — the thickness of the crust — is about 20 miles; beneath the ocean, only about 5 miles.[2] A hole drilled from land, therefore, would have to extend about 20 miles in order to reach the Moho, and the deepest hole yet drilled goes down only about 5 miles. But in some places in the ocean the crust is thinner than its average 5 miles, and the total distance from the surface to the Moho is only about 6 miles, 3 miles of which is water. If a drill string could be made 20 percent longer than that of the record hole on land, and if the drilling could be accomplished from a ship, the eventual Mohole seems possible at sea. The 20-mile depth, of course, ruled out a boring on land.

Before an experimental drilling program at La Jolla, Calif., in 3,000 feet of water that preceded the deep-water experiment, oceanographers had reached no farther than 75 feet below the bottom of the sea, using the standard piston coring apparatus lowered on a wire line. Not only did the new drilling technique produce the first deep cores, or cylindrical samples, of the deep ocean bottom, but it also sampled the mysterious "second layer" of the oceanic crust, hitherto studied only by seismic means. Findings proved that at least the top of the layer at the site of the drilling was basalt, a hard rock formed by the solidification of lava.

The significance of this discovery has only begun to be debated by the geophysicists and marine geologists. They are, for example, puzzled by the fact that the sediment layer is not deep enough for the amount of sediment estimated to have been deposited from the beginning of the oceans. The discovery that the top of the second layer is basalt could mean that the basalt, at 560 feet at the site, underlies only part of the total depth of sediment and that earlier sediment records lie still deeper. Conversely, it is argued that since the layer is basalt, it could be the beginning of a

---

[2] Geologists regard the continents as thick blocks of relatively light, or granitic, rock, "floating" upon the far denser supporting rock of the mantle. The rock of the oceanic crust, however, is relatively thin and dense.

ILLUS. 49—*Shown under way near San Diego, California, is the CUSS I, deep-sea drilling ship which participated in the experimental drilling program for Project Mohole during March and April 1961, near Guadalupe Island, off the west coast of Mexico. The program was undertaken with the support of the National Science Foundation to obtain engineering data and deep-sea drilling experience, and to provide scientific data on the composition of the earth's crust beneath the oceans. The Global Marine Exploration Co., Los Angeles, was the drilling contractor. (NSF Photo.)*

ILLUS. 50—*Aerial view of CUSS I in position off San Diego, California, at the start of the world's first deep-sea drilling. Note full pipe racks aft, and water turbulence created by the forward starboard steering engine.*

very deep layer of hard rock. This would mean that the hoped-for earlier sediments, with their evidences of the formation of the oceans, somehow have been lost.

WHAT CAN BE LEARNED?

What can be learned from the oceanic sediments? Today, at more than a dozen laboratories around the country, scientists are analyzing the bits and pieces of evidence resulting from the operation.

ILLUS. 51—*One of four 200-horsepower Murray and Tregurtha Co. diesel out-*
board engines used to power drilling ship CUSS I on experimental
drilling project off Guadalupe Island. (NSF Photo.)

First, there are the geophysical logs, the records obtained by lowering instruments down the various holes. Then, there are the
cores themselves, the sections of ooze and rock bitten out of the
hole by a specially designed coring apparatus. From these and
from subsequent tests will come facts that will be worked into existing hypotheses that try to explain what the ocean basins are
like, how they were formed, and how old they are. New facts may
force a revision of some hypotheses, or their rejection. In other
cases, the evidence may link with other facts, clarify concepts, or
point new directions. In addition, there is always the potential of
any basic research — discovery of the unexpected.

Within the sedimentary layers will be found many new pages of the history of the earth and the oceans. Mohole scientists at sea reported finding fossil evidence of a flowering of sea life roughly 25 million years ago in the Guadalupe Island area. More than 100 feet of nearly continuous core of the deep ocean ooze showed that sea life in the area was prolific for about 7 million years; by comparison the area is now an oceanic desert. The upper 500 feet of sediment was determined to be of late Miocene Age in the geologic time scale by correlating fossils with similar ones of known age found in continental rocks.

The geophysical logging hole reached a total depth of 576 feet, and penetrated to 20 feet within the basaltic layer. Geophones and seismic wave detectors were lowered into the hole to measure the velocity of sound in the deep rocks and to redetermine the thickness of the various layers beneath the reach of the drill. Preliminary analysis of the reading indicates that sound waves penetrate the soft sediment at a rate of 1.59 kilometers per second, a rate considerably less than the value generally assumed by seismologists. If this low velocity generally exists, oceanographic sediments could be thinner than has heretofore been supposed.

The geophysical logs also measured the heat flow coming through the layers of the earth beneath the ocean. These measurements provided improved scientific estimates of the earth's internal temperature. Readings off Guadalupe Island at 500 feet below the ocean floor showed a somewhat higher heat flow than was expected on the basis of earlier bottom measurements. The significance of this is not yet understood, but it is interesting in view of the fact that, while the heat flow through the ocean floor is less than that measured on land, it is still far too high to satisfy some theoretical considerations. According to present theories, heat flow through the oceans should be less than has been observed.

Most of the continental heat flow from within the earth derives from radioactive elements in granitic rocks. But the rocks thought to compose the oceanic crusts are supposedly low in radioactive material. Scientists believe, therefore, that there must be a suboceanic heat source other than the crust. There are many suggested explanations including an unsuspected radioactive heat source high in the mantle, or convection currents within the mantle.

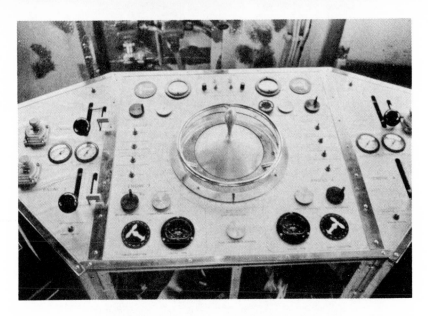

ILLUS. 52–a. Controls of integrated steering system for CUSS I. System was designed by AMSOC engineer Robert Taggart. It permitted four outboard engines to be operated simultaneously, regulating their speed and direction of thrust from single "joystick" on console.

b. The 8½-inch, $8,000 diamond drill bit used in the experimental drilling program for Project Mohole, shown aboard the CUSS I.

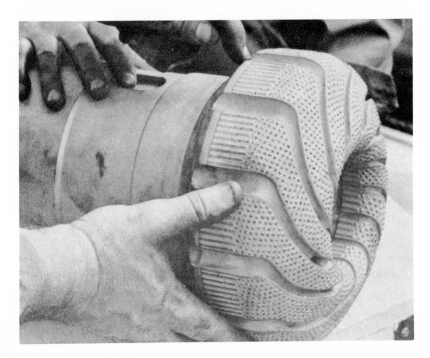

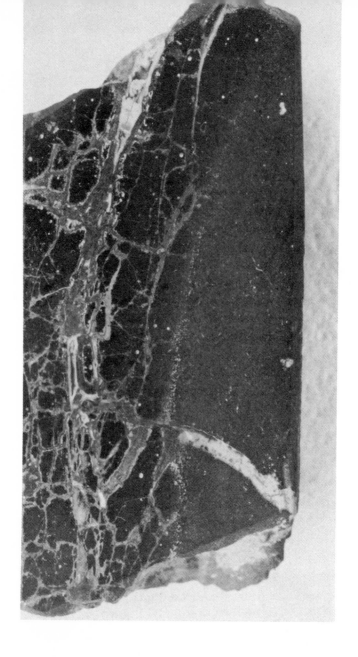

ILLUS. 53—Enlarged view of cut and polished section of a 1-inch core of glassy basalt recovered from near the top of the second layer of the oceanic crust, about 575 feet below the ocean floor under 11,700 feet of water, off Guadalupe Island, April 1961. (Photograph by U.S. Geological Survey.)

A more exact understanding of suboceanic heat flow will also provide new information that can be fitted to current theories of the earth's origin and to the conjectures of whether the earth is heating or cooling. It may also be possible to determine how much of the suboceanic heat is primordial and how much derives from radioactivity.

What may be the first fixed-position current measurements in the deep ocean were reported by the Mohole scientists. A velocity of 0.2 knot was observed at 1,500 feet in measurements for as long as 9.5 hours with a rotor-type meter suspended between the drilling ship and one of the deep-moored buoys. This velocity was considerably less than estimates used in designing the drilling string.

ONLY A BEGINNING

Present scientific and engineering results are only the beginning. Project Mohole, born as a purely scientific concept, has led to the development of equipment and techniques with the potential of opening the oceans to commercial activity. The theoretical work on the experimental drilling operation could speed the day of ocean-floor mining, deep-sea oil drilling, and practical construction techniques. It definitely has paved the way for more scientific exploration.

Meanwhile, the Mohole scientists are currently pushing ahead with surveys to determine the site for the eventual Mohole, seeking ways to improve the speed of drilling in hard rock, and experimenting with a host of new instruments and techniques, all aimed at the next immediate objective — a drilling program, perhaps within a year, to sample the third layer of the oceanic crust, and to prove out new methods for the eventual drill to the Moho.

SUPPLEMENTARY NOTE

Since this article was written, the plans for Project Mohole have progressed and evolved. In 1962 the National Science Foundation awarded a prime contract for the engineering design and logistic support of the project to Brown and Root, Inc. of Houston, Texas. After a thorough engineering study it was decided not to use smaller vessels for further testing but to proceed directly to the design and construction of a vessel capable of drilling to the mantle. Brown and Root have now completed the design of a large drilling platform together with new drilling and positioning equipment. Construction will start in the summer of 1965 and the platform should put to sea late in 1966. It will undertake a year's program of drilling through the sediments and into the deeper layers of the oceanic crust at a number of localities in the Pacific, finally settling down at a site 150 miles northeast of the Hawaiian Islands where the deep penetration to the mantle — the Mohole itself — will be undertaken.

COMMANDER JAMES T. STRONG

The Opening of the Arctic Ocean

[FROM THE SMITHSONIAN REPORT FOR 1962]

THIS ARTICLE *combines 20th century science with adventuresome exploration. The author, Commander Strong, U.S. Navy, in 1949 served in U.S.S.* Cochino, *which burned and sank in Arctic waters. Later he served in four different submarines and finally in 1960 was second in command aboard the nuclear submarine* Seadragon, *sailing from Portsmouth, N.H., to Pearl Harbor, Hawaii, by way of the Northwest Passage and the North Pole, with long stretches of the journey under the ice. Strong describes the significance of the pioneering voyages under the Arctic ice by the* Nautilus, Skate, *and* Sargo. *He describes first-hand the efforts of* Seadragon, *equipped with iceberg detector, upward-aimed fathometer, and underwater cameras, to prove the safety of traveling under icebergs. Later* Seadragon *also proved the feasibility of long journeys in shallow and narrow water under complete ice cover. The combination of nuclear power and electronic devices, plus the skill and courage of the men who man nuclear submarines, had conquered the last obstacles to prolonged under-ice travel. As a result, the entire 5 million square miles of Arctic seas were now open to navigation.*

Now only four years from the initial appearance of this article, many of the predictions of Commander Strong are already history. For example, during 1962 at least three nuclear submarines voyaged to the North Pole: the United States veterans Seadragon *and* Skate *and the Soviet newcomer, the submarine* Leninsky Komsomol.

F AR-REACHING voyages under the Arctic ice by nuclear submarines are now common enough to attract little interest. For the many who regard them as stunts, there now seems little reason to continue them. That they may well herald a new phase of naval operations, as important as any our Navy has ever seen, is perceived by only a few.

Until 1958 the Arctic Ocean was untraveled by ship. Polar bears, seals, and fishes shared this vast area with rare human intruders who traveled there by air or on foot or by sled at great effort. A few powerful armored icebreakers probed the edges of the perpetual icepack. These ships and others entered the fringes of this region at great risk; frequently they were trapped and remained until rescued at great cost.

Then *Nautilus'* crossing of the entire Arctic Basin under the icepack proved the feasibility of travel there by submarine. Within two years, succeeding voyages have removed all the major questions in under-ice navigation and the nuclear submarine has opened 5 million square miles of ocean to travel by ship. Before considering the implications of this breakthrough, a brief review of the conditions under which it occurred will be profitable.

The trip of U.S.S. *Nautilus* from the Pacific across the Pole to the Atlantic is well known. Earlier in 1957, *Nautilus* had prepared for this voyage by a brief but productive probe under the ice to within 180 miles of the Pole. Shortly after *Nautilus* crossed the Pole, the nuclear-powered submarine *Skate* arrived there on an intensive voyage of discovery. Among other significant achievements, *Skate* demonstrated the ability of submarines to surface in the open-water leads, and she also proved the existence of these leads throughout the Arctic pack during summer months. In

March 1959, less than seven months later, *Skate* proceeded to the Pole a second time. During this severest of all seasons in the Arctic, *Skate* developed a procedure for surfacing blind through the ice which completely covers the Arctic Ocean during the winter darkness.

In February 1960 *Sargo* became the third of the "ice boats" to undertake what many consider was the most hazardous task of all. Building on knowledge gained from *Nautilus* and *Skate,* and utilizing prototype equipment to guide her around shoals and deep ice, *Sargo* operated for many days in shallow waters under the unfavorable circumstances of complete ice coverage and round-the-clock darkness.

Several questions remained after *Sargo* successes. Could nuclear submarines operate under ice in proximity to icebergs without fear of colliding with this deep draft ice? Could nuclear submarines operate under the ice in the restricted waters between land masses? If a nuclear submarine could operate in narrow, shallow passages under the ice and in the vicinity of icebergs, it seemed likely that there were usable passages in the islands of northern Canada that should be sought out and used. Several ice-blocked straits crossed this area, but whether they were passable by submarine was not known.

Much had been learned about icebergs since the establishment of the International Ice Patrol in 1913 after the tragic sinking of *Titanic.* Icebergs are the droppings of glaciers which exist on many of the Arctic islands. The weight of centuries of snowfall shoves the glacier down the island slopes toward the sea where huge pieces break off, becoming icebergs. Time and pressure and temperature have converted snow to very hard ice by the time it reaches the sea. Once afloat, it may wander in Arctic waters under the effects of current — and to a lesser extent, wind — for years while a slow erosion occurs. Whenever currents take it into warmer waters, disintegration occurs within a few days.

Most of the world's icebergs occur in Baffin Bay. Greenland is by far the most important source; here 12 large glaciers alone have been recorded as calving 2,300 bergs in one year. Icebergs do not normally occur in the Arctic Ocean so that previous nuclear submarine expeditions have not confronted them.

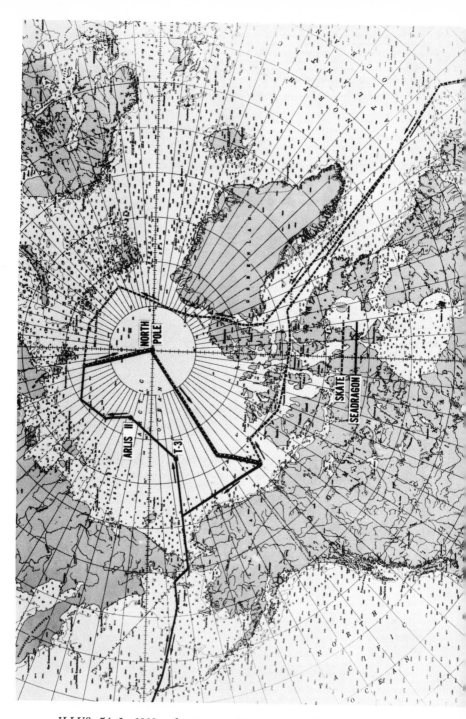

ILLUS. 54—In 1962, subsequent to the writing of this article, nuclear submarines USS Skate and Seadragon rendezvoused in the Arctic
and journeyed to the north pole together, making joint experiments and observations. Enroute to these operations the Skate
made the first survey and submerged transit of the Smith Sound
route between Greenland and the Queen Elizabeth Islands.

A new nuclear submarine, U.S.S. *Seadragon* (SSN-584) was having her post-shakedown shipyard availability at Portsmouth, N.H., at this time. *Seadragon* was scheduled for transfer to the Pacific Fleet at an opportune moment, and so it was decided to fit her with ice equipment and send her to Pearl Harbor by way of a Northwest Passage, if one could be found. On August 1, 1960, *Seadragon* sailed northward.

On August 9, *Seadragon* entered Baffin Bay, traveling at deep depths and at a speed of 14 knots. Attempts to locate icebergs reported to be disintegrating in the warm waters to the south had been unsuccessful. As the ship approached an area where several bergs were reported, speed was slackened. On August 10 *Seadragon* surfaced on the edge of a large area of loose sea ice which stretched as far as the eye could see to the north. This was what remained of the solid pack which had covered all of Baffin Bay the previous winter. Less than 2 miles away was a small piece of a berg — known as a bergy bit. Small compared to a full-sized berg, this bit was later computed to weigh 2,500 tons. At the limit of visibility to the north was a shape that must be an iceberg.

The bergy bit was a perfect target to use for final adjustments of the ship's iceberg detection equipment. Carefully the ship was conned under the bit for the first time — then again and again until the iceberg detector and the men who must use it were ready for bigger game. Going deep, the ship then headed in the direction of the full-sized berg.

Seadragon was surfaced in the open water before the berg, having traveled under 12 miles of loose pack. Slowly she approached the berg as the legendary David must have stalked his giant. Knowing that the underwater size was much greater than apparent, the Captain stopped the ship while still a mile away. The dangers of hitting a berg are well known to seamen. Ships that collide with icebergs are invariably severely damaged or lost. The above-water portion measured 74 feet tall with a 313-foot waterline. The submarine slowly circled the berg, surveying and photographing every angle. The berg was blocky on one side like the breastworks of a fort, while the reverse was hollowed out like the back side of a shield. The berg was clearly weathered, showing the multiple waterlines characteristic of the state of accelerated

ILLUS. 55—Underside of ice as photographed by diver.

disintegration. It would not be safe to approach close or send a party to this berg. A huge ice slide or rotation of the berg due to a change in center of gravity might occur as happened later on two other bergs.

After all possible study had been completed on the surface, *Seadragon* submerged. As expected, the iceberg detector traced out a huge underwater body in the direction of the berg. Except for size, it looked to the sonar no differently than the bergy bit earlier. But could the detector identify the berg as deep draft ice compared to shallow draft sea ice? The iceberg detector indicated that the berg was between 100 and 200 feet in draft. One theory held that the draft would be somewhere between one and five times the above-water height. Studying the above-water height

ILLUS. 56—Frogman from Seadragon *takes first pictures under the North Pole.*

and shape of the berg, the ice experts estimated the draft to be between 150 and 200 feet. There was no other way to check the iceberg detector measurement — or the theory — than to pass under the berg and let upward-beamed fathometers measure the distance precisely. At *Seadragon's* depth, the berg should clear by more than 200 feet. Beyond these prosaic reasons for passing under the berg was the urge to be the first submarine to do so. This magnificent crew had brought their ship 2,500 miles to find this berg. All were eager to conquer it in every way. A few runs were made at the berg to test equipment operation at every angle and speed, then *Seadragon* headed directly for the berg.

After many hours of preliminary steps, the long-awaited trip under the berg seem anticlimatic. The upward-beamed fathometer traced out an irregular bottom with a draft of 108 feet. A total of six runs were made under this berg in different directions to produce a complete picture of its shape. The maximum length of the underwater shape proved to be 822 feet compared to the 313-foot measurement above water. While proving her ice equipment, *Seadragon* corrected and proved many of the theories concerning the undersides of icebergs.

Soon the ship was operated routinely at speeds up to 20 knots with sure knowledge that every berg would be easily seen and avoided.

During the week that followed, 12 icebergs in all were selected and measured off. Six were passed under a total of 22 times. Six were too deep to be passed under safely. At one time in an area south of Kap York, Greenland, the bergs were so dense that 45 were in sight at the same time and the radar scope showed them to be undiminished in number beyond the range of visibility. Icebergs were clearly no hazard to a properly equipped nuclear submarine. In proving this fact, invaluable scientific information about the undersides of icebergs was produced to an extent never before possible.

Her first task completed, *Seadragon* turned west. In approximately the same position, 121 years earlier, a young English naval officer named William Edward Parry had directed his ships *Hecla* and *Gripper* in the same direction. He had entered a body of water called Lancaster Sound which was shown on his chart as a bay without an exit to the west. He was soon aware that it was not really a bay, but a strait, possibly the Northwest Passage, that he and many before him had sought.

It was a Northwest Passage and Parry lived to be knighted and have Parry Channel named after him. It took 121 years and nuclear power to see it navigated fully, however. In the winter this channel is completely ice covered. In the summer the eastern end, Lancaster Sound, is usually ice free. The western end, McClure Strait, and narrow center, Barrow Strait, are usually covered with rugged pack ice relentlessly forced there from the Arctic Ocean under pressure generated by the usual Arctic wind circulation. Parry was fortunate to have found the channel in a good year, the mildest ever recorded. He managed to travel all the way

ILLUS. 57—The largest iceberg encountered by Seadragon *on her Polar voyage.*

to Melville Island before being stopped by the pack. Here he wintered and returned home to a hero's rewards the next summer.

Because the usually unfavorable ice conditions keep ships away, Parry's soundings were all that existed in the main section of the channel. Ships since that historic voyage had traversed sections of the channel inshore in relatively shallow waters where the winds and presence of land frequently left channels through the ice. The many soundings along the coasts clearly revealed that a submerged submarine could not pass there. The half dozen or more soundings sparsely spread along the center of the Barrow Strait narrows indicated that the depth here was shallow as compared to the ends of Parry Channel. Five islands exist in the narrows, while another island and several shoals were marked as "existence doubtful" or "position doubtful." The best passage between the islands, or whether a passage even existed, was by no means clear from the chart. Whether the passage would be deep enough to pass a submerged submarine under the heavily ridged ice that normally was there was clearly uncertain.

On the morning of August 17, *Seadragon* submerged at the western end of Lancaster Sound and proceeded into the rapidly shoaling waters of Barrow Strait at slow speed. During the three days that followed she was never far from the bottom below or the surface above. The bottom proved to have many shoals that appeared on the fathometer trace with little warning. Grounding or collision with ice above was narrowly escaped many times by turning or changing depth rapidly. Although there was some ice on the surface, a lucky wind condition had cleared most of the ice from the Strait, permitting a more thorough survey than expected. *Seadragon* surfaced six times within the strait for navigational fixing to locate her survey accurately on the area's charts. The fixes revealed that several of the charted islands were 5 miles out of position. On August 19, the task was complete. Islands and shoals were carefully and accurately plotted on the chart. There was a channel there deep enough for any future nuclear submarine to follow, winter or summer, favorable ice or not. The survey had proved without reservation that the electronic equipment on *Seadragon* was capable of leading her through restricted channels between land masses.

At high speed, *Seadragon* entered the deep, unsounded waters of Viscount Melville Sound, passed the North Magnetic Pole, passed under the edge of the ice pack pushing into McClure Strait, and entered the Arctic Basin — all without surfacing once. Proceeding under the pack to the North Pole, the ship was surfaced frequently for scientific studies, tests of military equipments, and sightseeing by the crew. Departing the Pole on August 27 *Seadragon* continued this routine until emerging from under the ice north of Bering Strait. A brief stop was made at Nome, Alaska, and on September 14 *Seadragon* arrived at Pearl Harbor.

The final questions answered, all of the Arctic is now open to navigation by any nation having nuclear submarines. This is possible through the miracle of nuclear power. A hundred and nineteen years ago, Sir William Edward Parry could not have predicted *Seadragon's* voyage as he struggled through an icebound channel for the first time in a sail-driven wooden ship, misguided by a vexed magnetic compass. Neither can we predict today the nature of the change that will have occurred in the Arctic a hundred years hence. But change it most certainly will.

The Queen Elizabeth Islands of the Canadian Archipelago are rich in minerals. As those new materials become more valuable and as science makes them easier to obtain, commerce will surely move into the Arctic and flourish. *Seadragon's* route through the Parry Channel and many others yet uncharted will some day be important commercial routes just as they are today routes of military significance. Passenger routes across the Arctic of great importance are already in daily use in the air.

The idea of increasing importance of the Arctic is not a new one. Many years ago that venerable Arctic explorer and writer Vilhjalmur Stefansson gathered together the impressive evidence for this thesis in a book called *Northward the Course of Empire.* This book traces the center of civilization from its inception in a tropical climate, observes its slow movement north to temperate regions, and predicts an eventual center far to the north of where it exists now.

Across the Arctic Ocean from Canada there is already considerable activity. North of the 60th parallel, 6 million people live under Soviet direction, while north of the same parallel in Canada and Alaska live only a few hundred thousand. Just south of the Arctic Circle, Archangel has a population of 300,000, while the northernmost city of comparable size in North America is Vancouver, which is 15° farther south. Geography has aimed the great waterways of the Russian heartland to the north. While the Ob, Yenisei, and Lena rivers may never approach the same position of importance that the Mississippi River holds in the commerce of North America, they nevertheless are important commercial routes to north-central Asia. The northern sea route across the top of Eurasia is of growing importance as the main path for freight between the river systems and the population of the Soviet North. It is of increasing strategic significance as the only secure waterway between Soviet Pacific forces and the rest of the Soviet Union. The Russian interest in this route has produced the largest icebreaker fleet in the world. The more modern vessels of this fleet include four 11,000-ton *Stalin*-class ships and three Finnish built 5,500-ton *Kapitan*-class ships. The much heralded nuclear-powered, 16,000-ton *Lenin* will join the fleet soon.

For many years the Soviets have been systematically studying the science of the Arctic on a scale far beyond that of the Western world. Since 1937 this work has been carried out in the far north by groups of scientists established on ice floes. Since the floes drift very slowly, the scientists can thoroughly and deliberately carry out their studies over a long period of time. The pattern for this exploration was set by the first party in 1937 led by Ivan Papanin, who is now one of the most celebrated of polar explorers. Papanin and his three comrades were landed by aircraft on a floe at the North Pole. Nine months later, the floe had drifted clear of the ice and the party was removed by an icebreaker east of Greenland. Since that time, a series of eight expeditions have used aircraft to land men and equipment on the ice. The slow drift of the ice has carried them around this previously inaccessible region while they pursued their studies and research. Several of these expeditions manned their floes winter and summer for more than a year. During 1959, two of these stations, NP6 and NP8, were drifting in the Arctic.

While the drifting stations conducted long-time studies, the techniques and equipment developed to land the parties were used to extend the area of observations by short-time observations. During the 10 years after 1947, Soviet aircraft landed at more than 100 points all over the Arctic Ocean for brief hydrographic, oceanographic, meteorologic, and cryologic observations.

The nuclear submarine has proved to be a very efficient means for the gathering of certain scientific information in the Arctic on six cruises since 1957. This information has to a certain extent closed the gap that has existed between the Soviet exploration in the Arctic and the modest amount accomplished by all other countries. In 1960 it would appear that even though the Soviets have a far greater experience and interest in the commercial, scientific, and military opportunities of the Arctic, the United States has a fortunate, if temporary, advantage in the area because of her unique possession of nuclear submarines (1961).

The Arctic air has been a scene of large-scale military air operations ever since the U.S. and Soviet Air Forces began looking at each other across the Pole after World War II. The Arctic is ready for the first time for a corresponding interest by the two navies of these countries. The voyages of *Nautilus, Skate, Sargo,* and *Seadragon* have marked this area as the exclusive domain of the nuclear submarine. The Soviet submarine force — the largest submarine force in the world by a factor of more than three times — will most certainly soon have nuclear submarines. With their demonstrated interest in the Arctic commercially, scientifically, and strategically, the Soviets can be expected to direct their nuclear submarines north and under the ice.

The advantage to be gained by naval forces operating under the northern ice is fairly obvious. First, such a submarine force is secure from their traditional surface and air enemies. Second, ship targets in this area are especially valuable since there are few if any overland roads or rails to support the area, and air transport is practicable only to a limited extent. The sinking of a very few ships could cause whole areas to wither from lack of supplies. Third, the Arctic Ocean occupies a strategic position second to none. The search for missile-launching points clearly marks the Arctic Ocean as ideal for targets both in North America and Eurasia. The development of the Polaris submarine and its Soviet equivalent is bound to increase the desirability of operating submarines in the Arctic.

Beyond the three direct considerations is a subtle fourth consideration of great importance. Neither the Soviet Union nor the United States could possibly accept the establishment of an unfriendly Arctic nuclear submarine force without establishing a similar force. A nuclear submarine will be the only weapon able to counter a nuclear submarine under the Arctic ice in the foreseeable future.

The nuclear submarine is not per se an Arctic ship of war. It must be specially equipped, trained, and provided with information and procedures for offensive Arctic operations. The voyages of *Nautilus, Skate, Sargo,* and *Seadragon* have been nonmilitary in nature. Much remains to be done before nuclear submarines are ready for offensive naval operations in the Arctic.The equipment and environmental information already obtained by these submarines is a broad base to build on. The conclusion that their efforts have placed the United States several years in the lead because of voyages over a period of three years is not valid, however. The voyages so far accomplished have been widely spaced. Any determined opponent having several nuclear submarines and the published knowledge of these voyages could duplicate and exceed them quickly. It is possible to produce an Arctic naval force equal to that of the United States in a relatively short period of time.

History may well mark this period as a time of utmost significance in the Arctic. If accelerated naval penetration of this area does not result, it will be only because the challenge and opportunities that exist were ignored.

ELLIOTT B. ROBERTS

The IGY in Retrospect

[FROM THE SMITHSONIAN REPORT FOR 1959[1]]

THE DIVERSITY *of aims and immensity of accomplishments of the International Geophysical Year are unprecedented in the history of science. The scope of its investigations spanned the entire physical environment of mankind, and its scientists, numbering in the thousands, came from more than half of the world's nations. The author, Capt. Elliott B. Roberts, was a member of the U.S. National Committee for the International Geophysical Year and participated actively in the United States programs in geomagnetism and seismology. He was retired in 1962 from the post of Assistant Director, R. & D., of the Coast and Geodetic Survey, U.S. Department of Commerce, and now is active in the fields of writing, editing, and consulting. In this article he summarizes some of the results of the wide-ranging investigations of the IGY. To emphasize the magnitude of this international scientific undertaking, he states that the contributions toward its cost by all the nations involved totaled some 2 billion dollars. The IGY program of research included space studies, weather investigations, the earth's structure and its magnetic fields, earthquakes, glaciers, the oceans and the atmosphere, and the interrelations between earth and sun.*

[1] Revised as of February 1965 by the insertion of an addendum at end of article.

Vast quantities of records were accumulated by the conclusion of the IGY on December 31, 1958, and although a great deal has already been published, more new knowledge will continue to appear for years to come. Never before has so much vitally important geophysical knowledge been acquired in such a brief period of time.

O<small>N</small> DECEMBER 31, 1958, there was concluded a world-wide intellectual effort often characterized as the greatest cooperative enterprise for peaceful purposes in all human history. Between 20,000 and 30,000 scientists of 67 nations, with innumerable supporting workers, endeavored to expand man's understanding of his physical environment. This was the International Geophysical Year.

It is truly remarkable that such an enterprise was successfully planned and executed, in a period of unprecedented political passions and tension, through direct contact between scientists themselves without recourse to diplomatic intervention or formal treaties. As a result we have new and powerful ties on an individual level between leading scientists of many lands, mounting understanding for one another, a great breach in the Iron Curtain, and a demonstration that men of many races and political faiths can work together fruitfully. Even if these accomplishments cannot be exactly evaluated, their meaning for the world is deep and pervasive.

A number of great discoveries were made and more will inevitably grow out of the gradual assimilation, in years to come, of the accumulated data of the IGY. The borders of our knowledge of man's environment were pushed back in several important respects, with an already vast and growing store of new knowledge which will sharply influence the course of human development.

The space age was inaugurated under the auspices of the IGY; study and exploitation of our last geographical frontiers in Antarctica and over the oceans began to flourish in a new spirit of international cooperation; the age-old concern of all mankind with weather received tremendous new impetus; and human beings took bold steps toward better understanding of the earth itself, its physical structure and its gravitational and magnetic fields; of its earthquakes, orogenic processes and glaciation; of the chemical and physical processes of its oceans and atmosphere; and of its all-important relations to our sun.

One of the great physical-science discoveries of all time was made by a member of the small group of geophysicists who were the actual creators of the IGY. It was at an informal meeting at the Silver Spring, Md., home of James A. Van Allen that this group met on April 3, 1950, to discuss geophysical matters with a renowned visiting British upper atmosphere scientist, Sidney Chapman. Among those present was Lloyd V. Berkner, a foremost American scientist, then of the Carnegie Institution of Washington, who there proposed a successor to two previous international efforts known as International Polar Years. This was the genesis of the IGY — an undertaking destined to bring Dr. Van Allen to fame as discoverer of the great Van Allen radiation belts in space surrounding the earth. The implications of his discovery are as yet unimaginable, but they are certainly tremendous — quite possibly comparable with those attending the discovery of radio waves.

THE FIRST AND SECOND INTERNATIONAL POLAR YEARS

The first and second polar years were, in a sense, models for the IGY. The famous American naval officer M. F. Maury had suggested international scientific exploration of Antarctica as early as 1861, but his rather limited proposals did not meet with acceptance. Karl Weyprecht, an Austrian explorer-scientist, who had interested himself in the then inexplicable vagaries of weather, the compass, and auroral displays experienced by 19th-century Arctic explorers, later proposed an international effort to acquire simultaneously data from a circumpolar chain of stations. There resulted in 1882-83 a so-called International Polar Expedition, under what was later known as the International Meteorological Organization. The agreed term of occupation was a 13-month interval known as the International Polar Year beginning August 1, 1882. It happened that solar activity at the time was near a peak of the 11.2-year recurrence cycle.

Twelve countries rallied to Weyprecht's call, establishing 12 stations in the Arctic and two in sub-Antarctica. Weyprecht did not live to see the realization of his idea; however, the scientific world received an important new mass of data, a heightened awareness of complex relationships between several of the manifestations under observation, and the stimulus of working together without regard to political or racial barriers.

The Second International Polar Year followed a 1927 proposal by J. Giorgi of Hamburg. It was carried on by a special commission of the International Meteorological Organization, with D. LaCour of the Danish Meteorological Institute as its guiding spirit. The observing period, August 1, 1932, to August 31, 1933, was designed to be 50 years after the first polar year, and due note was made of the fact that this, unlike the former period, would be one of minimum solar activity. The objectives included investigations in the newer disciplines of ionospheric physics and cosmic-ray studies.

This second effort saw the establishment of 35 special stations by 20 nations, which, together with more than 60 regular establishments, made nearly 100 observing points. One was in Antarctica. J. A. Fleming and N. H. Heck of the United States served on the commission, and the major American contributions were magnetic, auroral, and ionospheric observations at Fairbanks and Point Barrow, Alaska, auroral studies in Greenland, and widespread weather observations.

The accomplishments included substantial progress toward understanding magnetic storms and other magnetic disturbances and associated auroral and ionospheric phenomena, and improved knowledge of wind and pressure systems in high latitudes of the Northern Hemisphere. A vast collection of data resulted, some of which still awaits types of analysis that only modern high-speed computers can provide.

BEGINNINGS OF THE IGY

The group in Dr. Van Allen's home in 1950, aware of the rapid advances in geophysics, especially in ionospheric investigations, perceived the desirability of a third and still greater effort, this time after a period of only 25 years and this time by design to coincide with another peak of the solar-activity cycle. It was recognized that the field of observation would be far wider than just the polar areas.

Sidney Chapman, then president of the International Union of Geodesy and Geophysics (IUGG) as well as of one of its constituent associations on terrestrial magnetism and electricity (IATME — later IAGA), and Lloyd V. Berkner, a member of the United States National Committee for the International Union of Scientific Radio (URSI), referred the matter to three international scientific organizations, of which the first to meet was the Mixed Commission on the Ionosphere (MCI), maintained by URSI with the cooperation of IUGG and the International Astronomical Union (IAU). The Commission, followed later by URSI and IAU, endorsed the proposal to the International Council of Scientific Unions (ICSU), a top-level coordinating body. In January 1951, ICSU commended the idea to its own executive board, which, in the following October, decided to form a special ICSU committee to run the show. This committee, which turned out to be of pro tem nature, together with other interested organizations, took preliminary steps resulting in several effective actions.

Nations adhering to ICSU were invited to form national committees to organize their own participation in the project. The polar-year concept was broadened to encompass the world, since the phenomena originally considered characteristic of the polar regions were now known to be but intense manifestations of worldwide phenomena, and the new name "International Geophysical Year" was adopted. A geodetic project of the IUGG and URSI for a new world-longitude determination was included. The World Meteorological Organization (WMO) and later the International Union of Pure and Applied Physics (IUPAP) were welcomed to the company. Most important, by early July 1953, a full Special Committee for the International Geophysical Year (CSAGI) had been convened. In its first meeting, Dr. Chapman and Dr. Berkner were elected president and vice president, and Marcel Nicolet of Belgium was designated permanent secretary. The committee contained representatives of IAU, IUGG, URSI, WMO, ICSU, the International Geographical Union (IGU), and later IUPAP, suitably distributed by nationality.

The IGY was considered at first as being divided among 11 disciplines comprising such representative coverage of geophysics as meteorology, latitude and longitude determinations, geomagnetism, the ionosphere, aurorae and airglow, solar activity, cosmic rays, glaciology, and oceanography. The work was planned to be supported by a variety of constructive operations such as the choice and announcement of selected World Days for intensive observations, the organization of world data centers for the collection and dissemination of technical results, and a program of publication covering all aspects of the IGY. The eventual performance of the work followed generally along the indicated lines; however, there were some changes, such as the later inclusion of gravity determinations and seismology, and the organization in some countries of such specialized logistic or operational activities as polar expeditions (notably to Antarctica), rocketry, and earth satellite experimentation.

The original plan, subject to extensive later additions, dealt with broad objectives toward which the participating countries would work. In meteorology it included global atmospheric circulation, energy content and dynamics, ozone, cloud physics, and radio atmospherics and electricity. In geomagnetism the principal problems were the morphology of magnetic storms and transient effects, relations with the ionosphere, and the equatorial electrojet. Synoptic studies of aurorae, especially in relation to magnetic storms, were planned, as well as the betterment of auroral charts, spectrographic and photometric studies, and corresponding treatment of airglow phenomena. Ionospheric work was to include extensive recordings of layer heights, radio absorption and scatter effects, and galactic noises. Solar-activity work was to be intensified and to include observations of radiation, sunspots and flares, the corona, and general spectroscopy. Cosmic-ray studies were

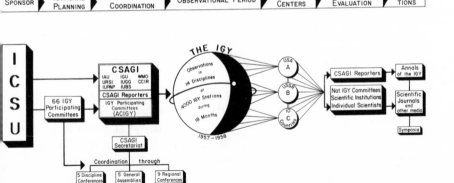

ILLUS. 58

important for their implications regarding solar and geophysical effects, especially in relation to magnetic fields of the sun, the earth, and space, and to cosmic-ray interactions with the atmosphere. Latitude and longitude work was directed to improve time determinations and star catalogues and to determine the irregularities of the earth's rotation. Glaciological and oceanographic work, originally considered not to be of synoptic nature, and therefore of minor IGY significance, eventually grew into major projects because of their importance in the heat balance and chemical problems of meteorology. Oceanography in particular loomed large because of the intimate relations of the oceans to many problems of weather and terrestrial dynamics and because of the vast natural resources of the oceans. Emphasis throughout was placed on worldwide views of all these geophysical phenomena, and particularly on intensive investigations in little-known Antarctica.

Inevitably many other detailed aspects of these disciplines, as well as entirely new and unanticipated problems, demanded attention before the IGY was even well started. While the original concept, derived from the polar-year experiences, envisioned a program concentrating on synoptic problems, secondary objectives presented themselves and were admitted to provide for types of work that would be facilitated by the basic IGY activities, or that could constitute epochal measurements for secular change studies.

ORGANIZATION OF THE IGY

One of the first aims of CSAGI was to enlist the cooperation of as many countries as possible — ideally all scientifically competent nations. At one of the formal meetings of CSAGI at Rome in 1954, Moscow sent a delegation to announce the intentions of the Soviet Union to participate — a development of strong accelerating effect, since no less than 66 nations eventually joined. Another significant event occurred at Rome. Following shortly after initial recommendations from URSI and IUGG, the CSAGI group formally proposed that countries able to do so undertake to place artificial earth satellites in orbit for the uniquely valuable observations seen to be possible by such means. Thus geophysicists hoped to acquire otherwise inaccessible information bearing on the cause and formation of the aurora, on the fluctuations of the earth's magnetic field, on the roles of the solar ultraviolet, X-ray and particle radiation, and on cosmic-ray phenomena.

Flights of earth satellites and space exploration were soon to become realities in any event. It was nevertheless a direct result of the agreement reached at Rome that the United States and the Soviet Union embarked at this time on what was to become perhaps man's most adventurous scientific enterprise. It was of course destined to produce results far beyond the initial expectations of CSAGI.

In the United States a national committee was established by the National Academy of Sciences, headed by Joseph Kaplan, and functioning with a secretariat headed by Hugh Odishaw as executive director. This committee became the focus of a large structure of technical panels, geographical committees, and other special groups, including a broad cross section of leading American geophysicists. The National Science Foundation, under technical guidance of the committee, prepared budget estimates and obtained congressional appropriations with which the large U.S. program was funded. Great logistic and operational contributions were made also by defense agencies, particularly for Antarctic expeditionary activities and rocket and satellite work.

The IGY grew to the status of big business. Directly appropriated U.S. funds amounted to some $43.5 million, and the estimated value of contributions from Federal agencies was in the order of $500 million, including logistics, Antarctic operations, missilery, etc. The effort of the Soviet Union was evidently equal to, and may have exceeded, that of America. The contributions of numerous other countries were impressive too — in a number of cases greater in relation to population or national wealth than the U.S. effort. A loose estimate of the total contributions of all nations would come to something like $2 billion.

THE SCIENTIFIC RESULTS OF IGY

No comprehensive account or full appraisal of the scientific results is yet possible. The IGY was primarily a period of observation and data gathering, and it will require years for the world scientific community to analyze so much material — masses of data not yet even collected in any one place. At this time we must be content, therefore, with some broad views suggestive of the scope of the work, with an indication of some major findings and a few of the implications. It is also impractical in a short account to refer to the many individuals and institutions deserving credit for what has been done.

In practically all disciplines the IGY work served dramatically to raise new problems and to broaden our realization of the vastness of the unknowns into which we are, so to speak, poking exploratory fingers. The IGY produced many more questions than it answered. Lloyd Berkner has said that it is like coming from outer space and finding a new planet.

The IGY investigations fit well into groupings based on major relationships between disciplines. One such scheme comprises: (*a*) the upper atmosphere, adjacent space, and solar influences; (*b*) the heat and water budget of the earth, comprising meteorology and related aspects of oceanography and glaciology; and (*c*) the solid earth.

PHYSICS OF THE UPPER ATMOSPHERE, SPACE, AND THE SUN

Interplanetary space suddenly became important — and useful. The IGY showed us much about it. We learned that there is no definite end to the atmosphere. In its vague outer regions, at perhaps 3,000 kilometers, it is almost indistinguishable from space itself. Solar and cosmic streams of elementary particles pass in undiminished intensity, forming with meteors the most important factors of the environment. The electrical and chemical activity of the upper atmosphere and of interplanetary space is due to X-rays and ultraviolet light, protons and electrons, meteors, and cosmic rays. There are present also electric and magnetic fields due to the movement of charged particles, and everywhere there is gravity, the weakest of known forces but perhaps the most important in the universe. Atomic hydrogen is also everywhere, in densities of perhaps 6 to 600 atoms per cubic centimeter. Previously unknown meteor streams were found, but the density of meteors and meteoritic dust, feared to imperil space vehicles, was found gratifyingly low.

Within 10 earth diameters there exists an actual hydrogen atmosphere, with a density at 500 kilometers as great as 100,000 atoms per cubic centimeter — this being ingeniously deduced from ultraviolet measurements made by nighttime and daylight rockets. Nearer the earth, atmospheric densities in the 200-500-kilometer band were found several times greater than previously supposed, as shown by observed retardation in the velocities of satellites. The density, moreover, exhibits strong variations supposedly due to the heating effect of particle collisions following solar bursts — this is suggested by satellite perturbations unquestionably related to the 27-day solar rotation, to specific solar flares, and to geomagnetic activity.

The sun. — The sun, generator and moderator of the physical forces affecting the earth, became a primary focus of attention. More than 100 patrols maintained watch upon it nearly every minute of the IGY, and 30 or more observatories, including 7 in the United States, photographed the sun at 3-minute intervals, comprising in effect an unprecedented motion-picture study. A notable achievement was the new order of fineness achieved in the photography of the granulation of the sun's surface, employing a combination of telescope and automatic sun pointer from a balloon at 80,000 feet. Thus we have the most detailed solar record in history, and for the first time an almost complete record of hydrogen gas flares, the influence of which upon the earth's ionosphere ranks among the most dramatic events in solar-terrestrial relationships. Sudden effects, caused by the bursts of ultraviolet light and soft X-rays, are seen in magnetic recordings, fadeouts of shortwave radio, enhancement of atmospherics (radio static), and reductions in cosmic radio noise level.

The sun cooperated notably by achieving the highest level of activity ever known. On Christmas Day of 1957 the greatest number of sunspots occurred since Galileo first reported them in 1612. Flares abounded. From this fabulous record a drastically modified concept of sun-earth relationships and of the conditions of interplanetary space has been derived.

Many sources of solar radiation were identified. Remarkably fine and detailed photographs showed the ultraviolet light source to be in patches closely associated with calcium plages (flocculi or clouds). Solar hydrogen flares are identified as a source of gamma radiation. Radio emissions of thermal generation were confirmed from coronal regions at much lower temperatures than previously believed possible. Radio noise emissions, noted to be associated with optical flares and energetic proton flux, await full explanation. Balloon measurements during eclipses have indicated the corona to be the source of X-rays, possibly an important factor in the causes of radio blackouts — the most widely known and troublesome of solar effects. Strong X-ray flux was discovered at 60,000 to 90,000 feet during auroral displays accompanying ionospheric disturbances.

The magnetic fields of the sun are perhaps the most important problem in solar physics, since therein can be found the forces that accelerate the solar particles affecting space and our upper atmosphere. A main magnetic field of minor intensity exists, with the property of puzzling polarity reversals that are presumed to be associated with the dynamic conditions of solar material. Intense local fields accompany sunspots and flares, and correlations between changes of field strength and flare occurrence have been found. Finely detailed mapping of the solar magnetic fields showed such small intensities as 1 gauss or less, with resolution in the order of 1 second of arc.

The corona is of vast extent and influence. Observations of electromagnetic waves of various frequencies from radio stars at times of near conjunction with the sun indicated a coronal structure alined with residual magnetic fields out to distances of 20 or more solar radii. It has no definite limits and may extend indefinitely outward beyond the outer planets. It is believed to reach 7,000,000° F. in some parts, and Sidney Chapman has speculated that much thermal energy is, in fact, transferred to the earth's atmosphere through direct contact with the thin but hot gases of the corona, perhaps at 350,000° F.

Radiation belts. — Space, we have seen, is far from empty. Among its features are the Van Allen radiation belts, intrinsically remarkable as well as an outstanding IGY discovery. Based on almost fantastically sparse probing up to the time of this writing, these two belts were tentatively described as annular shrouds about the earth, shaped by the typical force lines of the terrestrial magnetic-dipole field, and having northern and southern terminal cusps or edges pointing inward toward the auroral zones. Totally unexpected radiation intensities blocked the initial rocket probes with impossible counting loads, until Van Allen, with brilliant insight, provided modified counters. The vast outer belt of relatively soft, low-energy particles is most strongly developed in the zone between 3 and 4 earth radii distant from the earth's center, with maximum intensity perhaps in excess of 25,000 counts per second. It consists of charged particles — protons and electrons — captured by the geomagnetic field from clouds of plasma spewed forth from the sun. The inner belt, 2,200 to 5,500 kilometers from the earth's surface, consists of very high-energy particles of an origin yet unknown but suspected to be the decay products of cosmic-ray collisions. The particle count is somewhat lower than that of the outer belt. It has been said that despite the vast extent and intensity of the Van Allen belts, which would require billions of X-ray machines to duplicate, the materials present would amount to perhaps one-fifteenth of one ounce of hydrogen! Not enough is known about the identity and energy of the particles to provide good estimates of the radiation intensities.

The implications are tremendous. Notwithstanding our slender knowledge, it appears that the energy budget of the outer atmosphere and the theory of magnetic storms and aurorae will be dominated by these belts. Their presence means that many types of instruments must be shielded and that severe problems may confront human space travelers, although little is yet known of the biological effects. (It is because of this that one hears suggestions that future space voyagers may have to take off from the polar regions, escaping, so to speak, through the hole of the doughnut.) An interesting possibility is that similar belts may become useful as aids in detection of magnetic fields of other planets.

Cosmic rays. — Cosmic rays are another important factor of the space environment, with various consequences for the earth. They are charged particles of ordinary matter like those propelled from the sun, but generally of cosmic origin and of vastly greater energies — some are believed to travel at speeds near that of light and to carry energy up to 10^{19} electron volts — a billion times that achieved in man's best particle accelerators. They may represent half of all the energy in the universe. Through rocket and satellite observations, we know that such high-energy, or primary, cosmic rays are characteristic of space above the atmosphere and that in collisions with atmospheric molecules they produce showers of breakdown products of lower energy, called secondary cosmic rays, which reach lower levels. The sun has been found to influence cosmic-ray behavior near the earth, confronting us with an important factor in the study of magnetic space fields and magnetic storm effects. Cosmic rays display diminished intensity in general during sunspot activity, but there are shorter period fluctuations not so related. High-altitude aircraft observations of cosmic rays provided evidence leading to some refinement of our ideas about the configuration of the geomagnetic field at those and higher altitudes.

High-atmosphere phenomena. — Our outer atmosphere is thus under radiation of various types — X-rays, ultraviolet light, hard and soft cosmic rays, and charged particles from space or the radiation belts, which enter along lines of magnetic force. A whole family of related phenomena results. Under radiation the atmospheric gases produce the luminous effects of aurorae and airglow. Ionization of the thin outer gases occurs in layers comprising the ionosphere. These sheets of ions reflect or refract electromagnetic waves, providing the basis of long-distance radio communication, and they support electric-current systems and magnetic fields in grand patterns.

When the radiation becomes irregular, as at times of solar disturbances, the ionization is chaotic. Radio signals fade or black out, and the changing magnetic fields produce geomagnetic unrest and magnetic storms. Solar activity, radio-wave propagation disturbances, auroral displays, and magnetic storms had therefore to be considered together in broadly comprehensive views during the IGY.

The ionosphere. — This feature is in fact a series of concentric shells of ionized gases about the earth in configurations determined by the gas densities and chemical compositions. IGY observers carried out continuous intensive monitoring of the ionosphere, using vertical-incidence and oblique radio probes or soundings from the ground to determine ionospheric conditions by echo recordings. They observed radio-wave propagation characteristics under all manner of conditions, and they sought to find the extent, magnitude, and location of electric currents comprising streams of the ionized particles.

The ionospheric electric currents are particularly intense and complex in the auroral zones, but they exist everywhere in some form. Interesting features of local ionization and a strong electric current were found in the close vicinity of the magnetic equator. Much was learned about the neutral and ionized gases of the ionospheric regions — helpful information in the problem of determining the best working radio-frequencies to suit conditions. Scatter propagation of radio waves, often useful despite disturbed conditions, was studied intensively. Among the techniques responsible for such findings were geomagnetic studies and the analysis of radio signals from earth satellites.

Geomagnetism. — The geomagnetic program of the IGY was directed mainly toward the investigation of magnetic storms and other transient phenomena related to the ionospheric electric currents. Special arrays of recording stations were used to discover the dimensions of the magnetic fields in question, and thus to describe the current streams and systems. Among such arrays were ingenious "differential magnetographs" designed to record the field gradients across station arrays continuously as they fluctuate.

Stations in several places close to the magnetic Equator strongly indicated the intensity and extent of the previously mentioned equatorial electrojet — a powerful concentrated stream of current almost precisely along this zero-dip line. It exists chiefly on the sunlit side of the earth, and it must result from ionization by ultraviolet light or X-rays, rather than by energetic particles, which presumably cannot cross the magnetic field lines to that region. Electron and ion counts were made in the body of the current by rocket firings. The circuit return mechanism has not been determined.

The large number of special IGY magnetic observatories, particularly in Antarctica and other new places, provided working material for extensive investigations into many aspects of natural electric and magnetic phenomena and their relation to solar events. For the first time they furnished evidence of essentially simultaneous worldwide magnetic effects, and served to round out our global concepts. Telluric currents (in the earth's crust), the result of induction from the ionospheric currents, were found in unexpectedly great intensity and wide distribution, finely dissected by local ground conditions. The combined effects of ionospheric and telluric currents posed complex new problems impeding analysis attempts.

Pioneer work was done to disclose the secrets of geomagnetic field oscillations in the range between 1 and 100 cycles per second — a new area of research. Other experiments were designed to shed new light, if possible, on the old and unresolved question whether any real correlation of meteorological and geomagnetic effects exists. The Russian nonmagnetic ship *Zarya* discovered many unknown magnetic anomalies in ocean depths. Meanwhile, the main magnetic-field anomalies were said by Russian magneticians to be features of the depth of homogeneous magnetization, ruling out ferromagnetism of the crust as a source.

Aurora and airglow. — Auroral studies, difficult in a sense because by nature they do not submit to quantitative analysis, have nevertheless been prominent because of the public interest in the auroral displays and because amateur contributions are possible on a wide scale. The program included photography of various kinds, spectroscopy, position-finding observations, studies of extent and simultaneity, and even probes by rocket shots.

In general, it was found that aurorae are continuous throughout the extent of an isoclinic or magnetic dip line on the dark side of the earth. Motions within the aurorae progress from west to east — in this respect providing an unanswered mystery.

A variety of nonpolar and less spectacular aurora is the airglow. Solar energy is stored, as in a huge chemical reaction chamber, in the outer fringes of the atmosphere, where the energy synthesizes many chemical compounds. These gradually decay, emitting light, the wavelengths of which indicate the particular reaction. On moonless nights, the luminescence may contribute substantially to the night light — perhaps as much as the stars themselves. The airglow is many times stronger in the hours when the upper atmosphere can receive direct sunlight. The program for its study included expanded networks of ground stations as well as instrumented rocket flights for the exploration of the levels at which the various spectral lines are generated. Vast energy is involved which man may one day utilize with sufficient understanding of the circumstances.

Auroral displays may become very widespread following violent solar events, as in the case of the outstanding solar flare of February 9, 1958. This flare and its consequences were among the most intensively observed cosmic phenomena of all time and may have been the most important single event of the IGY. One day later, on the 10th, auroral displays as high as 800 kilometers and visible as far south as Cuba followed the entry of the earth into the great plasma cloud produced by the flare.

Protracted worldwide disturbances to communications by radio, as well as by land telegraph lines and ocean cables, accompanied this disturbance. The play of magnetic fields in the upper atmosphere induced potentials in transatlantic cables as great as 2,650 volts. From the moment of discovery of the original flare until the return of normal conditions several days later, all IGY scientists interested in space and the upper atmosphere had unexcelled opportunity to make coordinated observations, demonstrating the high value of the synoptic approach.

Artificial radiation effects. — An event of great interest, but not part of the IGY, showed, on August 1, 1958, that atomic bursts in the ionospheric regions are capable of producing artificial radiation and other widespread effects matching those of Nature itself. A nuclear explosion was produced by the United States in the ionosphere over the Pacific near Johnston Island, and within 1 minute a visible aurora was observed at Samoa — the first time in history! Simultaneously, Hawaii was aroused by a brilliant flash of light. Strong magnetic disturbances were recorded on the magnetographs at Honolulu, Samoa, Palmyra, Fanning, and Jarvis Islands. Radio blackouts of circuits over a large Pacific Ocean area persisted for one or more days. The radiation was detected and reported during many hours by the earth satellite Explorer IV during its passages over the area. Another such explosion at lower height 11 days later produced somewhat similar results.

A significant circumstance is that the location of the blasts and the vicinity of the Samoan aurorae are conjugate points respecting the geomagnetic lines of force. Charged particles introduced into the field of one of the points would predictably reenter the atmosphere at the other, as occurred at Samoa. Such controlled tests tell much about hitherto inaccessible phenomena.

A similar but even more dramatic demonstration was made, by definite design, in late August and early September 1958, when three small nuclear devices were exploded by the United States above the South Atlantic in the near vacuum of a region of relative minimum of natural radiation between the Van Allen layers. Immediately there were seen streaks of auroral luminescence along the magnetic lines of force, and a brilliant aurora was observed at the conjugate point near the Azores, where the particles, after spiraling along the lines out to distances as far as 6,500 kilometers into space, reentered the atmosphere. Theoretical predictions of the external figure of the geomagnetic field were verified. Following the now famous predictions of N. C. Christofilos, energetic particles immediately dispersed in a shell determined by the geomagnetic field, where they persisted during the battery lifetime of the satellite Explorer IV until late September. For the first time in history worldwide measurements were made on a completely controlled geophysical phenomenon, wherein a known quantity of electrons of known energies was injected into the earth's field at known times and places.

Another highly specialized investigation was directed toward the so-called whistler phenomenon. This involves the observation of electromagnetic radiation from lightning discharges, which similarly follows magnetic lines of force in the presence of a radiation field, to be heard finally through radio receivers at the conjugate points as rising or falling whistle sounds. This is explained as being due to differences in the propagation rates of the different radio frequencies produced by a lightning discharge. Unaccountably, however, whistlers have in some instances been heard over widespread areas not conjugate to each other; hence the radiation is not necessarily confined to magnetic-field lines.

New tools of man. — The use of rockets and earth satellites has in itself been a dramatic technical achievement, aside from the great value of the observational data so acquired. Ushering in, as they do, a new age of scientific exploration, they now provide exciting prospects of adding to human knowledge. Among the future objectives may be mentioned the further study of heat radiation, earth cloud cover, gravity and magnetic fields, the composition and processes of interplanetary media, life processes, the atmospheres, ionospheres, composition and structure of the planets, new fields of astronomy, solar nuclear processes, and the validity of Einstein's general relativity. As this is written plans are afoot to conduct a "clock" experiment, to determine by use of atomic clocks in space probes whether time goes slower with speed of the observer.

THE HEAT AND WATER BUDGET OF THE EARTH

Weather and climate are among the most immediate preoccupations of man. In everything that he does, but especially in his activities in the fields, on the sea, and in the air, they exert controlling influences over his very life and death. This, then, is nothing esoteric or "scientific" to the common man — it is his daily concern, and herein the IGY comes closest to his understanding.

Studies bearing on weather have historically suffered from a paucity of worldwide simultaneous data. The highly transitory and vastly complex phenomena of weather constitute the very prototype of a problem demanding the synoptic approach. The requirements are instantaneous pictures of the state of the whole atmosphere and broad vistas of the patterns of its activity everywhere on earth. These the IGY undertook to approach as nearly as possible, and thus meteorology became the greatest single sphere of IGY investigation.

Meteorology. — History's most effective steps toward the ideal of worldwide simultaneous data were taken in the IGY. For the first time it became possible to compile reasonably detailed pole-to-pole cross sections and synoptic charts. This was achieved by the establishment of three standard meridians — 10° and 140° E., and 70° W. — along which the participating nations concentrated their observing stations; by the opening of Antarctica to observation; and by a general intensification of station layouts everywhere. These improvements in coverage, and the relentless penetration of the stratosphere by soundings to new heights, are rapidly advancing the state of scientific meteorology.

Perhaps the most important IGY contribution to meteorology was the weather study of Antarctica. That bleak land has the world's coldest weather — a low temperature of 125.3° F. below zero is on record — but not all of Antarctica is that cold. Differences in the winter temperatures of portions of the continent equal those between Miami, Fla., and the Arctic. Old incorrect theories of the air circulation were laid at rest, and fundamental contrasts with northern polar weather were found.

The intensely cold air reaches perhaps only 1 kilometer above the ground; at greater heights the readings range 50° and more upward. It is accordingly believed that the Antarctic is not the major reason for the generally colder climate of the Southern Hemisphere. There are marked seasonal fluctuations of the stratosphere within a range as great as 150° F., a circumstance of high significance in the study of widespread climatic processes. The Antarctic stratospheric cyclone, unlike its mobile Arctic counterpart, tends to linger near the South Pole.

Air circulation is one of the main ingredients of the picture. It is now known that the Antarctic Continent presents no barrier to the free flow of tropospheric winds clear across the continent, distributing heat and moisture and greatly slowing the temperature fall during the polar night. In contrast, the stratospheric airmasses appear to be sealed off by a strong jet stream encircling the continent; thus its temperature drops continuously in the winter.

Important help in the exploration of upper air movements was afforded by modern balloon-borne radiosondes capable of reaching great heights. Natural radioactive tracer elements, such as tritium, also provided valuable clues. Worldwide circulation patterns exist. It was found that multiple jet streams at 9 to 12 kilometers exist even in high latitudes. Aside from research value, such information has already facilitated high-level jet-aircraft operations.

A great deal of investigation was carried out to determine atmospheric temperatures and the content of water and other compounds such as carbon dioxide and ozone, which have significant parts in the general mechanics of weather. The oceans, source of most of the water and much of the heat energy, were critically examined to determine their temperature characteristics and the circulation of their waters. For the first time, for instance, we have a full year of observations of temperature and salinity to 100 meters and of tides and sea level all the way across the Pacific from South America to Australia.

Among many special problems were such questions as the ocean-water absorption of carbon dioxide from the atmosphere, as well as the concentration of that gas with height. It has been suggested lately that the worldwide carbon-dioxide concentration is increasing, by the burning of chemical fuels in man's engines, at such a rate that noticeable climatic changes, if not already upon us, are soon to be detected. This follows from the so-called "greenhouse effect." Atmospheric concentrations of carbon dioxide do not interfere with heat intake but inhibit infrared reradiation, thus conserving heat energy and producing a general warming up. Little America now has a mean temperature 5° F. warmer than when first occupied in 1912, while that of Spitsbergen has risen

11° F. in the same time. Climatic studies showing mean temperature increases, and other evidences such as glacier recession and
the northern migration of warm-climate fauna, bear out this sup-
position.

Ozone, the three-atom form of oxygen, is present in substantial
concentrations, known to have some relationship with that of
carbon dioxide. Ozone traps the extreme ultraviolet radiation
which otherwise would interfere with the organic life of the earth.
Ozone transport is not fully understood, but it is known to be related to the general circulation and to be useful, therefore, as a
tracer element.

With the impact of increased observations, better theories and
high-speed computers, meteorologists are developing more certain
weather-prediction capabilities. It has been said that better and
long-range weather forecasts would be worth $100 million to the
petroleum industry alone. The value to transportation, business,
and agriculture cannot be imagined.

A vital factor in forecasting is the general synoptic view of water content, seen in part, at least, as cloud cover, and an important
development in modern meteorology is the weather robot, a cloud-
scanning earth satellite. Such a device provides a comprehensive
picture showing the extent and distribution of cloud cover at one
time over the whole earth. Post-IGY satellites have achieved brilliant success in this undertaking. Similar techniques will show the
wind patterns, weather fronts, rain pockets, airborne gases, and
temperatures. They will measure the heat soaked up by the earth
from the sun and how much is discarded in turn. This information is of great value in supplementing the reports from thousands
of ground stations, which altogether cover less than half the earth's
surface, and in tying these observations together to reveal patterns
unsuspected by the ground observer. Better storm warnings and
longer-range forecasts will result.

Many leading meteorologists believe that man's growing knowledge of atmospheric physics, and the acquisition of tremendous
energy resources, will one day give him the power to control the
weather. It is unnecessary to suggest the consequences for both
peaceful pursuits and war activities. When it does happen, we
can reflect that the IGY played a major role in producing such

revolutionary changes in the human environment.

Oceanography. — The seas, last geographical frontier on earth, prevent easy access to some 71 percent of the surface of the globe. They have borne the ships of the world since the dawn of history. Alexander the Great went down in a diving bell, yet man has but recently begun to explore them on a large scale. Now suddenly they are placed in a bright new limelight. Oceanic waters exchange water and energy with the atmosphere, producing major effects upon the weather and climatic cycles of the earth. We are told that they could provide more organic food materials than all the land areas of earth put together; on the other hand, they are perhaps a menacing frontier threatening submarine-launched missiles against our cities. All at once we have a need to learn everything about this well-nigh limitless environment, and to survey it forthwith. It is already trite to repeat that we know less of the ocean floor than of the visible surface of the moon. Thus the IGY embraced oceanography without restraint and it is just the beginning — a committee of the National Academy of Sciences has recommended an American oceanographic research program estimated to cost the Nation two-thirds of a billion dollars within the next 10 years.

As in the case of the atmosphere, the circulation within this great body of fluids had to be investigated, for tremendous thermal, chemical, and kinetic energy is involved. Indeed, ocean-water circulation may well be a clue to many mysteries of the weather.

The ocean is a complex layered structure with mighty rivers on diverse and mostly unknown courses, and with areas of turbulence and upwelling. Exploration of the circulation patterns requires ships and many instruments, including current meters, and some help is given by the evidence of radioactive tracers. Three major countercurrents have been investigated. One lies 9,000 feet below the Gulf Stream, traveling south at some 8 miles a day. Long known to exist, it took the IGY to provide definition of its characteristics. The Cromwell Current of the Pacific was discovered as late as 1952. Occupying a broad band south of the Equator, it flows east 200 to 1,000 feet below the westward drift known as the South Equatorial Current. It transports a billion cubic feet of water per second at 3.5 miles an hour. Even this prodigious movement is exceeded by the Pacific Equatorial Countercurrent, 200 miles north of the Equator, which carries eastward half again as much — the equivalent of more than 2,000 Mississippi Rivers! Oceanographers have not yet explained where all this water goes when it reaches the American Continent.

The sources of great water masses must be known in studying the general circulation. The ice caps of Antarctica and Greenland, and smaller glaciers everywhere, obviously provide substantial amounts of water. (Many persons are by now familiar with the statement that if the Antarctic ice were to melt completely the oceans would rise some hundreds of feet above present levels — luckily, a matter of no immediate hazard.) Analysis of the deep waters of the Atlantic shows staleness and oxygen starvation as compared with 30-year-old observations. This suggests a lessening in recent years of cold polar water to carry fresh oxygen to the depths, a matter of concern in marine biology. Anomalous warm-water masses in the Pacific in recent years have been accompanied by unusual fish distribution and by apparent effects on climates, but the causes are not yet explained.

The dynamic motions of the sea surface have had comparable attention. The U.S. island observatory program employed sensitive wave-metering devices and an unusual distribution of standard tide gages. Much information was derived leading to the analysis of water levels and the identification of short- and long-period waves up to several minutes in period, sea surges as much as an hour long, and other dynamic effects. Some of the motions may be related to tidal and earth-rotational mechanics; others are clearly meteorological in origin, with evidences of energy coupling between the water and atmospheric pressure systems even as high as the stratosphere. Possible benefits may be the future prediction of storms and damaging waves. Basic information was obtained about the steric sea level, which depends on total water volume, and we now have a growing idea of the changing shape of the sea surface during the period of the IGY.

Gropings toward that other boundary, the bottom about which so little is known, derived important facts of several kinds. Deep trenches and a 1,000-mile range of sunken mountains were found in the Pacific. The mid-Atlantic ridge was more extensively explored, and its geological substructure probed with sound waves from underwater explosions — a process termed "seismic exploration." Large Pacific areas were examined minutely with ship-towed magnetometers, which found magnetic characteristics of the bottom rocks having great significance in the compilation of geologic and tectonic history. Tests indicated that the flow of heat energy from the crust into the oceans is substantially larger than formerly thought — still another factor in the heat-engine cycle. Perhaps the most immediately interesting of the ocean-floor discoveries was a scattering of iron and manganese nodules, mixed with nickel, cobalt, and copper, over millions of square miles of the southeast Pacific, in concentrations worth hundreds of thousands of dollars per square mile. The economics of dredging appears promising.

Glaciology. — Like a smaller and less mobile counterpart of the sea, the ice deposits of the world store, and eventually release, water and thermal energy. Thus, they contribute their part to the endless cycle of weather and ocean phenomena. They also constitute valuable records of the past.

The ice in Antarctica is 40 percent greater than formerly believed but is now diminishing. It averages 10,000 feet in depth and contains 90 percent of all the ice in the world, some 6½ million cubic miles. In many places on the high icy plateaus, 10,000 feet and more above the sea, the ice has been found by seismic prospecting methods to rest on underlying earth thousands of feet below sea level. Such discoveries show that we may have there a great archipelago instead of a single land; however, the IGY seismic explorations indicate a crustal structure of continental type. Perhaps it is a "foundered continent." It seems likely that removal of the ice would disclose a broad strait between the Weddell and the Ross Seas, cutting Antarctica into two major land masses.

Ice borings in Greenland and Antarctica have reached layers formed by the precipitation of more than 1,000 years ago. These layers can be read like tree rings, and the thermal insulation is so good as to have preserved the temperatures of past centuries. Ancient climates are thus known, and clues to the future may be deducted. This is one of the ways in which we know of warming trends of world climates.

We know, through observation of precipitation rates, that the

Arctic has twice the snowfall of Antarctica. Pollen traces in perfect preservation and ash deposits at certain levels attest the atmospheric impurities of former times, and may give clues to ancient volcanic activity.

Glaciological studies of the great ice caps and smaller glaciers throughout the world provided first steps toward an understanding of the regimen, behavior, and physical properties of the great volumes of water withheld by climatic conditions from free circulation. An understanding of heat balances and interface reactions was gained. It was learned that glacier behavior throughout the world is synchronous — recession is going on everywhere. Incidental results were the creation of a corps of world scientists willing and able to endure the rigors of polar work and life, and in Antarctica, at least, a demonstration that scientists of competitive political regimes can work cooperatively without fighting over questions of land ownership or jurisdiction.

THE SOLID EARTH

Solid-earth aspects of the IGY program included geodesy, gravity, and seismology, with overtones of oceanography, glaciology, and the flights of earth satellites. These subjects, unlike those dealing with transient phenomena which call for synoptic treatment, found places in the enterprise because they fell within the logistic resources organized for other IGY activities or because they could provide measurements of importance. Some results were fortuitous, as when geodesists found the orbital characteristics of satellites divulging unique information about the figure of the earth. The organized programs in the solid-earth subjects were relatively small, and much of their technical results requires extensive study; few important implications, therefore, have yet come to light.

Geodesy. — The framework of international cooperation established for the IGY was seen at the outset to favor establishing a new and better measure of the longitude differences between continents and major isolated island groups, such as Hawaii. This was realized through use of new instruments and techniques, including the American dual-rate moon camera, which provided new precision in the relation of terrestrial positions to the celestial firmament. Better absolute knowledge of geographic locations of the earth's landmasses was obtained, with advantages in mapping, operation of earth satellites, scientific studies of the earth, and the mechanics of its rotation, including problems of timekeeping.

The incidental geodetic value of earth-satellite orbital observations, particularly of Vanguard I, has been substantial. Observations on such relatively near and fast-moving celestial bodies with well-determined orbits permit a new and higher order of positioning of isolated points beyond reach of the geodetic survey networks of the world. Analyses of orbital perturbations reflecting the irregular distribution of the earth's mass have already indicated that the theoretical or mean figure of the earth may be unsymmetrical — slightly pear-shaped rather than ellipsoidal, although the dissymmetry is very small. Active planning is in progress in the United States for the launching in the near future of geodetic satellites carrying special instruments in selected orbits designed for the fullest exploitation of these possibilities.

Gravity and seismology. — These fields of study profited by the strong upsurge of interest in geophysics and the many fieldwork opportunities produced by the IGY. They contributed in unique ways to our knowledge of the structure of the earth. New gravimeters, faster and more portable than the classic pendulum apparatus, permitted widespread detailed surveys of the earth's gravity field, supported by gravity surveys made in the search for petroleum. Thus are disclosed the effects of irregular earth-mass distribution, not only of mountains and ocean deeps that we can see but also of hidden ore bodies and structural irregularities of the earth's rocks. The new gravimeters are free of some of the limitations on use of the pendulum and have even been refined to cope with the accelerations of ship motion. Thus we may make gravity surveys of the watery three-fourths of the earth. It is believed, moreover, that airborne gravimeters will soon be an actuality.

The gravimetry program, aside from general survey coverage and the accomplishment of several important Antarctic profiles, dealt with the problem of earth tides, in the measurement of which gravity observations play a leading part. Gravimeters are sufficiently sensitive to indicate not only the changes in the lunar and solar tide-producing forces but also the small changes in distance involved in the rise and fall of the earth's crust. Such motion at Washington is nearly 6 inches in amplitude. Thus the gravity work contributed to our knowledge of the elastic constants of the earth and its crust, as well as of world mass distribution.

The gravitational force, which man has learned to measure with exquisite precision — one part in a million for absolute determinations, and a hundred times better for relative measurements — remains a scientific mystery, its true nature hidden somewhere outside man's conceptual capacity.

Seismological work also was stimulated by the unusual opportunities to place seismograph recorders in neglected parts of the world, particularly the polar regions. In the Arctic and sub-Arctic many gaps in coverage were filled, mostly by Soviet scientists. Antarctica, an aseismic continent except for one or two minor shocks a year, was nevertheless notable for its valuable readings on a broad range of far-southern quakes and for its clues to the seismicity of a vast region. Numerous readings of earth waves from Japanese shocks, agitating the seismographs after traveling the longest all-oceanic wave paths on record, helped in the determination of travel velocities through oceanic crustal formations.

A specialized application of seismology, in which reflected waves from small explosions on the surface are used to discover subsurface structure, disclosed the ice depths in Antarctica and Greenland, and indicated the continental structure of Antarctica. Similar exploration of the Andean massifs in South America showed that the underlying crust is unexpectedly thin, contrary to the normal expectation of a deep root structure.

Seismologists began the intensive development of seismographs sensitive to ground waves of ultralong period — waves which have already demonstrated unique value in the detection of distant earthquakes and subterranean explosions.

CONCLUSION

Sheer masses of data were collected in the IGY. The United States alone has brought out no less than 17 tons of records just from its

Antarctic stations. The total for the world is almost beyond comprehension. Now, to exploit such a fund of new information, we have comprehensive programs for its international exchange and for its orderly keeping in world data centers. There are new translating services, directed especially toward the large mass of Soviet-bloc science writings. General geophysics information in America is available in permanent journals such as *Transactions of the American Geophysical Union, Journal of Geophysical Research,* and *IUGG Chronicle,* and the temporary IGY journals, *Annals of the IGY* and *IGY Bulletin.* Complete technical data are available in the world centers.

The store of knowledge already amassed is great. It includes the story of Antarctica's striking geological history shown through the evidence of petrified trees and coalbeds. We have learned that the oceans may become a primary food source, "farmed" by man, and that their dark reaches may deliver up vast new riches for his benefit; that knowledge of solar processes may revolutionize our approach to energy problems; that space is far from a vacuum, but that despite its logistics problems and radiation hazards we will complete its conquest. The list could be well-nigh endless. And we have yet far to go with the digestion of IGY data.

To keep us from straying into scientific fantasy, we have a legacy of planning bodies at national and international levels — committees for oceanographic and polar research, and our Space Science Board — which will point out opportunities for the fullest exploitation of the possibilities.

The scientific fruits we have seen to be great. Yet it may be hard to say whether less tangible values may not be even greater. We have the lesson that science is not parochial — that we must deal broadly with interdisciplinary problems. We know now that men of all races and political faiths can work together. The press of the world has produced a radical change in public attitudes (with no little help, to be sure, from the Russian sputniks). There is a burgeoning public awareness of the importance of science and of scientists. The scientist is losing his reputation for wearing long hair and going absentmindedly through life. And we may now, for once and all, have laid the ghost of that stupid old question whether research and pure science are worth their own support.

ILLUS. 59—*First IGY Scanning Photoelectric Photometer, situated atop Fritz Peak, Colorado. This instrument selects and measures the intensity of airglow, light too faint for the human eye, and regards its changes, converting the light into electric signals. Airglow is the result of a complicated chemical process in the upper atmosphere. (National Bureau of Standards, Boulder Laboratories.)*

ILLUS. 60—Digging out at IGY Little America Station after the winter of 1957. Photograph taken from top of aurora tower shows in background the rawin tower and back right, meteorological instruments and radiation instruments used for scientific studies in these disciplines during the winter season. Accumulation around and over camp represents accumulation and wind drifting that has taken place since Little America was built by U.S. Navy Support Forces in December-January 1955-56. Melt holes around ventilation pipes and weak points in tunnel roofs interconnecting

ILLUS. 61—Earth Satellite. Juno II lifts from the earth at 12:11 A.M. EST,
March 3, 1959, carrying the gold-plated fiberglass IGY space
probe, Pioneer IV, toward a heliocentric orbit. Pioneer IV was
launched by Army Ballistic Missile Agency and the Jet Propulsion Laboratory of the California Institute of Technology as part
of the U.S. IGY program sponsored by the National Academy of
Sciences. (U.S. Army photo.)

ILLUS. 62—*Rocket launching aboard ship. The Deacon rocket, used for upper-atmosphere studies, is carried aloft by a balloon before it is fired. (Official U.S. Navy photograph.)*

ILLUS. 63—Observer Kenneth Toma, U.S. Weather Bureau, holding complete IGY airborne rawinsonde assembly, consisting of balloon, parachute and rawinsonde transmitter. In the background the fiberglass dome housing the GMD-1A rawinsonde receiver is on top of the inflation shelter. (National Academy of Sciences. IGY photo.)

ILLUS. 64—*Dual-rate moon position camera and telescope. Composite photograph shows how the moon appears through the dark filter at the center. The camera photographs the moon and surrounding stars simultaneously. The moon is held fixed with respect to the stars during the exposure by means of a dark filter which tilts. The photographs obtained enable the position of the moon to be determined accurately, and, from this, precise determination of latitudes and longitudes can be made, completely free of the distortion of gravity. The dual-rate camera was designed by Dr. William Markowitz of the U.S. Naval Observatory. (Official USNO-IGY.)*

ADDENDUM

Possibly foreseeable, but probably not fully anticipated, was the tremendous stimulus given geophysics investigation by the IGY. At the outset, much of the IGY program was continued for an additional year by the participating nations, in a program called International Geophysical Cooperation 1959. More significant has been the rising level of continuing activity. This includes particularly oceanography, polar investigations, geomagnetism, and space, among others. Knowledge of the oceans is now seen as vital to the future of man on earth. An era of permanent friendly collaboration between nations has been established in Antarctica. Space studies have continued to yield remarkable new understanding of radiations, energetic particles, and the electromagnetic fields of interplanetary space. Indeed the expansion of local interest in the old Polar Years to one of worldwide interest in the IGY has already been overshadowed by the assimilation into geophysics of the broader areas of interplanetary physics and astrophysics.

There is now a well-organized system for the preservation and availability of IGY records in the World Data Center establishment. The records are in use. A recent count of IGY-inspired technical papers in the United States alone exceeds 2,800, and they appear at an ever-increasing rate!

GEORGE W. BEADLE

The Place of Genetics in Modern Biology

[FROM THE SMITHSONIAN REPORT FOR 1962[1]]

THE BRANCH *of biology known as genetics is unquestionably the subdivision of that science of the most fundamental importance to mankind and should be of greatest interest to him. For it is genetic research that has taught us what we know of the incredibly complex processes that make a human being out of a submicroscopic fertilized egg. Dr. George W. Beadle, distinguished President of the University of Chicago and a renowned biochemist and geneticist, tells the fascinating story of how the chemistry of that miracle is being unraveled. The key factor in the story is deoxyribonucleic acid (DNA), which Dr. Beadle describes as "a kind of molecular code written in four symbols." To emphasize the enormous complexity of encoding the information needed to make a man, he states that some 1,000 large volumes of coded directions would be required in the egg nucleus for a human being to develop from it. The author goes on to explain how mutation operates to bring about evolution in life forms and how natural selection eliminates unfavorable mutations, the process sometimes given the ominous name, "genetic death."*

[1] Eleventh Annual Arthur Dehon Little Memorial Lecture. Reprinted, with additions and modifications, by permission of the Massachusetts Institute of Technology.

Many years ago Dr. William Morton Wheeler, a distinguished and admired professor of biology and Dean of the Bussey Institution of Harvard University, wrote a small essay[2] in which he said, "Natural history constitutes the perennial rootstock or stolon of biologic science. . . . From time to time the stolon has produced special disciplines which have grown into great flourishing complexes. . . . More recently another dear little bud, genetics, has come off, so promising, so self-conscious, but alas, so constricted at the base." I am sure Professor Wheeler was convinced that this bud would be abortive.

More recently there appeared in *Science*[3] a related essay by a distinguished and likewise much admired biologist, Sewall Wright, who was a graduate student at the Bussey Institution during Wheeler's time. After quoting the above words, Wright points out that, far from aborting, the little bud genetics has flourished mightily and has in many respects replaced natural history in the sense that it has become the rootstock of all biological science and has bound "the whole field of biology into a unified discipline that may yet rival the physical sciences."

Why such a change in 36 years? For despite the fact that Wheeler was not above giving his friends and colleagues in genetics a bit of ragging, he was basically serious. There has been a great change. We have come to recognize that genetics does in fact deal with the very essence of life. This is why at the present time in the biology laboratories of M.I.T. there are physical chemists, biophysicists, biochemists, microbiologists, virologists, zoologists, and other varieties of biologists devoting much effort to the study of genetic material.

I should like to begin a development of this thesis that genetics is the keystone of modern biology by reminding you that every one of us — you and I — starts development as a tiny sphere of protoplasm, the almost microscopic fertilized egg; and that somehow in this small sphere there must be contained the specifications, the directions, or the architectural blueprints for making one of us

[2] *Science*, vol. 57, p. 61, 1923.
[3] *Science*, vol. 130, p. 959, 1959.

out of that bit of jellylike material. Of course, the process by which this happens is enormously complex, and we do not yet understand very many of the details. But we do know that a substantial part of these directions is wrapped up in the centrally located nucleus of the cell. These directions are the material heredity that we received from our parents.

In addition to this set of directions in the nucleus, there must be more. There must be an architectural organization of the rest of the cell — the cytoplasm — and this is indispensable. And for the carrying out of the directions there must be a proper supply of raw materials in the form of food — perhaps 10 or 20 tons — for the egg to grow and differentiate into a mature person. Time, too, is essential — 16, 20, 25 years, or more. Finally, there must be a proper environment, initially a very precise one. Later, as we develop the ability to regulate our own environments, we become less fussy. The environment adds to the information in the original egg. This is particularly impressive in our own species, for in addition to all the other environmental information fed into us during development we are continually bombarded with a cultural inheritance — language, art, music, religion, history, science, and so on — that in man supplements biological inheritance to a far greater degree than in any other species.

All these factors are essential to our development, and many of them continue throughout life. In these halls I do not need to emphasize the significance of cultural inheritance, for it is a primary function of M.I.T. to add to that cultural inheritance and to teach us how more effectively to pass it on in a manner that will be cumulative from generation to generation.

What I wish to talk about are the directions in the nucleus. What are they and how do they specify that from this minute cell one of us will come? I shall ask five questions about these specifications:

First, how do we get them and how do we transmit them? I shall dispose of this one briefly, for it is answered by classical genetics — the Mendelian genetics now found in every elementary textbook of modern biology. You know about classical genetics: about blue eyes, brown eyes; curly hair, straight hair; good hemoglobin, bad hemoglobin; and so on.

Perhaps you know less about the remaining four questions:

How are the specifications written — that is, what is the language of genetics?

How are the specifications replicated? From the time we start development as a fertilized egg until we transmit them to the next generation there are perhaps 16 to 25 successive replications of these specifications, depending on whether the carrier is female or male. Each time the material is replicated it doubles, so 20 replications represents more than a million copies. How does replication occur with the precision necessary to avoid intolerable numbers of mistakes?

How are the specifications — the directions or the recipe for making us — translated? This is an enormously difficult question, and I shall say right now that we know very little about it.

How are specifications modified during the course of evolution? Most of us believe in organic evolution, and we want to know how we have come to be different from our ancestors. In other words, what is the nature of the mutation process?

A few years ago, seven or eight years ago, we would have had a very difficult time answering the four questions that I have just asked. We did not know enough, and we did not have many good clues even as to how we might go about searching for answers to these questions. But within the past half-dozen years or so excellent clues have turned up. In 1953, shortly before the M.I.T. Dorrance Laboratories of biology and food technology were opened and dedicated, there occurred an important turning point in modern biology. What was it and what does it have to do with answering the questions I have posed?

By this time it had become quite clear to a number of biologists that a particular chemical substance called deoxyribonucleic acid was important in transmitting hereditary information in bacteria and in viruses. Since the cells of all higher plants and animals contain deoxyribonucleic acid, it seemed probable that this substance served to carry genetic specifications in all living systems.

I shall attempt to explain how and why this substance, DNA for short, is important. And I shall try to do it without considering the

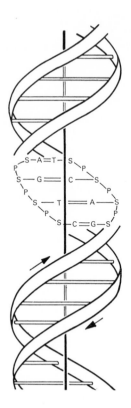

ILLUS. 65–*The Watson-Crick structure of DNA schematically represented. The parallel spiral ribbons represent the paired polynucleotide chains. Hydrogen bonding is represented by transverse parallel lines. P = phosphate group, S = sugar unit, A = adenine base, T = thymine base, G = guanine base, C = cytosine base. Arrows indicate that polynucleotide chains run in opposite directions as specified by the sugar-phosphate linkages. Redrawn form Watson and Crick (1953).*

details of its rather complex chemistry. DNA has been known for a long time. And it was known to consist of long chainlike molecules made of four kinds of units called nucleotides. But it was not known exactly how DNA molecules were internally organized until 1953, when two investigators — Dr. James D. Watson, now at Harvard University, and Dr. Francis H. C. Crick of Cambridge University — succeeded in formulating a structure that has proved to be substantially correct.

From the information then available from classical organic chemistry, from X-ray diffraction studies, from analyses of the relative proportions of the four kinds of nucleotides, and through ingenious model building, Watson and Crick proposed the structure illustrated in Illus. 65.

This Watson-Crick structure was at once exciting to the biologists. Why? Because it suggested such plausible answers to the four questions: How is genetic information written? How is it replicated? How is it translated? And how does it mutate?

How does the model help answer these questions? The key to the structure of DNA is that its molecules are double in a special way. There are two parallel polynucleotide chains wound around a common axis and bound together through specific hydrogen bonding.

You can more easily visualize the essential features of DNA if you will imagine a four-unit segment of it pulled out in two dimensions as follows:

ILLUS. 66—

Here the four letters represent the four nucleotides; and the colons, hydrogen bonds. In fact, you can very nicely represent such a segment with your two hands. Place your forearms vertically before you and parallel. Fold your thumbs against your palms and place homologous finger tips together as though they were teeth on two combs vertically oriented in a single plane, tooth tip to tooth tip. In this arrangement the two index fingers represent the A:T nucleotide pair and so on.

Imagine many fingers along your forearms — of four kinds corresponding to the nucleotides A, T, C, and G. The four kinds of fingers or nucleotides can be arranged in any order on one arm but must always have the complementary order on the other. T opposite A, A opposite T, G opposite C, C opposite G. Thus if one knows the sequence of nucleotides in one chain, the sequence in the other can be determined by the simple rule of complementarity.

This structure suggests that genetic information is contained in the sequence of nucleotides; in other words, DNA is a kind of molecular code written in four symbols. One can think of the code as a sequence of nucleotide pairs or of nucleotides in a single chain, for it is obvious that the double chain and the two single component chains all contain equivalent information. In essence the two complementary chains are analogous to forms of a single message, one written in conventional Morse code, the other in a complementary code in which each dot is changed to a dash and vice versa.

Let us now ask the question: how much information is packed away in the nucleus of a human egg? It is estimated that there are about 5 billion nucleotide pairs per single cell. How much information does this correspond to in terms of, say, information spelled out in the English language? Francis Crick has expressed it this way: If you were to make an efficient code for encoding messages in English in the four symbols of DNA, and with this started encoding standard library volumes of 500 pages, 500 words per page in this DNA code, you could get the contents of 1,000 such volumes in the DNA in the nucleus of a single fertilized egg cell. This is another way of saying that it requires the equivalent of about 1,000 large volumes of directions in the egg nucleus to specify that a human being like one of us will develop properly from it, given a cytoplasm, proper food, and a suitable environment.

Said in another way, that is the size of a genetic recipe for building a person.

This is supposedly the way the genetic information is carried from generation to generation — in a language we might call DNA-ese. Each gene is a segment of DNA of perhaps 3,000 or 4,000 nucleotides.

ILLUS. 67—

Now let us ask about the replication. The double structure of DNA suggested immediately to Watson and Crick how this could happen. If, during cell division, the two chains were to come apart, obviously each could serve as a template for picking up additional units to make new half chains. And this is happening in each of us right now. In many cells nucleotides are continually being made from food components. The replication of DNA according to this scheme can be illustrated as shown at the left.

You can represent the process with your hands. Indicate the double molecule as already directed as paired hands. Take the two hands apart. Imagine free fingers (nucleotides) moving around at random. Each single hand serves to select in proper order the one-fingered units necessary to make a complementary hand. The right hand is a template for making a left hand and vice versa. So with a double molecule, represented by a pair of hands, two single molecules arise by breakage of hydrogen bonds, with each then directing the synthesis of a new complementary single partner.

This process of replication takes place with every cell division and, as we shall see, with a high degree of precision.

This hypothesis by which two identical bipartite molecules arise from a single such double molecule is very satisfying in its simplicity and elegance. If true, it is presumably the basis of all biological reproduction at a molecular level. Can the hypothesis be tested? The answer is yes. In fact, several kinds of experiments can be and have been made to see if the hypothesis agrees with observed facts.

In one kind of experiment DNA units are labeled with radioactive phosphorus. Each nucleotide has one phosphorus atom, and a certain number of its phosphorus atoms can be made radioactive by growing an organism, say a bacterium, in a medium containing radioactive phosphorus for several generations until it becomes equilibrated. Then both chains of its DNA molecules will be labeled. If the bacteria are then allowed to multiply in a medium in which there is no radioactivity, the two chains of each DNA molecule, both labeled, should come apart, each then directing the synthesis of an unlabeled partner. The new double molecules should then be labeled in one chain but not in the other. In the next generation the labeled chain should separate from the non-labeled one. With synthesis of non-labeled partners by these, there should be produced labeled and non-labeled double molecules in equal numbers. The observed results are consistent with this expectation.

Another way of doing essentially the same experiment is to replace the normal nitrogen atoms of DNA with "heavy" nitrogen, the stable isotope N^{15} instead of the usual N^{14} counterpart. DNA molecules so labeled become heavier but not larger. Hence they are denser. DNA containing only N^{15} can be cleanly separated from that containing N^{14} in an analytical centrifuge cell in which an appropriate density gradient is established. In such experiments it is found that bacteria containing DNA fully labeled with N^{15}, if allowed to multiply once (double in number) in a medium containing only N^{14}, give rise to descendants in which all the DNA molecules are "hybrid" as though one nucleotide chain of the double molecules contained N^{15} and the other N^{14}. This, of course, is what is predicted by the hypothesis. In a subsequent generation, also in N^{14} medium, half the DNA molecules are hybrid and half are fully light. Again this is what would be expected if the hypothesis is correct.

While experiments of this kind do not prove that the Watson-Crick hypothesis of DNA replication is correct, they do strongly suggest it.

An even more dramatic way of testing the hypothesis is the one used by Professor Arthur Kornberg and his associates, now at Stanford University. They have devised a test-tube system in which there are present the four nucleotides A, T, C, and G as triphosphates, a buffer solution, magnesium ions, and a polymerizing enzyme. DNA molecules added to this system appear to be replicated. Is the new DNA like the primer molecules added? One important observation suggests it is. The ratio of A:T nucleotide pairs to C:G pairs of the product is like that of the primer DNA. It is not easy to see how this could be if the primer were not being copied in a precise way. On the other hand, if DNA having known biological activity (as determined by ability to transform the genetic constitution of a bacterium) is used as a primer, both the product and the primer added end up being inactive. Why this is so is not known, but it is strongly suspected that the polymerizing enzyme added contains a small amount of depolymerizing enzyme that breaks up DNA chains and thus destroys activity.

Again, the Kornberg synthesis does not prove that the hypothesis is correct. It is just possible that an unkind nature could have evolved a system that would do just exactly what the hypothesis predicts but by a different mechanism.

About the next question: How is genetic information translated? How do we develop from that minute egg cell? These are enormously difficult questions, and we know relatively little in detail about the answers. They involve the whole of development, differentiation, and function. There are working hypotheses — widely used and useful ones — that suggest how some of the steps occur.

We know that in our bodies there are many thousands of kinds of protein molecules — large, long molecules made of amino acids and very specific in their properties. One, for example, is hemoglobin. It is built of 600 amino acids strung together in a particular way. There are two kinds of chains of amino acids per hemoglobin molecule, each in pairs, with each chain about 150 amino acids long. And we know that there are segments of DNA — two, we postulate — in our chromosomes that say how to build the two protein subunits.

A widely used working hypothesis assumes that against a single chain of DNA there is formed a chain of another kind of nucleic acid, called ribonucleic acid or RNA. RNA, like DNA, is built of four nucleotides. The DNA code is translated into a complementary sequence of RNA. RNA then moves from the nucleus into the cytoplasm. There it is incorporated into microsomes, submicroscopic structures in which protein synthesis occurs. In the microsome, RNA units are believed to serve as templates against which amino acids are lined up in proper sequence.

Amino acids, derived from the proteins in our food, are first activated by enzymes and subsequently hooked to small carrier segments of RNA that serve to carry the amino acids to their proper places on the microsomal RNA templates.

For each amino acid there is a specific carrier RNA, made up of about 80 nucleotides. Each of the 20 carrier RNA's contains a coding unit of 3 nucleotides presumably complementary to a 3-nucleotide coding unit in the template RNA in the microsome. When all coding units in the template are matched by their complements, the amino acids are lined up in proper order along the template and are joined chainlike through peptide linkages. The resulting protein then peels off the template and the process is repeated. For hemoglobin, for example, there are assumed to be two DNA segments, one for each of the two protein chains, and two RNA templates.

Protein synthesis can be carried out in a cell-free system in which are present ribosomes, template RNA, carrier RNA, amino acids, the requisite enzymes, and other necessary components. By means of radioactive labels it can be shown that proteins are synthesized step-wise beginning at the free amino end and ending up with a free carboxyl group in the last amino acid to be added to the chain. Thus there is a good experimental evidence suggesting that the translation process does occur as postulated.

A large number of proteins serve as enzymes or essential components of enzymes. Enzymes catalyze chemical reactions that would otherwise occur at rates so low that life processes would essentially cease. For each enzyme protein there is supposedly a segment of DNA information in the nucleus — a gene — and corresponding microsomal RNA templates in the cytoplasms of those cells active in synthesis of that particular enzyme protein. An important question of present-day biology is concerned with the nature of the mechanism by which the 4-symbol code of DNA is related to the 20-symbol code of proteins. It is obvious that single symbols of DNA cannot stand for amino acid, for there are only 4. Likewise pairs of DNA symbols will not do, for there are only 16 such pairs if the DNA molecule is read in one direction. If one reads in one direction and uses 3 symbols per amino acid, there are 64 possibilities.

Recent genetic evidence strongly suggests that the code is in-

ILLUS. 68—DNA molecule model

deed a triplet code read in one direction from a starting point on the template RNA. Each successive triplet normally encodes an amino acid. Thus if we assume a segment of a template beginning: UCG UUU UGA UUA UGU UUG - - -, where U (uracil nucleotide) replaces A in the DNA code, the amino acids arginine, phenylalanine, glutamic, tyrosine, valine, and cysteine might be incorporated by the successive underlined triplets. The order of nucleotides is determined by making use of synthetic template RNAs. Thus such an RNA template consisting of...UUUUUUUUA incorporates only phenylalanine and tyrosine. Tyrosine appears to be at the carboxyl end of the polypeptide so synthesized (preliminary reports from S. Ochoa's laboratory). Thus the triplet encoding tyrosine must be read UUA. Now from mutational replacement of amino acids in proteins such as occurs in hemoglobin on mutation from normal hemoglobin to sickle cell hemoglobin in which one glutamic acid unit in the chain is changed to glutamic acid, one can deduce the nucleotide sequence in the code triplets for other amino acids. Thus if it is assumed that the order of the G, U, and A nucleotides in the glutamic acid code is UGA, then the lysine triplet which is known to contain two A and one U nucleotide must be UAA, thus

$$UGA - - - - \rightarrow UAA,$$

assuming the mutation responsible resulted from a change of a single nucleotide.

Study of intra-coding-unit recombinants reveals nucleotide sequence just as classical crossing over indicates gene order and permits the assignment of a unique linear order to genes in a chromosome. This method is being used by Dr. Charles Yanofsky and co-workers.

There is good reason to believe that the genetic code is degenerate in the sense that a single amino acid may be specified by more than one triplet.

The task of deciphering the total genetic code is well along toward solution and one may confidently predict that it will be completed in the near future.

My fourth question concerns the nature of mutation. How is genetic information modified during the replication in a manner that permits organic evolution?

During DNA replication, mistakes are occasionally made. Presumably, during replication a nucleotide does not pick up a complementary partner as it should but instead picks up a noncomplementary one. It has been postulated that such mistakes result from an improbable tautomeric form in which a hydrogen atom is in an improbable position at the exact moment the nucleotide picks up a partner. A wrong partner is therefore selected. In the next round of replication the "wrong" partner will pick up what is its complementary partner, and this will result in substitution of one nucleotide pair for another. This is somewhat like a typographical error. In typographical errors it is possible to have extra letters, too few letters, one letter substituted for another, or transposed letters. Presumably similar kinds of mistakes can be made in genetic information during replication. In fact, there is genetic evidence that these four basic types of mistakes do occasionally occur.

How often do such mistakes occur? Quite infrequently, we believe. From the time one receives a set of directions in the fertilized egg until one transmits it to the next generation — and remember this is perhaps 17 to 20 successive replications of information equivalent to about 1,000 printed volumes — a significant and detectable mistake is made perhaps about once in 100 times. This is clearly a high order of precision.

What happens to such typographical errors as are made? First of all, it is clear that the DNA molecules will replicate just as faithfully whether the information in it makes sense or not. Its replication is a purely mechanical one, it seems. Therefore mistakes in genetic information will be perpetuated.

It is obvious that if there were no way of eliminating errors in such a process, such errors would accumulate from generation to generation. Perhaps an analogy will make this clear. If a typist types in a purely mechanical way, never proofreading, never correcting, and types successive copies of the same material always from the most recently typed copy, she will accumulate mistakes at a rate dependent on her accuracy until eventually the sense of the original message will be entirely gone. In the same way this would have to happen with genetic information if there were no way of taking care of mistakes. With genetic information something does happen that takes care of mistakes. By extending the analogy perhaps I can make clear what does happen. The typist, typing mechanically, can correct a mistake by a second random typographical error, but obviously the probability of this is extremely low. It is likewise so with genetic information, and it is clear therefore that this is not the principal way in which mistakes are prevented from accumulating. Let us pretend the typist has an inspector standing beside her. When she makes a mistake, he says, "Throw that one away. Put it in the wastebasket and start over." If in the next try she makes no mistake, he says, "All right, now you may type another from the one you have just finished." Each time she makes a perfect copy he allows her to go ahead, but each time she makes a mistake he insists she throw the copy away. That is what happens with genetic information. The inspector is analogous to natural selection. Bad sets of specifications in man are eliminated by natural selection.

A more dramatic term for elimination of unfavorable specifications by natural selection is "genetic death," as used by Dr. H. J. Muller. Individuals developed from unfavorable specifications do not reproduce at the normal rate, and ultimately a line so handicapped dies out. To avoid progressive accumulation of mistakes from generation to generation, it is obvious that every error in replication that is unfavorable must be compensated for by the equivalent of a genetic death. That is why geneticists are concerned about factors that increase the mutation rates.

You may quite properly ask, "Are there no favorable mutations?" The answer is yes, there are occasional favorable mutations; they are, in fact, the basis of organic evolution.

However, because many mutations involve subtle changes that may be favorable under special circumstances of environment or over-all genetic constitution, it is not easy to estimate the proportion of favorable to unfavorable mutations. Theoretical considerations and a certain amount of experimental evidence agree in indicating that the great majority are unfavorable. Organisms are in general already so highly selected for success in their normal environments that the chance of further improvement by random mutation must be very small. Perhaps an analogy with a fine watch will dramatize the point. Assume the watch is very slightly out of adjustment. A random change brought about, say by dropping it, could conceivably improve the adjustment. Clearly, however, the chance of making it run less well or not at all is enormously greater. Now let us extend our typing analogy. Assume our inspector exercises judgment. When the typist makes an error that improves the original message, he passes it. Thus improved messages will replace their ancestral forms and the improvement will be cumulative. Something like this happens with living systems. Specifications improved by occasional favorable mutations are preferentially reproduced and thus tend to replace their ancestral forms. This is natural selection.

In recent years many factors have been found to increase the frequency of mutations. High-energy radiation that penetrates to the cell nucleus is mutagenic in proportion to its amount. A number of chemical agents are likewise mutagenic. It is now possible, for example, to alter nucleotides in known chemical ways that will produce mutations. Oxidation of amino groups of nucleotides with nitrous acid is one way. It is encouraging that biochemists and geneticists who study the mechanisms involved are beginning to be able to predict successfully the types of mutations that are most likely to be produced by specific chemical agents. It is not, however, possible to do this specifically for certain genes only.

Let us now turn to the general question of evolution. What do mutations have to do with the processes by which evolution occurs? It is especially appropriate at this time to discuss this aspect of my subject, for, as you know, this is the hundredth anniversary of the publication of Darwin's *Origin of Species.*

Organic evolution is interesting and important in many respects. For one thing, it is not logically possible to accept only a small amount of it, for one cannot imagine a living system that could not have evolved from a very slightly simpler system. Starting with man, for example, and working backward toward simpler systems one sees no obvious stopping place. Our ancestors were presumably a bit simpler than we. Early in man's evolution there were primitive men. And before primitive man there were prehuman ancestral forms capable of evolving into true man. This is true however one defines man. The point is that no matter what living system one thinks of, another is conceivable that is one mutation simpler or different. And so one can go backward in the evolutionary process to simpler and simpler forms until finally one begins to think of systems like present-day viruses, the simplest of which consist of little more than nucleic acid cores (DNA or RNA) and protein coats. One can easily imagine that before systems of this type there were smaller and smaller systems of nucleic acid and protein capable of replication and of mutation which in turn had ancestors consisting of only nucleic acid.

We know that nucleic acids can be built up from nucleotides and these from simpler precursors. In a lecture recently delivered in this auditorium, Prof. Melvin Calvin talked about the origin of some nucleotide precursors and presented evidence suggesting that some such compounds, or their relatives, are found in certain meteorites. It is assumed that these were formed by natural chemical reactions that went on and are still going on outside living systems. Presumably precursors of nucleotides were formed through such reactions. Professor Calvin also mentioned the evidence that amino acids are made from such simple inorganic molecules as methane, ammonia, hydrogen, and water under conditions assumed to have obtained on primitive earth. It is, I believe, justifiable to make the generalization that anything an organic chemist can synthesize can be made without him. All he does is increase the probability that given reactions will "go." So it is quite reasonable to assume that given sufficient time and proper conditions, nucleotides, amino acids, proteins, and nucleic acids will arise by reactions that, though less probable, are as inevitable as those by which the organic chemist fulfills his predictions. So why not self-duplicating viruslike systems capable of further evolution?

I should point out that nucleic acid protected with a protein coat has an enormous selective advantage, for it is much more resistant to destruction than is "raw" nucleic acid. Viruses can be stored for years as inert chemicals without losing the capacity to reproduce when placed in a proper environment. Of course present-day viruses demand living host cells for multiplication, but presumably the first primitive life forms inhabited environments replete with spontaneously formed building blocks from which they could build replicas.

Before molecules like methane, hydrogen, water, and ammonia there were even simpler molecules. Before that there were elements, all of which nuclear physicists and astrophysicists believe have evolved and are now evolving from simple hydrogen. That is why I say if you believe in evolution at all there is no logical stopping place short of hydrogen. At that stage I'm afraid logic, too, runs out.

The story can, of course, be repeated in reverse. When the conditions become right, hydrogen must give rise to other elements. Hydrogen fuses to form helium, helium nuclei combine to give beryllium-8, beryllium-8 captures helium nuclei to form carbon, and carbon is converted to oxygen by a similar process. In this and other known ways all the elements are formed. As one goes up the scale, the number of possibilities rapidly increases. As elements begin to interact to give inorganic molecules, the number of possibilities becomes still greater. I do not know how many inorganic molecules are possible, but I do know there must be a very large number. With organic molecules the number becomes truly enormous, particularly with large molecules like proteins and nucleic acids. For example, there are something like 4 raised to the 10,000th power ways a modest-sized DNA molecule can be made. There appears to be no stage at which there is a true qualitative change in the nature of evolution. The number of possibilities goes up gradually, the complexity goes up gradually, and there appears to be no point at which the next stage cannot be reached by simple mutation.

Let us suppose we have a small piece of DNA protected by a protein coat and capable of replication in the presence of the proper building blocks and a suitable environment. During replication, the system will occasionally make mistakes. It is a mutable system. Given sufficient time there will eventually occur a combination of mutations of such a nature that the protein coat will become enzymatically active and capable of catalyzing the formation of a nucleotide or amino acid from a slightly simpler precursor. If this particular building block happens to be limiting in replication, the mutant type will obviously have a selective advantage. It can replicate in the absence of an essential building block by making it from a simpler precursor. If two such units with protein coats having different catalytic functions combine to form a two-unit system, they will be able to make two building blocks from simpler compounds and will be able to survive under conditions in which their ancestral forms would fail. In the same way it is not too difficult to imagine systems arising with successively three, four, five, and more units with every additional unit serving a catalytic function. With each additional unit the total system would become one step less dependent on spontaneously preformed precursors. With perhaps 10,000 such units the system might be able to build all its necessary parts from inorganic materials as we know present day green plants do.

How many units to reach the stage of man? Perhaps 100,000 units carrying out 100,000 functions are necessary. However many it is, we know they carry the specifications for the development of a complex nervous system by which we supplement blind biological inheritance with cultural inheritance. We reason, we communicate, we accumulate knowledge, and we transmit it to future generations. No other species we know of does this to anything like the same degree. We have even learned about organic evolution and are on the verge of learning how to start the process.

I pointed out that in the Kornberg system with the four nucleotides present, nothing happens unless a primer is added. That is not entirely true. After a delay of some three or four hours something does happen even without a primer. What happens is that a DNA molecule is spontaneously formed. It differs from most naturally occurring DNA in that it contains only two of the four nucleotides. Now if this two-unit co-polymer is used as a primer in a new system, it immediately initiates the synthesis of co-polymers like itself. In other words, it starts replicating. Remember, it arose spontaneously. If you believe in mutation — and you must if you accept scientific evidence — you must believe that if you start with a two-unit co-polymer and let it undergo successive replications, there will eventually occur a mutation with which a pair of nucleotides will be replaced by the pair originally excluded in the process. This conceivably could have been the origin of the four-unit DNA of all higher organisms.

Knowing what we now know about living systems — how they replicate and how they mutate — we are beginning to know how to control their evolutionary futures. To a considerable extent we now do that with the plants we cultivate and the animals we domesticate. This is, in fact, a standard application of genetics today. We could even go further, for there is no reason why we cannot in the same way direct our own evolutionary futures. I wish to emphasize, however — and emphatically — that *whether* we should do this and, if so, *how*, are not questions science alone can answer. They are for society as a whole to think about. Scientists can say what is possible and perhaps something about what the consequences might be, but they are not justified in going further except as responsible members of society.

Some of you will, I am sure, rebel against the kind of evolution I've been talking about. You will not like to believe that it all happened "by chance." I wish to repeat that in one sense it is not chance. As I have said, the mutations by which we believe organic evolution to have occurred are no more "chance" reactions than those that occur in the organic chemist's test tube. He puts certain reactants in with the knowledge that an expected reaction will go on. From the beginning of the universe this has been true. In the early stages of organic evolution the probabilities were likely very small in terms of time intervals we are accustomed to think about. But for the time then available, they were almost certainly not small. Quite the contrary; the probability of evolving some living system was likely high. That evolution would go in a particular direction is a very different matter. Thus the *a priori* probability of evolving man must have been extremely small — for there were an almost infinite number of other possibilities. Even the probability of an organism evolving with a nervous system like ours, was, I think, extremely small because of the enormous numbers of alternatives. I am therefore not at all hopeful that we will ever establish communication with living beings on other planets, even though there may well be many such on many planets. But I do not say we should not try — just in case I am wrong!

Some of you will no doubt be bothered by such a "materialistic" concept of evolution. Ninety years ago in Edinburgh, Thomas Henry Huxley faced this question of materialism in his famous lecture on the physical basis of life. And it has been faced many times since — for example, a few years ago by Dean George Harrison of M.I.T. in his book *What Man May Be*. What Huxley said can be said today with equal appropriateness. He said in effect that just because science must by its very nature use the methodology of materialism, scientists need not necessarily be materialists. A priest wears material clothes, eats material food, and takes his text from a material book. This does not make him a materialist. And so it need not with a scientist. To illustrate, the concept I have attempted to present of the origin of life and of subsequent evolution has nothing to do in principle with the problem of ultimate creation. We have only shifted the problem from the creation of man, as man, to the creation of a universe of hydrogen capable of evolving into man. We have not changed the problem in any fundamental way. And we are no closer to — or further from — solving it than we ever were.

THEODOSIUS DOBZHANSKY
AND
GORDON ALLEN

Does Natural Selection Continue to Operate in Modern Mankind?

[FROM THE SMITHSONIAN REPORT FOR 1958]

THE QUESTION *posed in the title of this article is obviously of vital significance to the future of the human race. If the answer is in the negative, mankind is doomed, according to many present-day writers, to decadence and possible extinction. The authors, Theodosius Dobzhansky, professor at the Rockefeller Institute, in New York, and Gordon Allen, of the National Institute of Health in Washington, D.C., attempt to clarify the thinking about the effects of natural selection and adaptation as they apply to the human race. After discussing the "survival of the fittest" theory and the genetic variations produced by the irresistible process of mutation, the authors give their definite answer to the question in the title. In concluding, they feel that mankind may not be able to rely wholly on biological natural selection, but may eventually have to obtain sufficient genetic knowledge to "take over the controls from nature."*

THE PROBLEM

THE PURPOSE of the present article is to examine the validity of the assertion, frequently made in medical, biological, and sociological writings, that natural selection has been relaxed or even done away with altogether in modern mankind, particularly in advanced industrial societies. With this assertion as a premise, dire predictions of biological decadence of the human species have been uttered, especially in popular scientific literature. It is of course not our intention in this article to grapple with this immense problem in its entirety, and we mean neither to affirm nor to refute the predictions of decadence. We feel, however, that the thinking in this field may gain in clarity from a reexamination of the concepts of natural selection and adaptation, particularly as they apply to man. Such a reexamination is the more needed since these concepts have not remained stable even in biology since they were advanced by Darwin. Particularly rapid change has taken place in recent years in connection with the development of population genetics.

Natural selection is regarded in modern biology as the directing agent of organic evolution. The process of mutation yields the genetic variants which are the raw materials of evolutionary change. Sexual reproduction then gives rise to innumerable gene combinations or genotypes. However, which mutants arise, and when, have nothing to do with their possible usefulness or harmfulness to the species. Natural selection, nevertheless, so maneuvers the genetic variability that living species become fitted to their habitats and to their modes of life. Organic evolution consists of a succession of threatened losses and recapturings of the adaptedness of living matter to its environment. But the environment does not change the genotype of a living species directly, as some evolutionists of the past have wrongly assumed. The role of the environment consists rather in that it constantly presents challenges to the species; to these challenges the species may respond either by adaptive modification or by extinction.

It would be an exaggeration to say that the above view of the evolutionary process is universally accepted. Few biological theories really are. However, the importance of natural selection, at least as an agent which guards against degenerative changes in populations, is denied by scarcely anyone. We need not labor the point that the evolution of the ancestors of the human species was brought about by the operation of the same fundamental biological processes which act elsewhere in the living world. A new situation has arisen with the advent of the human phase. Species other than man become adapted to their environment by changing their genes. In man, the adaptation to the environment occurs in part through development and modification of his learned tradition and culture. Man is able to adapt by changing either his genes or his culture, or both.

Another innovation has also occurred in the evolutionary pattern of the human species. Owing to the protection conferred upon certain weaker genotypes by civilization, natural selection against these genotypes has become weakened or removed. Individuals and populations which would die out under allegedly "natural" conditions survive and procreate in civilized societies. A large share of the blame for this interference with "normal" evolutionary processes is laid at the door of modern medicine. Although man possesses methods of adaptation which are peculiar to his species, he is still subject to general biological laws. Biological evolutionary processes operate in the human species within the unique evolutionary pattern conditioned by human intellectual powers; yet it would certainly be a dangerous matter to abolish the controlling influence of the processes of selection.

STRUGGLE FOR EXISTENCE AND SURVIVAL OF THE FITTEST

According to Darwin's own testimony, the theory of natural selection was suggested to him in 1838, when he "happened to read for amusement" Malthus's *Essay on the Principles of Population*. Any living species is able to multiply in geometric progression, and hence to increase in numbers until it outgrows its food supply. In reality this happens quite rarely, and populations of most species are stable within relatively narrow limits. The causes which bring about the relative constancy of numbers are by no means well known even at present (see Andrewartha and Birch, 1955, and Lack, 1954, for relevant information).

Nineteenth-century authors said simply that excessive production of progeny was balanced by wholesale destruction in the "struggle for existence," in which "famine, war, and pestilence" were the principal factors. Actually, things are more complex. Thus, with many species of birds, the number of eggs in a clutch is such that under average environmental conditions the greatest number of young survives to maturity. Larger clutches produce fewer, not more, survivors, since the parents are unable to take proper care of their brood. Among insects, starving females or females that develop from underfed larvae deposit fewer eggs than do well-fed females. Scarcity of food, destruction by predators, disease, unfavorable weather conditions, and accidents of every kind are all involved. One or more of these factors may occasionally be decisive in different species or at different times and places in the same species. Struggle, in the sense of actual combat, is a rare occurrence among members of the same species, although it doubtless exists. To give just one example: adults and larvae of ladybird beetles, which normally feed as predators on other insects, resort to cannibalism when the food is scarce.

Destruction of a large proportion of the progeny certainly does not by itself guarantee that natural selection will take place. The contrary may be the case. When death or survival and production or nonproduction of offspring are due mainly to chance, large-scale destruction actually hampers selection for anything except fecundity. Selection as an evolutionary force is most effective where each individual's success or failure in life is a consequence of his over-all excellence or imperfection. In precisely this situation, most nearly approached by higher animals, the number of young produced is usually small and survival rates are high (Schmalhausen, 1949).

To put it simply, in order to be effective natural selection must be selective. On the average, survivors must be better fitted to live than nonsurvivors. The survivors must be stronger, or more intelligent, or better able to get along on little food, or more resistant to weather, or better able to escape from diseases, parasites, or predators. But not even all these virtues combined will improve the quality of the progeny unless the fitness of the survivors and the unfitness of the nonsurvivors are due to their genes. This proviso is obviously most important in human evolution. In man, individual and group success is often due to better means rather than to better genes.

Natural selection is, then, brought about by the survival of the genetically fit, not of the genetically fittest. Spencer's "survival of the fittest" was an effective slogan in the struggle for acceptance of the evolution theory. But the rhetorical superlative misrepresents the actual situation by overstating the ferocity of the struggle for existence. Nietzschean superman is biologically a dubious foundation on which to build the future of the species. In nature, even under most stringent conditions, the survivors are usually fairly numerous and possess a variety of genetic equipment. Without going into the details of this matter, it can be stated that too severe a selection is likely to be less effective than a moderate one, because severe selection tends to deplete too soon the reserves of genetic variability.

REPRODUCTIVE SUCCESS

The version of the theory of natural selection which invokes survival of the fittest in the competitive struggle for life was remarkably well suited to the intellectual climate of Darwin's times. It has often been pointed out (e.g., Barzun, 1941) that the popularity of Darwinism had more to do with the social and political implications which some people read into the theory than with its scientific validity. Those who believed that limitless progress will inevitably result from unrestricted competition of private enterprise were beguiled to learn that their economic views found support in a universal law of nature. With colonial empires in the expansion stage, it was a comforting thought that the exploitation of the weak by the strong was merely a part of "the stern discipline of nature which eliminates the unfit." An eminent anthropologist was able to advocate withholding education from most people, in order that competition might occur under "natural" conditions. This "social Darwinism" continues to exist even today, and it has recently been given a modern biological dress by Darlington (1953).

With the development of genetics, and particularly of population genetics, the theory of natural selection has been recast in a more exact, though emotionally less impressive form. Consider a population of a sexually reproducing and cross-fertilizing species, such as man. A Mendelian population of this sort consists of individuals which differ from one another in certain genes. The population has a gene pool, in which different gene variants are represented with different frequencies. Now, in any one generation, the carriers of the different genes are likely to make unequal average contributions to the gene pool of the next generation. Therefore, the gene frequencies in the gene pool will change from generation to generation. Some genes will be perpetuated at rates greater than their alternative genes. The former are, then, favored by selection, and the latter are discriminated against. The genes which are selected for may eventually be established in the population, while those selected against may be lost.

Selection consists in differential perpetuation of genetic variants in the gene pool of a population. Selective success is reproductive success. The Darwinian fitness, or adaptive value of a genotype, is measured by the mean contribution of the carriers of this genotype, relative to other genotypes, to the gene pool of the succeeding generations. The highly fit genotypes are those which transmit their genes most efficiently; the less fit ones have a mediocre reproductive efficiency; the unfit ones have no surviving and fertile progeny.

Under this sober appraisal, the "fittest" is nothing more spectacular than a parent of the largest family. He is no longer the mighty conqueror who has subdued countless competitors in mortal combat. He need not necessarily be even particularly hale and hearty; strength and toughness increase Darwinian fitness only insofar as they contribute to reproductive success. Mules are at least as vigorous and resistant to harsh conditions as their parents, horses and donkeys. But the Darwinian fitness of mules is zero, because of their sterility. Conversely, a hereditary disease which strikes after the close of the reproductive period does not diminish the adaptive value of the genotype. An example of this is Huntington's chorea. This is a dominant disease due to a single gene, the incapacitating effects of which do not usually appear until its carrier has passed most or all of the reproductive period. There has even been a suspicion that the carriers of this gene have on the average a greater number of children than their normal siblings. The infirmities of old age are easily accounted for by the theory of natural selection. What happens to the organism after the reproductive age is of no concern to natural selection, or only insofar as the condition in old age is correlated with some traits which appear during the reproductive age. In a social organism like man, natural selection may, however, control survival in later years, because what happens to the older members of the family or community also affects the welfare of its younger members. The tendency of this control might be to shorten the interval between the close of the reproductive period and death because, as Haldane has pointed out, in some societies the oldsters prove a useless drain on the resources of the group. But comparison of the post-reproductive years in man with those in other primates would probably show that the net effect of selection has been to lengthen this period.

The question whether modern man is subject to natural selection can now be answered. He certainly is. Natural selection would cease only if all human genotypes produced numbers of surviving children in exact proportion to the frequencies of these genotypes in the population. This does not, and never did, occur in recorded history. Quite apart from the hereditary diseases and malformations for which no remedies are known and which decrease the reproductive fitness, the inhabitants of different parts of the world have different reproductive rates.

The selective forces which now act on the human species are natural, rather than artificial, selection. It is of course conceivable that natural selection may some day be replaced by artificial selection. Indeed, "To replace natural selection by other processes that are more merciful and not less effective" (Galton) was the original theme of eugenics. To make this dream a reality, the contributions which various genotypes made to the gene pool of the next generation would have to be decided on the basis of genetic considerations either by parents themselves or by some outside authority. An alternative idea has been developed, especially by Osborn

(1951); instead of substituting artificial selection for natural selection, he suggests a reorganization of social and economic institutions so that natural selection could be relied upon to favor intelligence and social adaptability.

The frequent allegation that the selective processes in the human species are no longer "natural" is due to persistence of the obsolete 19th-century concept of "natural" selection. The error of this view is made clear when we ask its proponents such questions as, why should the "surviving fittest" be able to withstand cold and inclement weather without the benefit of fire and clothing? Is it not ludicrous to expect selection to make us good at defending ourselves against wild beasts when wild beasts are getting to be so rare that it is a privilege to see one outside of a zoo? Is it necessary to eliminate everyone who has poor teeth when our dentists stand ready to provide us with artificial ones? Is it a great virtue to be able to endure pain when anesthetics are available?

The words "fitness" and "adaptedness" are meaningless except in relation to some environment. Natural selection involves interaction between the genotype and the environment, and this interaction leads to furtherance of congruity between the interacting entities. For this reason, organic evolution has on the whole been adaptive. It is, nevertheless, a function of an imperfect world. One of its limitations is that it is opportunistic. Selection enhances the adaptedness of genotypes only to the currently existing environments. Therefore, the direction and the intensity of natural selection are as changeable as the environment. Selection in modern man cannot maintain our fitness for the conditions of the Old Stone Age, nor can it prepare us for novel conditions of the distant future except by increasing our general adaptability.

Man's environments are decisively influenced by his cultural developments. For good or for ill, natural selection fits man to live in the environments created by his own culture and technology. In these environments, the ability to subsist on uncooked foods is probably now less important than it once was; the ability to resist certain infections prevalent in crowded towns is probably more important than it was. So is the ability to learn, to become educated, and to live in reasonable accommodation with one's neighbors. Natural selection now works in what some may call unnatural conditions, but it is still natural selection.

RELAXATION OF SELECTION

The hoary fallacy which is perpetuated by some modern writers is that for a genetic variation to be selected it must be important enough to decide between the life and death of the creature. In reality, even a slight advantage or disadvantage which increases the probability of one genotype leaving more offspring than another will be effective in the long run. It has recently been found (Aird, Bentall, Mehigan, and Roberts, 1954) that the proportion of people with blood group O is slightly higher among patients suffering from duodenal ulcer than it is in the general population. This does not mean either that everybody with O blood gets a duodenal ulcer, or that those with other blood groups are immune. But the possibility that the frequencies of O bloods in human populations may be influenced by the greater susceptibility of O persons to duodenal ulcer is a real one.

The fitness, the adaptive capacity of the carriers of a given genotype is continuously changing. Suppose that the contribution of one genotype to the gene pool of the following generation is equal to unity. The contribution of a different genotype may then be represented as $1 - s$. The value s is the difference in reproductive success between the two genotypes and is called the selection coefficient. Now, the magnitude of the selection coefficient depends upon the environment. Selection coefficients grow larger as selection becomes more stringent and they diminish as selection is relaxed. When s is zero, the genotypes are equal in fitness, and selection does not operate upon them.

There can be no doubt that modern technology, and especially modern medicine, have greatly mitigated the disadvantages of many genetic weaknesses and disabilities: In other words, in an environment which includes modern technology and medicine, selection coefficients operating against certain human genotypes are smaller than in a primitive environment. But this amounts to saying that the fitness of the carriers of these genotypes has increased. A person afflicted with hereditary diabetes mellitus can live reasonably happily and may even raise a family if his environment includes proper doses of insulin administered at proper intervals. Genetically considered, a disability that can be corrected by environmental means so that it no longer causes an impairment of reproductive efficiency ceases to be a disability when a suitable environment is provided.

This reasoning applies also to any relaxation of selection that may result from sociological progress. There is supposed to exist a danger of loss or "erosion" of genes for high intelligence, owing to the higher reproductive rates of the social classes in which such genes are supposedly rare. Cook (1951, p. 260) describes this danger in the following way:

> As this process continues . . . the average level of intelligence and the proportion of gifted individuals decline. Should the feeble-minded level be reached, most of the plus-genes will have been eliminated. But before that time growing inefficiency and incompetence would cause the collapse of modern industrial society. The Dark Ages which spread over Europe with the fall of Rome were a cultural blackout that lasted for a thousand years. The Dark Ages which would be caused by continued gene erosion could last five to ten times as long.

It would not be appropriate here to discuss how far this eschatology is justified by available evidence. It should, however, be pointed out that the fearsome process, if it actually occurs, means that in our society high intelligence decreases the average biological fitness of its possessors, while less intelligent people tend to be more fit. This appalling circumstance would be due not to the cessation of natural selection, but to the relative intensification of selection for personality traits other than intelligence. It would be unfortunate only insofar as the most favored genotypes gave rise to certain characteristics which could be regarded as undesirable on other grounds. If the humble and the meek inherit the earth, it will mean simply that under social conditions which obtain in modern industrial civilizations humility and meekness are favored by natural selection, while pride and egotism are discriminated against.

It should be noted that relaxation of natural selection does not by itself change the genetic composition of populations; it does so only in conjunction with mutation. The process of mutation constantly and irresistibly generates genetic variations, and most of the mutants are deleterious to the organism. Increase of mutation rates would, then, lower the fitness of the population even if the selection pressure remained constant. But the relaxation of selection would necessarily mean that the "bad" genes will have become rather less dreadful than they were.

SELECTION AND ADAPTEDNESS

More than half a century ago, in the heat of polemics, Weissmann wrote about the "omnipotence of natural selection." This unfortunate exaggeration is not wholly absent in the writings of some modern authors. Natural selection is a remarkable enough phenomenon, since it is the sole method known at present which begets adaptedness to the environment in living matter. But it has its limitations. As pointed out above, it is opportunistic and lacking in foresight. Moreover, any genotype which possesses a higher net reproductive efficiency has a higher Darwinian fitness, and is, by definition, favored by natural selection. Higher Darwinian fitness usually goes together with superior adaptedness to the environment; however, the correlation is not perfect.

A single example will suffice to illustrate the occasional miscarriages of natural selection. Dunn (1953) found a recessive gene in the house mouse which is lethal when homozygous. A population of mice in which this gene occurs in a certain proportion of individuals produces, then, some inviable embryos. The gene is clearly deleterious. But this gene possesses the curious property that a male which is heterozygous for it and for its normal allele yields more spermatozoa carrying the abnormal than the normal gene. This automatically confers upon the abnormal gene an advantage in the population, and causes it to spread until its lethal effect in homozygotes checks its propensity to increase in frequency. Dunn has found that the lethal is actually common in many "normal" mouse populations, outside of genetic laboratories. Up to a point, therefore, natural selection favors the spread of a lethal gene in mouse populations because this gene happens to be able to subvert the male reproductive processes in its own favor. The reproductive success of a genotype is, in this case, opposed to adaptive success of the population.

This discrepancy between reproductive and adaptive success arises because the former has but one dimension: the rate of perpetuation of a gene from generation to generation relative to that of an alternative gene. Adaptation is multidimensional, and herein lie some unresolved problems about natural selection, particularly as it occurs in the human species. The pioneers of Darwinism were already aware that, in a social animal, the qualities which promote success in an individual are not necessarily those which are most useful to the society in which the individual lives. A gene for altruism (if such existed) might be discriminated against by natural selection on the individual level, but favored on the population level. The outcome of selection would, therefore, be difficult to predict. One might speculate that it would depend on the population structure of the species. A gene for altruism might be lost in large undivided populations, but might become frequent in a species subdivided into numerous competing colonies or tribes. Moreover, adaptedness to a certain environment, however perfect, need not go together with adaptability to changeable environments (flexibility, according to Thoday, 1953). For example, it is to be expected that of all the genotypes which are successful in times of abundant food supply, relatively few will be adaptable to periodic starvation; genotypes which can resist a large variety of infections are not necessarily the most successful ones in disease-free environments.

It can be granted that some genotypes which were being eliminated under primitive conditions are enabled to survive and to perpetuate themselves in civilized environments. As pointed out above, this necessarily means that the Darwinian fitness of these genotypes under civilized conditions has risen relative to what it was under primitive ones. The possessors of such genotypes, if they take proper care of themselves, may even be able to secure their share of the joy of living. Does it follow, however, that these genotypes may now be considered desirable in the human species?

The answer may, unfortunately, be in the negative. Muller (1950) has portrayed the state of mankind which might result from failure to eliminate weakening mutant genes in the following way:

> This means that despite all the improved methods and facilities which will be in use at that time the population will nevertheless be undergoing as much genetic extinction as it did under the most primitive conditions. In correspondence with this, the amount of genetically caused impairment suffered by the average individual, even though he has all the techniques of civilization working to mitigate it, must by that time have grown to be as great in the presence of these techniques as it had been in paleolithic times without them. But instead of people's time and energy being mainly spent in the struggle with external enemies of a primitive kind such as famine, climatic difficulties and wild beasts, they would be devoted chiefly to the effort to live carefully, to spare and to prop up their own feeblenesses, to soothe their inner disharmonies and, in general, to doctor themselves as effectively as possible. For everyone would be an invalid, with his own special familial twists.

The outlook seems grim. Natural selection under civilized conditions may lead mankind to evolve toward a state of genetic overspecialization for living in gadget-ridden environments. It is certainly up to man to decide whether this direction of his evolution is or is not desirable. If it is not, man has, or soon will have, the knowledge requisite to redirect the evolution of his species pretty much as he sees fit. Perhaps we should not be too dogmatic about this choice of direction. We may be awfully soft compared to paleolithic men when it comes to struggling, unaided by gadgets, with climatic difficulties and wild beasts. Most of us feel most of the time that this is not a very great loss. If our remote descendants grow to be even more effete than we are, they may conceivably be compensated by acquiring genotypes conducive to kindlier dispositions and greater intellectual capacities than those prevalent in mankind today.

SELECTION OF WHOLE GENOTYPES

The propensity of evolution to produce unfavorable changes in plants and animals may at first sight appear astonishing. Consider the absurd difficulty which the human female has in giving birth to her young. Here is a process which is assuredly essential for the perpetuation of the species. Natural selection could be expected to make it pleasant, or at least painless. Instead, childbirth is attended with intense pain, and often imperils the life of the mother, of the fetus, or of both. Although the later stages of pregnancy and parturition are to some extent incapacitating in all mammalian females, they are much more so in the human species. This and the other flaws in our biological organization Mechnikov called "the disharmonies of human nature." We cannot but suppose that these disharmonies have arisen during the natural course of human evolution.

The situation will appear less incomprehensible if the mechanics of natural selection are considered. Natural selection cannot develop this or that organ apart from the rest of the body, nor can it foster this or that gene apart from the rest of the genotype. What is selected in the process of evolution is the genotype as a whole. It is the whole organism which survives or dies, and successfully reproduces or remains barren. The genotype is a mosaic of genes, but it is wrong to think of the organism as though it were a mechanical sum of parts, each determined by a single gene. In the process of individual development all genes act in concert. The whole genotype, not just some genes, decides what an individual will be like as a fetus, in childhood, in adolescence, in maturity, and in old age. Moreover, the development of different individuals takes place in different environments; and the genotype may be required to adapt its carrier to any one of the possible environments. Certain differences between individuals (such as differences between some blood groups) are ascribable to single genes, but even the expression of these differences may vary; what an individual is like is always due to all the genes this individual carries.

The evolutionary success or failure of a species is determined by the fitness of its entire genotype, and of its entire developmental pattern, in those environments which the species inhabits. An observer may discern, however, that some particular feature or aspect of the organization is most instrumental in bringing about success or failure. Thus with man: his body is remarkable neither by its strength nor by its endurance. The evolutionary success of our species has been due to brain power, not to body power. Evidently, some genotypes which enhance brain power have been selected in spite of their tendency to decrease body power. Darwinian fitness is the resultant of all the advantages and disadvantages which one genotype may have compared to other genotypes. In man, the ability to learn and to invent and use tools influenced this balance more significantly than did muscular strength or resistance to inclement weather, although these were not negligible.

It is certainly reasonable to suppose that genotypes which combined the greatest brain power with the greatest body power would yield the highest fitness. Why, then, is man not always as wise as Socrates, as strong as a lion, and as hardy as a dog? If we had unrestricted power to plan the evolution of the human genotype we would probably equip it with all these qualities and some others besides. But natural selection does not work according to any plan. Selection is opportunistic; whatever can survive does. Man's evolution was not designed or arranged beforehand. It took the course which it did because man's genotype, imperfect as it was, was good enough to survive, and in fact good enough to make our species a tremendous biological success.

Specialization is a common feature of the evolutionary pattern in many kinds of organisms at the expense of all-around perfection. The former is evidently more easily achieved than the latter. This is true not only of unplanned evolution which occurs in the state of nature but also of evolution under domestication, which to some extent is planned. Among cattle, there exist dairy breeds and beef breeds; there exist also some unspecialized breeds, but no breed combines the maximal performances of the best dairy and the best beef breeds. Why this is so is hard to tell; it may be that a combination of the above sort is a physiological impossibility, since the qualities which one may wish to combine may be antagonistic. On the other hand, it may be that a perfect breed of cattle is simply yet to be obtained.

Perhaps the most impressive example, other than man, of an

organism whose biological success appears to be due to an outstanding development of just one ability, and a mediocre development of others, is the man-of-war bird *(Fregata)*. Those who have had the opportunity to observe these superb fliers procure their food from the tropical seas can hardly imagine a more perfect flying machine. Yet, the legs of these birds are so weak that they cannot rise into the air from a flat surface, nor can they alight on water since their plumage becomes waterlogged. Man is certainly the best thinking machine which protoplasm has produced. This confers upon him a biological adaptedness so great that he continues to prosper as a species despite his relatively weak body, his several biological disharmonies, and his many follies. He need not fear biological extinction so long as his genotype as a whole enables him to live in some environments, either "natural" or devised by his own ingenuity.

EVOLUTIONARY PROCESSES ACCENTUATED BY CIVILIZATION

Many traits that were essential for bare survival in a paleolithic culture are unnecessary in New York City, but we have emphasized that natural selection is not restricted to the struggle for survival. For all organisms, reproduction is the essential step in selection, and reproduction in man involves not only bearing children, but rearing them to maturity. In modern civilization, furthermore, parental influence may often be decisive in determining the success of children in their own marriage and reproduction. If so, the reproductive success of an individual may be more adequately gauged by the number of his grandchildren than by the number of his children. Also, if parental influence is so important, the existing negative correlation between intelligence and family size may be compensated in some cultural groups by a positive correlation between intelligence and successful preparation of one's offspring for adult adjustment. This extension of parental functions appears to represent a trend in human cultural evolution; in our own society, as class differentials in fertility diminish, it may restore some of the biological value which intelligence seems to have lost.

Under civilization, reproduction and successful child rearing have come to depend more upon individual adjustment patterns and less on survival or reproductive capacity. Individual and family adjustment is the modern theater of the "struggle for existence." In our culture biological adaptedness, that is, optimal reproduction and child rearing, seems to bear no direct relation to economic or educational status, but probably depends in part upon personal and social adjustment patterns. Though physical and mental handicaps rarely eliminate persons completely, they probably affect such adjustment. Among the traits capable in this way of influencing reproduction, the relative importance of physical health is presumably diminished and that of mental health magnified in comparison with selection in primitive man. In addition, some physiological defects would appear to contribute to personal maladjustments more frequently in a modern than in a primitive culture. Likely examples of such defects are color-blindness, left-handedness, and allergic diathesis. With respect to genetic factors underlying these traits, present-day natural selection may be reinforced both relatively and absolutely. Finally, the capacity to compensate for gross physical or sensory handicaps probably has more selective value now than it did under conditions of existence which eliminated most cripples completely.

Further speculation is unwarranted here, but it seems safe to assume that most sensory or mental characteristics that were developed in our primate ancestors in response to the demands of an increasingly complex, variable environment, are even more important to civilized man. If so, they surely play some role in determining which persons shall marry, which shall have stable families, and which shall raise more children. When handicapped individuals defy these determinants and become parents, their children pay the price in a relatively severe selection by the adverse physical and social environment. As a result of this stringent selection in such families, on the average, survivors in the third generation are probably superior to the grandparents genetically.

Selection for many traits at once always makes slower progress than selection for one or a few traits. Insofar as natural selection formerly maintained genetic traits that have now become useless, civilization has eliminated a probable source of interference that impeded selection for cultural adaptability. Whether selection in the latter respect is in an absolute sense stronger or weaker than formerly, it is probably operating more efficiently.

Whatever emphasis is placed here on the positive aspects of natural selection under civilization is not intended as a denial of all negative aspects. Man's increasing physical dependence on his cultural heritage, beginning with clothing and cooked food, can be taken as a historical fact, and accelerated specialization in this direction is to some extent inevitable. Conflicts in our present culture between reproduction and higher education, or between reproduction and self-control, are almost completely new selective forces in human evolution. It is not at all apparent how these conflicts would be resolved in the natural course of cultural progress. On the other hand, artificial attempts to counter such selection by "eugenic" support of culturally desirable types would inevitably lead to another type of dangerous specialization; the very need of these types for such support, insofar as the need exists, proves their failure to adapt biologically to civilization. Dependence of society upon complex reproductive controls seems to be a higher order of specialization, whether better or worse, than dependence of the individual on medical and technical aids.

From a long-term point of view, another effect of civilization may be more important than changes in selection pressures per se. Individual genetic variation is the basis for selection, and this has been accentuated in modern man for several reasons. First, relaxation of selection in any respect immediately increases the proportion of minor and extreme abnormalities in the surviving population. Second, new environments, as well as the increasing proportion of deviant individuals, permit fuller expression of genetic differences formerly masked in uniform phenotypes. An example of this is perhaps to be seen in some childhood reading disorders, which would make little or no difference in an illiterate population. Third, migration and intermarriage of formerly separate races or groups produce a great new diversity of genotypes. Fourth, increased survival of mutations results, to a small extent, in greater prevalence of genes that raise the mutation rate.

Even if selection should be reversed for a brief period of time the above sources of increased genetic variation will, in Schmalhausen's words, mobilize the variability of the species. Thus, civilization is now preparing man for rapid evolution in whatever direction long-term selection may determine. As long as populations remain large, and as long as competition exists in any form, degenerative evolutionary trends are likely to be outweighed by adaptive changes, but the direction of these changes is uncertain.

CONCLUSIONS AND SUMMARY

The idea explicit or implicit in many writings, that all would be well with the human species if obstructions to natural selection were removed, does not stand critical examination. Man, like any other biological species, is constantly subject to natural selection. The genotypes which possess the highest Darwinian fitness in the environments created by man's inventive genius are, however, not the ones which were most favored by selection in the past. Natural selection cannot maintain the adaptedness of modern human populations to environments which no longer exist, nor can it pre-adapt them to environments of the future.

Natural selection is opportunistic; it does not always lead to improved adaptedness. After all, extinction has been the fate of countless biological species which lived in the state of nature and which were at all times subject to natural selection. It would be folly for our species to risk the same fate for the juggernaut of blind biological force. One of the causes of extinction is too narrow an adaptedness to a circumscribed biological opportunity which proves only temporary. Man has reached a solitary pinnacle of evolutionary success by having evolved a novel method of adapting to the environment, that by means of culture. Having ventured on this biological experiment, our species cannot any longer rely entirely on forces of natural selection as they operate on the biological level. Man must carefully survey the course that lies ahead and constantly study his genetic progress. He can then prepare to take over the controls from nature if it should become necessary to correct the deficiencies of natural selection. Only thus can he insure for himself continued evolutionary advance.

REFERENCES

AIRD, IAN; BENTALL, H. H.; MEHIGAN, J. A.; and ROBERTS, J. A. FRASER. 1954. Blood groups in relation to peptic ulceration and carcinoma of colon, rectum, breast, and bronchus. British Med. Journ., vol. 2, pp. 315–321.

ANDREWARTHA, H. G., and BIRCH, L. C. 1955. The distribution and abundance of animals. Chicago.

BARZUN, JACQUES. 1941. Darwin, Marx, Wagner: Critique of a heritage. Boston.

COOK, ROBERT C. 1951. Human fertility: the modern dilemma. New York.

DARLINGTON, C. D. 1953. The facts of life. New York.

DUNN, L. C. 1953. Variations in the segregation ratio as causes of variations in gene frequency. Acta Gen. et Stat. Med., vol. 4, pp. 139–151.

LACK, D. 1954. The natural regulation of animal numbers. Oxford.

MULLER, H. J. 1950. Our load of mutations. Amer. Journ. Human Gen., vol. 2, pp. 111–176.

OSBORN, F. 1951. Preface to eugenics, 2d ed. New York.

SCHMALHAUSEN, I. 1949. Factors of evolution: the theory of stabilizing selection. Philadelphia.

THODAY, J. M. 1953. Components of fitness. Symposia of the Society for Experimental Biology, vol. 7, pp. 96–113.

EDGAR ANDERSON

Man as a Maker of New Plants and New Plant Communities

[FROM THE SMITHSONIAN REPORT FOR 1956[1]]

WHILE *the two preceding articles deal with theoretical considerations of genetics and evolution in general, this discussion of the part man has played in creating new plants and plant communities is documented by specific practical examples. The author, Edgar Anderson, is the Curator of Useful Plants at the Missouri Botanical Garden and also professor of botany at Washington University in St. Louis. He shows that many of the common plants and weeds that we think of as having always been where we now find them have in a great many instances been brought by man from other regions, often from as far distant as other continents. Also it is brought out that man has hybridized and otherwise altered crop plants and ornamentals to a degree that they are actually entirely new creations. He concludes that the evolution of plants (as well as of animals) has been to a marked degree affected by the efforts of modern and ancient man, and that a more thorough study of the subject will teach us much concerning the story of prehistoric man as well as the process of evolution before the advent of man on the earth.*

---

[1] Revised as of March 1965.

THAT MAN changes the face of nature may be noted
by any casual observer; not even the ablest and most experienced
scholar can yet estimate just how far this has reclothed the world.
Whole landscapes are now occupied by man-dominated (and in
part by man-created) faunas and floras. This process began so long
ago (its beginnings being certainly as old as *Homo sapiens*) and
has produced results of such complexity that its accurate interpretation must await research as yet scarcely begun. Though answers
to many basic questions remain unknown, they are by no means
unknowable.

The average thoughtful person has little inkling of this recloth-
ing of the world; even professional biologists have been tardy in
recognizing that in the last analysis a significant portion of the
plants and animals which accompany man is directly or indirectly
of his own making. The average American supposes that Kentucky
bluegrass is native to Kentucky and Canada bluegrass native to
Canada. A few historians and biologists know that these grasses
(along with much of our meadow and pasture vegetation) came
to us from Europe. The research scholar inquiring critically into
the question realizes that some of this vegetation was as much a
Neolithic immigration into Europe as it was a later immigration
into the New World. Like Kentucky mountaineers, this vegetation
has its ultimate roots in Asia, and spread into central and western
Europe at times which, biologically speaking, were not very long
ago.

It is obvious that landscapes such as the American Corn Belt
have been transformed by man. Other man-dominated landscapes
do not betray their origin to the casual observer. Take the grass-
lands of California, the rolling hills back from the coast, the oak-
dotted savannas of the Great Valley. Here are stretches of what
look like indigenous vegetation. Much of this mantle is not obviously tended by man; it has the look of something that has been in
California as long as the oaks it grows among, yet the bulk of it
came, all uninvited, from the Old World along with the Spaniards.
Most of it had a long history of association with man when it made

the trip. Wild oats, wild mustards, wild radishes, wild fennel — all of these spread in from the Mediterranean, yet over much of the California cattle country they dominate the landscape. Native plants are there, even some native grasses, but it takes a well-informed botanist going over the vegetation item by item to show how small a percentage of the range is made up of indigenous California plants.

For those parts of the tropics where plants grow rapidly it will take careful research before we can have an informed opinion about such questions. Thorn scrub, savannas, bamboo thickets, weedy tangles of quick-growing trees and shrubs are known to have covered vast areas in the last two or three millennia. Yet Standley, our greatest authority on the vegetation of Central America, digging up a small tree in what appeared to him to be a truly indigenous forest in the Lancetilla Valley, came upon a layer of potsherds (Standley, 1931). What is the relation between the supposedly wild avocados of such a forest and the avocados eaten in the village that once covered that site? We now have various techniques (pollen profiles, carbon-14 datings, chromosome analysis, extrapolated correlates) which can give critical answers, but they are time-consuming, and their application to such problems has just begun.

The total number of plants and animals that have moved in with man to any one spot on the earth's surface is way beyond what even a biologist would estimate until he looked into the problem. There are the cultivated plants both for use and for display, the domesticated animals, the weeds, and their animal equivalents such as houseflies, clothes moths, rats, and mice. A much larger class comprises organisms not purposely introduced by man, which are neither eyesores nor plagues, but which, like weeds, have the capacity to get along in man's vicinity. Such are the daisies and yarrows and buttercups of our meadows. Such, in a sense, are even those native species that spread under man's influence. Take, for example, the sunflowers of Wyoming. They are certainly native to North America and may possibly in part be prehuman in Wyoming. They line the roadways yet seldom are elsewhere prominent in the native landscape. They appeared along with the road, even though they may have moved in from not so far away. But how did they get into the spot from which they spread, and did pioneers or primitive man have anything to do with making this previous niche? This is the sort of question we are now making the subject of decisive experiments; we do not yet have enough results for decisive answers.

For microorganisms the problem of the species that travel about with man staggers the imagination. Microorganisms seemingly fall into the same general categories as macroorganisms. Brewers' yeasts are as much cultivated plants as the barleys and wheats with which they have so long been associated for brewing and baking. The germs of typhoid and cholera are quite as much weeds as are dandelions or Canada thistles. The microorganisms of our garden soil are apparently the same mixture of mongrel immigrants and adapted natives as our meadow and pasture plants. Soils are good or bad quite as much because of the microcommunities they contain as because of their composition. Man's unconscious creation of new kinds of microorganisms is an important part of his total effect on the landscapes of the world. Think, then, of this total composite mantle of living things which accompanies man: the crops, the weeds, the domesticated animals, the garden escapes such as Japanese honeysuckle and orange day lily, the thorn scrub, the bamboo thickets, the English sparrows, the starlings, the insect pests. Think of the great clouds of algae, protozoa, bacteria, and fungi — complex communities of microorganisms that inhabit our soils, our beverages, our crops, our domesticated animals, and our very bodies.

If we turn to the scientific literature for an orderly summary of where these species came from and how, there is a depressing lack of information. The crop plants and domesticated animals have been somewhat studied, the ornamentals and the weeds scarcely investigated. Even for the crop plants one notes that for those that have been the most carefully studied — wheat (Aase, 1946), cotton (Hutchinson et al., 1947), maize (Mangelsdorf and Reeves, 1938) — there is now general recognition that their origins, relationships, and exact histories are much more complex problems than they were thought to be a generation ago. In spite of these wide gaps in our knowledge, I believe the following generalizations will stand:

1. All the major crops and most of the minor ones were domesticated in prehistoric times. *Modern agriculture, classified solely by the plants it uses, is Neolithic agriculture.*

2. For none of the major crops can we point with certainty to the exact species (or combination of species) from which it was derived: for some we can make guesses; for a number we can point to closely related weeds. This merely complicates the problem. We then have to determine the origin of the crop, the origin of the weed, and the history of their relationships.

The world's knowledge of crop plants, in other words, does not tell us very much. All we know is that we are dealing with man's effects on certain plants in the Neolithic or before. Yet for weeds and ornamental plants even less is known. A few general observations may be offered, parenthetically, about their origins.

1. We can now point to crops that are definitely known to have been derived from weeds. For instance, rye as a crop originated from a grainfield weed (Vavilov, 1926). As barley and wheat spread farther north onto the sandy Baltic plain, the weed gradually replaced the crop. The origin of rye as a weed is a far older and more complex problem. Stebbins and his students are far enough into it to tell us that it is a story with several chapters, most of them unsuspected until recently.

2. We can point to weeds that originated from crop plants. The bamboo thickets that cover whole mountainsides in the Caribbean came from cultivated bamboos. It now seems much more probable that teosinte the weed was derived from maize the crop than that maize was derived from teosinte.

3. Crop plants and their related weeds frequently have a continuing effect upon each other. We have documented evidence of weeds increasing their variability by hybridizing with crop plants and of crop plants consciously or unconsciously improved through hybridization with weeds. These processes recur repeatedly in the histories of weeds and crop plants. For wheat it is clear that a minor grain was in very early times built up into one of the world's great cereals through the unconscious incorporation of several weeds from its own fields (Anderson, 1952, pp. 57–64).

As a whole, ornamentals (though little studied as yet) provide the simplest keys and the clearest insights into the basic problems

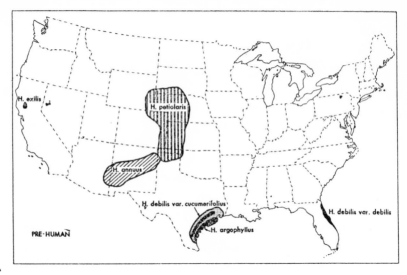

ILLUS. 69—*Annual species of North American sunflowers as presumed to have existed in prehuman times: 1)* Helianthus exilis, *a highly localized endemic in the serpentine areas of California; 2)* H. petiolaris *on bare sandy areas in the western Great Plains; 3)* H. annuus *in playas and other raw-soil habitats of the southwestern deserts; 4)* H. argophyllus *on the sands of the Texas coastal plain; and 5)* H. debilis *in Florida and Texas.*

of domestication of any class of plants or animals. Some have been domesticated within the last century — the African violet, for instance — but are already distinct from the species from which they arose. Such recent domesticates provide unparalleled experimental material for determining what happens to the germ plasm of an organism when it is domesticated. Others of our garden flowers originated in prehistoric times. They seem to have been associated with magic and ceremony; some of them may have been with us for as long as or even longer than our crop plants. Take woad, *Isatis tinctoria*, now known only as a garden flower, though it persisted as a commercial dye plant until Victorian times (Hurry, 1930). When Caesar came to Britain, he found our semisavage ancestors using it to paint their bodies. There are various other ornamentals (*Bixa, Amaranthus, Helianthus*) whose earlier associations were with dyes and body paints. Which is older, agriculture or body painting?

The cultivated grain amaranths (known to the Western world mainly through such bizarre late-summer annuals as love-lies-bleeding) demonstrate that we shall be in for some rude shocks when we

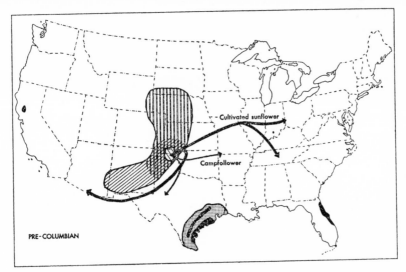

ILLUS. 70—Hypothetical origin of the North American sunflower as a weed and as a cultivated annual in pre-Columbian times. In the areas where annuus and petiolaris had begun to introgress, this process is being unconsciously accelerated by the activities of early man.

make serious studies of these apparently trivial plants. J. D. Sauer found (1950) that this whole group was domesticates, divisible into several different species, none of which could be equated to any wild amaranth; that the whole group was of American origin; and that the varieties cultivated since ancient times in Kashmir, China, and Tibet were not (as had previously been taken for granted) derived from Asiatic amaranths. They are instead identical with those cultivated by the Aztecs and the Incas.

It is now becoming increasingly clear that the domestication of weeds and cultivated plants is usually a process rather than an event. None of them rose in one leap from the brain of Ceres, so to speak. The domestication of each crop or weed went on at various times and places, though by bursts rather than at a regular rate. For many it still continues. Our common weed sunflowers, for example, are at the moment being bred into superweeds. In California, by hybridization with a rare native sunflower, these weeds are increasing their ability to colonize the Great Valley (Heiser, 1949). In Texas (Heiser, 1951), by similar mongrelizations with two native species, they are adapting themselves to life on the sandy lands of the Gulf Coast (see Illus. 69, 70, 71).

The story of the American sunflower is significant because it dem-

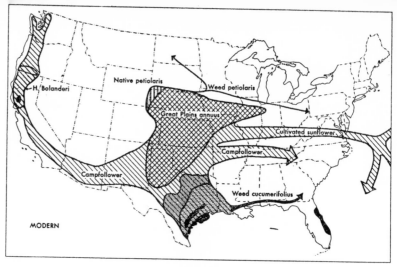

ILLUS. 71—Spread of annual species of North American sunflowers in modern times. In the Great Plains extensive introgression of annuus and petiolaris produced the Great Plains race of Helianthus annuus, which has spread eastward through the prairies as a somewhat weedy native. The camp-follower weed (sometimes mixed with Great Plains annuus) has spread as a weed throughout the East and to irrigated lands in the West. In California, by extensive and continuing introgression with exilis, it has created the semiweedy H. bolanderi, which is still actively spreading. Similarly on the sands of the Texas coast and the Carrizo ridge, H. argophyllus is introgressing actively with H. annuus to produce weedier strains. Over an even wider area in Texas extensive introgression of annuus, petiolaris, and cucumerifolius is producing a coastal-plain weed sunflower which is actively spreading along the coast. In spots it has already reached the North Carolina coastal plain. Eventually this will react actively with H. debilis var. debilis, breeding a superweed for the American Southeast but, fortunately, a not unattractive one. The Texas and California phenomena have already been documented by Heiser (1949, 1951), and research on other facets of the problem is going forward rapidly.

onstrates the kinds of processes that went on in the Stone Age and before, when our major crops were domesticated. It is because the domestication of weeds and cultivated plants (using the word "domestication" in its broadest sense) is a continuing process that it came to my professional attention. Thirty years ago I started out to study (and if possible to measure) such evolution as was still going on. As I analyzed example after example, the fact became increasingly clear that evolutionary activity is concentrated in (though by no means confined to) disturbed habitats — to times and places where man's interference with the prehuman order of things has been particularly severe. Post-Pleistocene evolution, it seems, has been very largely the elaboration of weedlike plants and animals.

Now why should this be? What is there about the presence of man that stimulates his plant and animal companions into increased evolutionary activity? A growing body of observational and experimental data bears directly upon that question; rather than summarizing it, let me describe in considerable detail one particularly illuminating example. It concerns the hybridization of two California species of wild sage, *Salvia apiana* and *S. mellifera*. They have been meticulously studied by Epling — in the field (1947), the herbarium (1938), the laboratory, and the experimental plot (Epling and Lewis, 1942). Burton Anderson and I (1954) have made an exhaustively detailed analysis of the variation pattern of several populations, confirming and extending Epling's conclusions.

These two species of sage are so unlike that any ordinary amateur would immediately recognize them as radically different plants; only an occasional botanist would see that they are really quite closely related and that their differences, though conspicuous, are superficial. This was what first drew Epling's attention to them. He found that they hybridized readily when artificially cross-pollinated. The hybrids grew vigorously in an experimental plot and were fertile enough to produce abundant and variable offspring. In spite of this fertility, hybrids were ordinarily not found in nature or occurred mainly at spots where the native vegetation had been greatly altered by man's activities. Yet on the rocky slopes where they were native, these two kinds of sage frequently grew intermingled. Burton Anderson and I worked with samples of wild populations of both species so intensively that eventually we could distinguish between mongrels, seven of whose great-grandparents were from one species and one from the other, and plants with all eight grandparents from one species. With this yardstick we learned that, though the plants on the mountainside were prevailingly of one species or the other, yet along the pathway from which we collected them we could find a few mongrels. These were mostly plants closely resembling typical *Salvia mellifera* but showing slight indications of *S. apiana* in one character or another. Apparently the very rare hybrids which Epling had found were not completely without issue. Some of them had crossed back to *S. mellifera*, and, of these three-quarter bloods, a few of those similar to the recurrent parent had been able to fend for themselves.

At one point along the path we found conspicuous hybrids resembling those produced by Epling; careful investigation of this area gave us new understanding. With repeated visits we gradually realized that these bizarre mongrels were limited to a definitely circumscribed plot having a greatly altered habitat. It was at a point where the trail swung down along the slope. Originally a forest of live oaks had abutted on the rocky, sunny slopes where the salvias grow. The oaks had been cut and a small olive orchard planted and then abandoned — abandoned so long ago that native plants had flowed in and the whole site looked quite natural. A collection of salvias made exclusively from among the olives was almost entirely hybrids and hybrid descendants. Though the bulk of the plants looked somewhat like *Salvia apiana*, there was not a single plant which in all its characters agreed exactly with the *apiana* outside this plot. Furthermore, they resembled artificial backcrosses in that their differences from *apiana* were all in the direction of *S. mellifera*. These "sub-*apianas*" graded into plants closely resembling the first-generation hybrids raised by Epling. There were a few "sub-*melliferas*" similar to those we had detected along the pathway on the mountainside and a few plants which on our index scored as typical *melliferas*. However, in the field *none* of them looked quite average. Dr. Anderson and I had to work in St. Louis on pressed and pickled material previously collected in California. Had we been able to go back and add characters such as flower color and flower pattern to our battery of measurable differences between *S. mellifera* and *S. apiana*, I believe we could have demonstrated that the entire plot was colonized with hybrids and mongrels, most of them first or second or third backcrosses from the original hybrids to one or the other species.

The results indicate that hybrids are being constantly produced on this mountainside, but one does not ordinarily find them, because there is no niche into which they can fit. The native vegetation had a long evolutionary history of mutual adaptation. Plants and animals have gradually been selected which are adapted to life with each other like pieces of a multidimensional jigsaw puzzle. It is only when man, or some other disruptive agent, upsets the whole puzzle that there is any place where something new and different can fit in. If a radical variant arises, it is shouldered out of the way before it reaches maturity. In a radically new environment, however, there may be a chance for something new to succeed. Furthermore, the hybrids and their mongrel descendants were not only something new; they varied greatly among themselves. If one of them would not fit into the strange new habitat, another might. Though virtually all of them had been at a selective disadvantage on the mountainside, a few of them (aided and abetted no doubt by the vigor which is characteristic of these and many other hybrids) were now at a selective advantage. They consequently flowed in and occupied the old olive orchard to the virtual exclusion of the two original species.

Furthermore, to take up an important fact about which biology as yet knows very little, the habitat among the olives was not only something new; it was *open*. It was not full of organisms which had been selected to fit together. Remember that for the mountainside, on those rare occasions where a first-generation hybrid plant had been able to find a foothold, virtually none of its highly variable descendants was able to persist. Such species crosses can father hundreds if not thousands of distinguishably different types of mongrel descendants. Only along the pathway had *any* of these been able to find a place for themselves and then only those that differed but slightly from *Salvia mellifera*. Hybridization does not advance in closed habitats.

The plants in the olive orchard had no such history of long association. The olives were new to California. The societies of microorganisms in the soil were originally those that go with live oaks, not those accompanying the salvias on the sunny slopes. These must have been greatly changed during the time the olives were cultivated. Furthermore, the olives, being planted at considerable distances from each other, did not re-create either the fairly continuous shade of the oaks or the open sunshine of the upper slopes. The orchard became the site for evolutionary catch-as-catch-can, and under these circumstances, as we have seen, the new and variable had a decisive advantage.

Now that we know this much about these salvias, it would be interesting to work experimentally with them and the species with which they are associated to determine just what factors allow two different but closely related species to fit together with their associates so perfectly that all hybrid intermediates are excluded. From experience with other similar problems I would predict that among the most important factors would be fairly specific reactions between some of the other associated plants and these two sages. In our experimental work with sunflowers we have discovered that one of the strongest factors in determining where weed sunflowers may or may not grow is their reaction to grass. Many grasses apparently give off a substance highly toxic to weed sunflowers. The various species of weed sunflowers differ in their sensitivity to this poison. When two such sunflowers hybridize, one of the factors affecting the outcome is the grassiness of the site. Such relationships seem to be very general among plants. On the whole, many species grow where they do, not because they really prefer the physical conditions of such a site, but because they can tolerate it and many other organisms cannot.

Generally speaking, the plants which follow man around the world might be said to do so, not because they relish what man has done to the environment, but because they can stand it and most other plants cannot.

Are these salvia weeds? I would put forward the working hypothesis that those in the abandoned olive orchard are on the way to becoming weeds. The small exceptional communities of hybridizing colonies similar to this one, which can be found here and there over southern California, are worth considerably more attention than they have hitherto received. They demonstrate the way in which man, the great weed breeder, the great upsetter, catalyzes the formation of new biological entities by producing new and open habitats.[2]

---

[2] This same area was reexamined in 1957 after it had begun to recover from one of the most destructive fires in many years. This had resulted in an explosion of *S. mellifera* and segregates resembling it (including two pure albinos) spreading way down the slope. A series of collections made at that time between Pomona and Palm Springs demonstrated the increasing importance of introgression into *S. apiana* from *Salvia apiana* var. *compacta* Munz, as one approached the desert. In such sites as pastures at Riverside (now part of the new campus) the plants of *S. apiana* were all gray-white and lower than on the mountainsides above Pomona or in the nearby washes.

The salvia case is not unique. We now have over a score of similar well-documented studies of the connection between hybridization and weedy, disturbed habitats. This relationship had long been known to observant naturalists, though not until the last few decades was its significance stressed or experimental work undertaken. One other example demonstrates the role of man's operations on the habitat. Riley (1938) studied the hybridization of two species of *Iris* on the lower delta of the Mississippi in a neighborhood where the land-use pattern had produced something as demonstrable and convincing as a laboratory experiment (Anderson, 1949; Illus. 72). Property lines ran straight back from the river; the farms were small, only a few hundred yards wide, and very narrow. Under these conditions it was easy to see that the hybrids between these two irises were virtually limited to one farm. They grew in a swale which crossed several of the farms, yet were nearly all on one man's property. On his farm they went right up to the fences and stopped, and this could be demonstrated at either side of his property. Unlike his neighbors, he had kept the swale heavily pastured. His cattle had held in check the grasses which are serious competitors of swamp irises. They had also, tramping about in wet weather, turned the swale into more of a quagmire than existed on any of the neighboring farms. They had at length produced an open environment in which the pasture grasses were at a disadvantage and the resulting hybrid swarm of irises at a very real advantage. Hybrids in various patterns of terra cotta, wine, purple, and blue flooded out into this swale until it had almost the appearance of an intentionally created iris garden.

Though Riley never published the sequel, it might be inserted here, parenthetically, since it points up some kind of a moral. The farmer himself did not remove the irises, even though they interfered seriously with the carrying capacity of his pasture. The irises were conspicuously beautiful, and garden-club members from New Orleans dug them up for their gardens, at so much per basket, until they were eventually exterminated. The hybridization that nature began in this and other pastures around New Orleans has been continued by iris fans. These Louisiana irises are now established as cultivated plants both in Europe and in America. Until the arrival of the garden-club ladies, they were nascent weeds (Illus. 73).

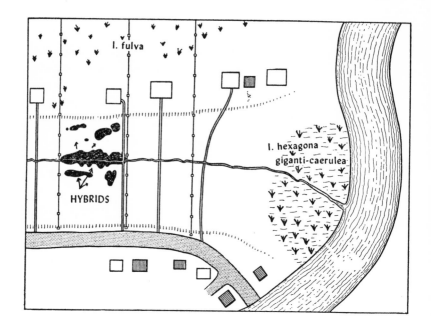

ILLUS. 72—*A demonstration of man's unconscious role in creating new plants. (From Riley, 1938). At the far right one of the minor bayous of the lower Mississippi Delta. At right angles to it and running nearly across the figure is the abandoned channel of a former stream, now drained by a ditch. The natural levees of the stream are slightly higher than the surrounding country. Their sharp inner edges are indicated on the map by hachures. The road has been run along the lower levee, and houses have been built along the opposite one. The property lines (as in many old French settlements) produce a series of long narrow farms, which for our purposes serve as so many experimental plots. Each farm has its house on a low ridge with a long entrance drive connecting it across a swale to the public road on the opposite ridge. The farms (including a score of others which are out of sight to the left of the figure) were originally essentially similar. At the point where the ditch joins the bayou is a large population of* Iris hexagona giganti-caerulea. *Behind the levee on which the houses were built,* I. fulva *grows on the lower ground as well as farther upstream along the ditch. The key fact to be noted is that the hybrids are on only one farm, that they are abundant there, and that they go up to the very borders of the property on either side. Nature is evidently capable of spawning such hybrids throughout this area, but not until one farmer unconsciously created the new and more or less open habitat in which they could survive did any appear in this part of the delta.*

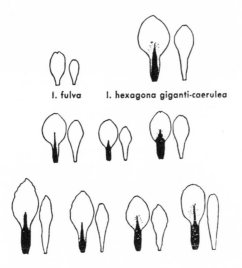

I. fulva   I. hexagona giganti-caerulea

ILLUS. 73—Sepals and petals of some hybrids of Iris hexagona giganti-caerulea *and* I. fulva, *somewhat diagrammatic but accurately to scale. In each case the sepal (the so-called "fall" of iris fanciers) is shown to the left; the petal, "standard," to the right.* I. fulva *has small lax terra cotta sepals and petals.* I. hexagona giganti-caerulea *has large crisp petals and sepals of bright blue. The sepal has a brilliant yellow signal patch (shown in black) surrounded by a white area (shown by stipples) shading off into the blue. Note that in the various hybrids the small-sized flowers (characteristic of* I. fulva) *tend to be associated with the lack of a white area (another* fulva *characteristic). Note the variability of the hybrids. In color they varied from deep wine to very pale light blue.*

A little reflective observation will show that the ways in which man creates new and open habitats, though various, can mostly be grouped under a few headings: (1) dumps and other high-nitrogen areas; (2) pathways; (3) open soil; (4) burns. The last is probably the oldest of his violent upsettings of the natural order of things. It must have stimulated evolutionary activity very early — whole floras or certainly whole associations must have come to a new adjustment with it here and there; fire should be, of all man's effects upon evolution, the most difficult to analyze. Until valid experimental and exact historical methods deal with this problem, it inevitably must spawn more polemic activity than scientific analysis.

In contrast to fire, the creation of open-soil habitats as a really major human activity belongs much more to the age of agriculture and industry than to prehistory. It may be that is why it seems to be the simplest to analyze. In Europe and eastern North America, in the humid tropics and subtropics, open soil — bare exposed earth — is scarcely part of the normal nature of things. Most of the flora truly native to these areas cannot germinate in open soil or, having germinated, cannot thrive to maturity. Make a series of seed collections from wild flowers and forest trees and plant them in your garden just like radishes or lettuce. You will be amazed to learn how small a percentage of them ever comes up at all. Make similar collections from the weeds in a vacant lot or from the plants (wanted and unwanted) of your garden. Nearly all of them will come up promptly and grow readily. Where did these open-soil organisms come from in the first place, these weeds of gardens and fields, these fellow travelers which rush in after the bulldozer, which flourish in the rubble of bombed cities? Well, they must have come mostly from prehuman open-soil sites. River valleys did not supply all of them, but rivers are certainly, next to man, the greatest of weed breeders. Our large rivers plow their banks at flood times, producing raw-soil areas. Every river system is provided with plants to fill this peculiar niche; all those known to me act as weeds in the uplands. One of the simplest and clearest examples is our common pokeweed, *Phytolacca americana,* native to eastern North America. It will be found growing up abundantly in the immediate valleys of our major rivers (Sauer, 1952; see Illustration 74). On the uplands it is strictly limited to raw soil, though, once established in such a habitat, it can persist vegetatively for a long time while other kinds of vegetation grow up around it. Being attractive to birds, its seeds are widely scattered. I remember, from my Michigan boyhood, how pokeweed came in when a woodland near our home was lumbered over. We had never noticed this weed in that community, but the birds had been planting it wherever they roosted. When the felling of the big oaks tore lesser trees up by the roots, pokeweed plants appeared as if by magic for the next few years in the new craters of raw soil. Man and the great rivers are in partnership. Both of them are upsetters. Both of them breed weeds and suchlike organisms. The prehuman beginnings of many of our pests and fellow travelers are to be sought in river valleys. River valleys also must have been the ultimate source of some of the plants by which we live: gourds, squashes, beans, hemp, rice, and maize.

The examples of the salvias and irises show how quickly evolution through hybridization can breed out something new and different under man's catalytic influence. What we should most like to know is the extent to which weeds and similar organisms, created or at least extensively modified through man's influence, are built up into whole associations. It is clear that such things can happen; the *maqui* vegetation of the Mediterranean, the *shiblyak* and *karst* vegetation of the Balkans, the *carbón* scrub of Central America, are obviously very directly the results of man's interference. One would like to analyze the dynamics of these associations. We must do so if man is to understand his own past or to be the master of his own future. For such purposes we need ways of studying vegetation which are analytical as well as merely descriptive — methods not based upon preconceived dogmas. I should like to suggest that the methods used in analyzing the *Iris* hybrids and the *Salvia* hybrids, if combined with other experimental techniques, would allow us to get a long way into these problems. Let me illustrate what I mean by describing some recent studies of *Adenostoma*, a fire-resistant shrub, which is a common component of the California chaparral (Anderson, 1954).

Between the Great Valley and the Pacific Coast, *Adenostoma fasciculatum* is one of the commonest shrubs in the California landscape. Noting that it varied conspicuously from one plant to the next, I made collections of it near Palo Alto and applied to them the methods of pictorialized scatter diagrams and extrapolated correlates. The details of these techniques need not concern us here, since they have been adequately published elsewhere, both in technical journals and in books for the intelligent public. They allow us (through a meticulous examination of variability in such mongrel complexes as the salvias of the abandoned olive orchard) to determine precisely the good species (or subspecies or varieties) from which these complexes must ultimately have arisen. Furthermore, though it takes considerable hard work, these methods can be used successfully by one with no previous knowl-

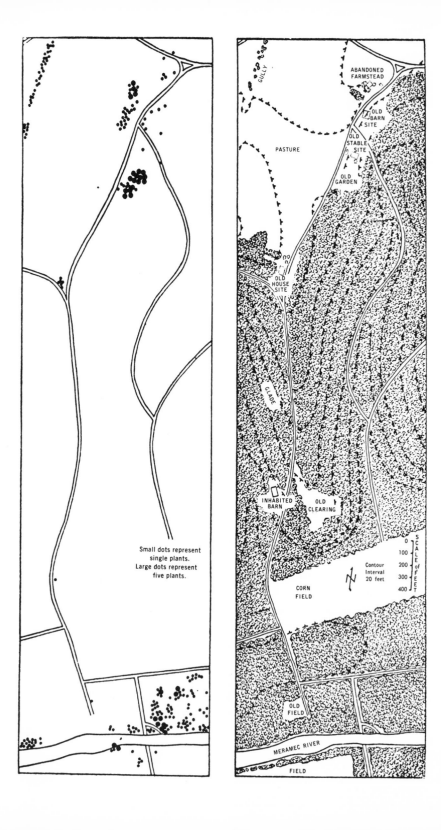

Small dots represent
single plants.
Large dots represent
five plants.

GULLY

ABANDONED
FARMSTEAD

OLD
BARN
SITE

OLD
STABLE
SITE

PASTURE

OLD
GARDEN

OLD
HOUSE
SITE

GLADE

INHABITED
BARN

OLD
CLEARING

0
100
Contour
Interval
20 feet   200
300
400

SCALE of FEET

CORN
FIELD

N

OLD
FIELD

MERAMEC RIVER

FIELD

ILLUS. 74—Occurrence of pokeweed in two different habitats. Pokeweed (Phytolacca americana) is an example of a species which is apparently native in the open soil along American rivers but a weed in the open soil of disturbed habitats. Small dots represent single plants. Large dots represent five plants. It will be seen that the pokeweed is occurring in two quite different kinds of habitats: in the raw soil of repeatedly flooded woodlands on the immediate banks of the river and as a weed around farm buildings, gardens, and the like. (Map from Sauer, 1952.)

edge of the organisms or of the faunas and floras from which they may have come.

Using these methods, I have shown that the common *Adenostoma fasciculatum* of coastal California arose from the hybridization of two very different adenostomas. One of these was *A. fasciculatum* var. *obtusifolium*, a low-growing shrub of the headlands and islands along the California coast. The other is now found in its purest form in the Mother Lode country of the Sierra foothills, a tall, branching shrub which, when in flower, somewhat resembles a small-leaved white lilac. Each of these had its own contributions to make to life in coastal California. The coastal shrub brought in a tolerance of brilliant sunlight and the ability to grow in thin, rocky soil. However, it was accustomed to fog and drizzle even during the dry season. The inland form could go months without a drop of water, but it is used to deeper soil and to less extreme radiation. When these two centers of variation had been identified, it was easy to demonstrate that the common *Adenostoma* is a great, plastic, hybrid swarm, including approaches to these two extremes and many intermediates between them. On dry, rocky ridges in sites that are frequently foggy, one finds plants very close to the island extreme. On deeper soils and in the shade of small oaks are bushes scarcely different from those of the Mother Lode country. Around old ranch buildings and in other peculiar habitats one finds strange and bizarre recombinations of various sorts.

Just as these studies came to a close and it was time for me to leave California, I realized that many of the other plants in the chaparral association were similarly variable. There were swarms of hybrid oaks and hybrid ceanothus and hybrid manzanitas. The entire association seemed to be in a state of flux. Unlike the coastal sages which I had studied in southern California, there was room for hybrid recombinations within the association itself. The entire chaparral seemed to be ecologically in the same general class of disturbed habitat as the abandoned olive orchard.

I do not wish to jump to conclusions from one small experiment. I would merely suggest that these methods are appropriate for the analysis of such problems, particularly if combined with experimental work (for instance, the removal of a single species or species complex from a small area using modern herbicides followed by measurement of the effect of this removal on the other complexes in the association). Here is a field in which we could very rapidly get down to some of the basic principles concerning closed versus open habitats. In my opinion, the degree to which such associations as the California chaparral are manmade is a better subject for study than for debate. They have certainly been greatly affected by man. To learn to what degree, I should prefer to look for more facts rather than to listen to more opinions.

Even among biologists there has been a strong tendency to avoid such problems — to study the plants and plant association of mountaintops and jungles rather than those of dooryards and gardens, to think of plant and animal communities as they must have been in some blissfully innocent era before the advent of man. It seems to me far healthier and far more logical to accept man as a part of nature, to concentrate one's attention as a naturalist on man's activities, since he is the one species in the world we most nearly understand. It is because we know from inside ourselves the problems in which man is deeply involved that we appreciate their bewildering complexity; experiments with laboratory insects would not seem so beautifully simple if we knew as much about them as we do about man. The population genetics of garbage-pail flies (Dobzhansky, 1949) would appear more complex if we understood from within what it is like to be a *Drosophila*. The apparently standardized environment of flour in a bottle (Park, 1938) would not seem undifferentiated to any investigator who had once been a flour beetle and who knew at firsthand the complexities of flour-beetle existence. Imagine a nonhuman investigator of human populations recently arrived from Mars. What could he understand of the relationships of Catholics and Protestants? How long would it take him to discover that, though most of the shortest girls in New York City get married, the very tallest seldom do? Having discovered this phenomenon, how much longer would it take him to understand it? When we attempt to work with laboratory insects, our ignorance of their social complexities makes them seem far simpler material than they really are.

I must confess that when, from being a student of variation in natural populations, I was of necessity led to being a student of man's upsetting effects on his environment, my own thinking was too much colored by this attitude. Only gradually did I come to realize that, though man is now the world's great upsetter, he is not the first. There were others before him, and they played a similar role in evolution. Stebbins and I have recently suggested (1954) that the great bursts of evolutionary activity in the past, the times of adaptive radiation, were caused by such upsets. The formation *de novo* of a great fresh-water lake such as Lake Baikal produced a new and open habitat in which the organisms from various river systems could meet and mongrelize and, under the hand of selection, evolve as rapidly into new paths as did the salvias in the abandoned olive orchard. What must have happened when the first land vertebrates at last arrived on continents whose vegetation had no experience of such beasts? What occurred when the giant reptiles of the Mesozoic churned like gigantic bulldozers through the ferny swamps of that period? Must not the plants of those periods have gone through the same general experiences as are now facing the adenostomas of the California chaparral?

Man has been a major force in the evolution of the plants and animals that accompany him around the world, in the midst of which he largely spends his days. The detailed study of this process (1) should illuminate for us the course of evolution in prehuman times; (2) should be as well one of our truest guides to the history of prehistoric man; and (3), most importantly, should enable us at last to understand and eventually to control the living world around us.

REFERENCES

AASE, HANNAH C. 1946. Cytology of cereals, II. Bot. Rev., vol. 12, No. 5, pp. 255–334.

ANDERSON, EDGAR. 1949. Introgressive hybridization. 109 pp. New York.

1952. Plants, man, and life. 245 pp. Boston.

1954. Introgression in *Adenostoma*. Ann. Missouri Bot. Garden, vol. 41, pp. 339–350.

ANDERSON, EDGAR, and ANDERSON, BURTON R. 1954. Introgression of *Salvia apiana* and *Salvia mellifera*. Ann. Missouri Bot. Garden, vol. 41, pp. 329–338.

ANDERSON, EDGAR, and STEBBINS, G. J., JR. 1954. Hybridization as an evolutionary stimulus. Evolution, vol. 8, No. 4, pp. 378–388.

DOBZHANSKY, TH. 1949. Observations and experiments on natural selection in *Drosophila*. In Bonnier, Gert, and Larsson, Robert (eds.), Proc. Eighth Internat. Congr. Genetics (July 7–14, 1948, Stockholm), pp. 210–224. Lund.

EPLING, CARL C. 1938. The California salvias. A review of *Salvia*, Section Audibertia. Ann. Missouri Bot. Garden, vol. 25, pp. 95–188.

1947. Natural hybridization of *Salvia apiana* and *Salvia mellifera*. Evolution, vol. 1, Nos. 1–2, pp. 69–78.

EPLING, CARL C., and LEWIS, HARLAN. 1942. The centers of distribution of the chaparral and coastal sage associations. Amer. Midl. Nat., vol. 27, No. 2, pp. 445–462.

HEISER, CHARLES B., JR. 1949. Study in the evolution of the sunflower species *Helianthus annuus* and *H. bolanderi*. Univ. California Publ. Bot., vol. 23, No. 4, pp. 157–208.

1951. Hybridization in the annual sunflowers. *Helianthus annuus* × *H. debilis* var. *cucumerifolius*. Evolution, vol. 5, No. 1, pp. 42–51.

HURRY, JAMEISON B. 1930. The woad plant and its dye. 328 pp. London.

HUTCHINSON, J. B.; SILOW, R. A.; and STEPHENS, S. G. 1947. The evolution of *Gossypium* and the differentiation of the cultivated cottons. 150 pp. London.

MANGELSDORF, P. C., and REEVES, R. G. 1938. The origin of maize. Proc. Nat. Acad. Sci., vol. 24, No. 8, pp. 303–312.

PARK, THOMAS. 1938. Studies in population physiology, VIII. The effect of larval population density on the post-embryonic development of the flour beetle, *Tribolium confusum* Duval. Journ. Exp. Zool., vol. 79, No. 1, pp. 51–70.

RILEY, H. P. 1938. A character analysis of colonies of *Iris fulva, I. hexagona* var. *giganticaerulea* and natural hybrids. Amer. Journ. Bot., vol. 25, pp. 727–738.

SAUER, JONATHAN D. 1950. The grain amaranths: A survey of their history and classification. Ann. Missouri Bot. Garden, vol. 37, No. 4, pp. 561–632.

1952. A geography of pokeweed. Ann. Missouri Bot. Garden, vol. 39, pp. 113–125.

STANDLEY, P. C. 1931. Flora of the Lancetilla Valley, Honduras. Field Mus. Nat. Hist. Bot. Ser. No. 10. 418 pp. Chicago.

VAVILOV, N. I. 1926. Studies on the origin of cultivated plants. Bull. Appl. Bot. and Plant Breed., vol. 16, No. 2, pp. 138–248.

R. E. SNODGRASS

Some Mysteries of Life and Existence

[FROM THE SMITHSONIAN REPORT FOR 1962]

THE AUTHOR *of this wide-ranging article, the late Robert E. Snodgrass, was until his death in 1962 an Honorary Research Associate of the Smithsonian Institution. He was a world-renowned insect morphologist and the author of widely used textbooks on insect morphology, as well as of innumerable articles on many phases of insect structure and insect life in general. In his later years he became interested in the broader aspects of the phenomenon of life itself, and in this article he brings together the findings of the latest researchers in many branches of science including astronomy, paleontology, biochemistry, genetics, and animal behavior. Workers in all these disciplines finally arrive at a point in their researches where the possibility of actual proof fails, and at these points begin the mysteries discussed by Dr. Snodgrass. If the biochemists, for example, do finally succeed in synthesizing life in the laboratory, the author points out, there would still remain "the mystery of the nature of the chemical forces in organic compounds by which they give life to lifeless matter."*

393

INTRODUCTION

THE ANATOMISTS, the cytologists, the embryologists, the physiologists, the biochemists are continually giving us more and more facts about the structure, development, composition, and activities of living things. Yet beyond their farthermost advances there still remains in each phase of life an unresolved mystery. The mysteries of life are the various activities constantly going on in living matter, which can be observed, but cannot yet be explained.

The universe itself is one vast mystery. All matter, in a last analysis, consists of the component particles of atoms — protons, neutrons, and electrons. These are united in about a hundred kinds of known atoms, which combine to form innumerable kinds of molecules, gaseous, liquid, gelatinous, and solid. It is the energies inherent in these elementary cosmic units that account for all the activities of matter, both inanimate and animate. The final mystery of the universe and of everything in it, then, is the nature and origin of matter. The basis of life in its simplest form is the chemical interaction of certain kinds of molecules when the latter come together in appropriate conditions. Life, therefore, is one with the movements of the stars and the planets, the heat of the sun, radiant energy, volcanic eruptions, and simple chemical reactions, all of which are manifestations of atomic and molecular energies. While this thought greatly simplifies our concept of the universe, it only magnifies the mystery of it all.

The biologist studies the various phases of life in plants and animals, but generally he regards it as no part of his science to explain the invisible forces that activate living matter. The general public gives little thought to such subjects. We plant a tiny seed knowing that it will give rise to a plant of the kind from which it came, perhaps a huge tree, for example, which will put out thousands of leaves all essentially alike, and repeat the same year after year. We see all this without emotion, just as we see young animals, or even our own children, grow up to be adults of their species. Such things are so commonplace that we take them for granted, not realizing that we live in the midst of mysteries, or that we ourselves are one of the greatest mysteries in nature.

From this paper the reader must not expect to get any factual information beyond what is well known. The discussions that follow are simply ratiocinations about things we do not know, and theories that attempt to explain them.

IN THE BEGINNING

We begin with the most abstruse of all mysteries, the question of how did the universe come into existence. In the book of Genesis we are definitely told that on the first day, whenever that was, the heavens and the earth were created and that, on the third day following, the sun and stars were made. No astronomer can accept this statement. To say the least, the writer got his dates badly mixed, since it is certain that the earth did not float around in space for 4 days before making connections with the sun. Moreover, "creation," as we must now visualize it, did not begin with the formation of stars and planets all ready-made, but with the elemental particles of matter. Since atoms are no longer indivisible units, the first forms of matter should have been protons, neutrons, and electrons.

There are only two possible ways to account for the existence of the universe; either matter was created, or it has always existed. The technique of creation, making something out of nothing, no one has even attempted to explain, and the process is quite impossible for us to understand. On the other hand, that anything can exist without a beginning is something we cannot visualize; "always" is a stretch of time our finite minds cannot grasp. Yet we can hardly conceive of time having had a beginning — we rather confidently speak of eternity in the opposite direction — nor can we think of space as having limits. Time can be limited only by more time, and space by more space. However, there is the theory of some astronomers that radiation from the sun and stars is produced by the annihilation of atoms. In this case, Jeans (1921) points out, the present matter of the universe could not always have been here, and so he postulates that annihilation must be compensated by creation, but he is not explicit as to how the latter takes place. Material existence has to be taken as a fact, but the question of origins will forever remain a double mystery. As said by Jeans, there is "a growing conviction that the ultimate realities of the universe are at present quite beyond the reach of science, and may be — and probably are — forever beyond the comprehension of the human mind." It is a relief to feel that there are things so far beyond us that we need not even try to understand them.

Material existence has to be accepted as a fact, and we can endure perpetual ignorance concerning the origin or beginning of the universe. The important thing to realize is that, however it may have begun, the universe is still composed of the elemental particles of matter and that the energy with which these particles were originally endowed is the source of all energies and activities, inanimate and animate, later developed as the universe evolved.

Gamow (1952), under the misleading title of the "creation" of the universe, gives us a very good picture of its evolution from a vast, hot, seething, gaseous mass of the primary particles of matter. Later, as the mass began to cool and expand, protons, neutrons, and electrons combined to form atoms, and atoms united into molecules. Cloudlike condensations formed galaxies, condensations in the galaxies became stars, and finally the planets were formed. It is wonderful what atomic physics, mathematics, and imagination can do for astronomy, but still it is disconcerting to find how much of it is theoretical. Urey (1952), for example, lists five theories, beginning with that of Laplace, which have been proposed to explain the origin of the solar planets. Of these theories he discredits all except the idea that the sun was first surrounded by a vast cloud of dust which condensed into the planets. However, we need not here be concerned with cosmic theories; they all have to come out with things as they are, the earth a globe fitted for life, the other planets still to be investigated in this respect.

The earth at last, perhaps 3 billion years ago, acquired a solid rocky crust, but still it was intensely hot, and volcanoes everywhere were throwing out liquid matter from below. All was shrouded in dense cloud masses. Given a billion years to cool, the clouds condensed into torrential rains that filled depressions on the earth's surface and formed the primitive oceans. (Never again until the time of Noah was there such a rain as this.) The rain brought down chemicals from the atmosphere, washed them out of the rocky hillsides, from the volcanic lava, and poured them all into the standing waters. With the clouds dispersed, sunshine floods the earth and ultraviolet radiation penetrates the atmosphere. The stage is now set for the beginning of life.

The picture above presented of conditions on the earth before the advent of life is that visualized by theorists on life's origin. However, as generally in matters incapable of proof, different writers have advanced quite different theories on the nature of the young world (see Urey, 1952).

THE ORIGIN OF LIFE

Ideas concerning the beginning of life on the world are necessarily theoretical, but the biochemists have worked out a theory that is now generally approved or accepted. It is derived from the fact that the basis of all life at present is the chemical interaction of organic substances in the units of living matter called cells. It is reasoned, therefore, that if similar substances were first brought together in pools of water or along the shores of the primary seas, the same chemical reactions would take place as at present, and thus give the beginning of life. This theory has been particularly well worked out by Oparin (1938, 1961), whose ideas have been so closely followed by others, as by Wald (1954), Adler (1957), and Lehrman (1961) here cited, that fortunately we have only one plausible theory on the subject to deal with, which fact in itself is a good recommendation for it. The general reader may find the theory well presented by Platt (1961) in the *Reader's Digest*. Briefly reviewed, this modern scientific concept of the origin of life is as follows:

Among the chemicals poured into the waters of the earth by the rains were simple organic compounds freely formed in nature. As time went on, some of these substances came together in small groups forming droplets of organic material in a gelatinous or colloidal state, such as are known as coacervates. When organic molecules get together in a water medium, things begin to happen. Some are broken down into simpler molecules, some of which are thrown out, while others are taken in from the surrounding water and assimilated to restore the internal balance. Thus *metabolism*, the basic activity of life, began on a small scale. Though most of the coacervates were highly unstable and soon went to pieces, those in which a balance of output and intake was preserved endured. These persisting coacervates could now be said to be alive. With feeding, the mass became too large and simply broke into two parts, perhaps as a lump of jelly might be divided. Thus the simple organisms multiplied; those best fitted to survive were preserved by natural selection and became the progenitors of future life forms. In the words of Adler (1957), "through the slow accumulation of changes during hundreds of millions of years, coacervates finally developed that had the complex, delicately balanced, and stable chemical processes that we call life."

Some writers, as Moskin (1962), refer to the origin of life in matter as "creation" of life, but clearly there is no act of creation involved.

The materials that first became living matter had been in existence since the beginning. They were simply brought together under circumstances that allowed their inherent energies to interact in a new way.

The chemical activities of living matter require a constant supply of energy. The principal source of life's energy today is the oxidation of food, but the theorists tell us that when life began and for a long period afterward there was no oxygen or very little in the earth's atmosphere. At this time it is supposed that energy was produced by fermentation, a very slow process, but there were millions of years during which living matter could leisurely develop and improve. It was not until plants acquired chlorophyll and developed the process of photosynthesis that oxygen was liberated from carbon dioxide and energy became available by oxidation. Thereafter organic substances were produced in abundance by living things themselves, and the life processes were speeded up by the acquisition of enzymes. Since all the earliest known animals were air breathers, the plants must have had the water well oxygenated by the time of the Pre-Cambrian, and made the land habitable for all the air-breathing creatures that came later to populate the earth. There is no doubt that plants are now the ultimate source of all animal food; it is difficult to believe, however, that we are indebted to them also for all the oxygen we breathe today. Another theory contends that oxygen and other gases have seeped through the earth's crust from the interior.

The biochemical theory of life's origin here reviewed should be as convincing as any visionary theory on the subject could be. It is the hope of the biochemists that it may sometime be demonstrated by the artificial synthesis of life in the laboratory. In this event, the mystery of life would not be its origin, but the nature of the chemical forces in organic compounds by which they give life to lifeless matter.

There have been other theories concerning the origin of life on the earth. A fanciful idea that once appealed to the credulous held that germs of life pervaded the universe and that drifting through space they have developed on any planet that offered favorable conditions. This theory neatly avoids the question of life's origin. It may readily be admitted that if the same chemicals and the same conditions are present on some other planet as on ours, life may have appeared there as on the earth. But it is highly improbable that evolution followed the same course and produced higher forms of life comparable to those that have evolved here. The "man from Mars" will probably be found to be just as fictitious as the "man in the moon."

Down to almost modern times a belief has persisted in the spontaneous generation of living creatures, such as the production of maggots from the flesh of dead animals, or the origin of microorganisms from the scum of foul water. Even in the writer's early days we never doubted that threadworms (*Gordius*) found in the old horse watering troughs were animated horse hairs. Modern biology has callously put an end to all such romance.

From the theoretical primitive forms of life it is still a long way to the organized cell with its nucleus, chromosomes and genes, centrioles, and mitochondria. Unfortunately, however, as Oparin (1938) says, "the origin of the cell is perhaps the most obscure point in the whole study of the evolution of organisms." No intermediate forms are known, and theories have not yet bridged the gap. Viruses are not a primitive form of life because they can reproduce only in other organisms, and bacteria cannot live alone in nature. If, however, we can once account for the origin of an amoeba, evolution from Protozoa to man is relatively easy.

CELL DIVISION, REPRODUCTION, AND HEREDITY

Since no form of life is individually immortal, there would be no living thing on the earth today if the first living creatures had not devised a means of multiplication. The simplest type of reproduction is the division of a unicellular animal into two duplicating cells, and cell division is still the basis of reproduction in all higher animals. In the simpler Protozoa it begins with a division of the nucleus, followed by a constriction of the cell between the daughter nuclei, and ends with a complete separation of the cell into two cells. In others the mechanism becomes variously more complex until it comes to resemble that characteristic of the Metazoa. In some of the Protozoa the successively formed cells, instead of separating as individuals, adhere in a mass, forming a many-celled animal of a sort, such as *Volvox*, in which there is some coordination among the individuals, but little differentiation of structure, except that certain cells assume the function of reproduction. With the true many-celled animals, or Metazoa, however, the cells are so closely adherent that they practically lose their individualities, and groups of them differentiate into complex organs of various functions.

In some of the lower Metazoa the body cells may retain a reproductive potential sufficient to regenerate lost appendages or even a large part of the body including the head. Among the higher animals this faculty becomes reduced to wound healing. In general, reproduction is the function of special cells set apart for the purpose. The germ cells are differentiated into male and female cells which, with few exceptions, must first unite in pairs before development begins. The combination of the male and female elements in the zygote, or egg, combines hereditary material from two parental sources, and is usually accredited with inducing more structural variations in the adult for natural selection to work on in the evolution of species. Sexual reproduction occurs among the

Protozoa, some of which come together in pairs and unite, while others simply exchange nuclear material. Among the metazoic animals and in the flowering plants it is all but universal. Bisexual reproduction, therefore, evidently has had a strong evolutionary influence. Only in a few invertebrates, as in the honey bee, does the unfertilized egg develop.

Since the number of chromosomes in the body cells of the Metazoa is typical for each species, the primary germ cells undergo a reduction division by which the number of chromosomes is halved. Union of the sex cells at the time of fertilization then restores the normal chromosome equipment of the species. Sexual reproduction, therefore, is dependent on chromosome reduction in the conjugating cells, but the same thing takes place in every dividing cell. In ordinary cell division, however, the chromosomes are first doubled.

When we turn from the gross structure of an animal to what goes on within its cells, we leave the realm of anatomy for that of biochemistry. Here we find ourselves in a totally different world of life, in fact, in that of life itself, and we encounter phenomena quite different from anything we have experienced before.

The mechanism of cell division in the Metazoa is highly developed in a form known as *mitosis* (see Mazia, 1953). In the resting cell the nuclear chromosomes are long, tangled filaments, but preceding mitosis they condense into darkly staining bodies usually of a definite number in each species. Prior to this the chromosomes have divided each into two, so that now they are present in identical pairs. A small body in the cytoplasm, known as the centriole, then divides and the two parts move to opposite poles of the cell. Threadlike fibers radiate out from each centriole, forming a spindle through the nucleus, which now accommodatingly loses its wall. Some of the threads extend from pole to pole, others attach to individual chromosomes. The two chromosomes of each pair then move to opposite poles as if pulled by the threads, but the mechanism of their movement is not fully understood. Each chromosome group becomes a new nucleus. Finally the cell constricts at the equator between the nuclei and eventually divides into two duplicate cells.

All this coordinated activity observed in the dividing cell appears to take place automatically. It can be followed under the microscope, but there is no visible evidence of what causes the phenomena seen.

The biochemists have shown that the principal substance of the chromosomes in all animals is a chemical known as deoxyribonucleic acid, of highly complex molecules. This acid, called DNA, is truly a most remarkable stuff; it is the "dictator" of all the cell activities, including cell metabolism and the growth of the embryo developed from the egg. Intensive studies of these subjects have been made by the biochemists in recent years. A dramatic example of the creative power of DNA is seen in the infection of a bacterium by a virus. The virus cell discharges its DNA into the bacterium, and here, at the expense of the bacterial cytoplasm, the DNA molecules not only replicate themselves but form complete new virus cells, as many as 200, which are discharged with the rupture of the bacterium (Jacob and Wollman, 1961).

The cytoplasmic changes that differentiate the multiplying cells are said to be done strictly "on orders" from the DNA of the nucleus, and are carried to the cytoplasm by a related substance RNA (ribonucleic acid) catalyzed by enzymes from the DNA. In connection with nodules (ribosomes) in the cytoplasm RNA then synthesizes the amino acids of the cell into the proteins and enzymes necessary for the specific function the cell is destined to assume.

The fertilized egg is the mother cell of her offspring. To each cell is given explicit "instructions" as to just what is to be its role in duplicating the form and structure of its immediate ancestor. The biochemists are attempting to explain all this, but still it seems one of the most mysterious things in the whole physical realm of nature. As said by Fischberg and Blackler (1961), "Long before men knew anything about cells, much less molecules, they were familiar with one of the most tangible mysteries in nature: out of a simple-looking egg emerges a living organism, complete and perfect in every detail and unimaginably complex. Each organ just the right size and in the right place and contains the right kind of cell to carry on its specialized function. Today we are scarcely less mystified. How does the undifferentiated cell of a cleaving egg turn into a specialized cell of heart, liver, nerve, bone, or muscle?" Needham (1942) gave an exhaustive review of the status of biochemistry and morphogenesis as of 20 years ago, occupying 677 pages based on more than 2,400 citations. Bonner (1962) now gives us an up-to-date account of more recent developments in the biochemistry of the genetic materials. Yet both authors leave us still with the mystery of *how* chemical substances determine and control the development of the egg into an embryo that reproduces the structure of its parents, whether a mouse, a bird, a dog, a man, or an insect. According to Bonner the mechanism of cell differentiation is still unknown. The biochemists, of course, ardently believe that some day the mystery may be dispelled; but let us hope this will not be too soon, for when all the facts of life are known, biology will lose its interest.

The specific factors of heredity we have long been told are bodies called *genes*, thousands of them distributed along the length of the chromosomes. We might then suppose them to be something like seeds in a pod. However, it appears that not yet has a gene been isolated and studied individually. They are parts of the DNA molecules, which the biochemists now regard as the basic material of heredity. That the genes are specific somethings, however, is evident from the fact that changes (mutations) attributed to them are reflected in hereditary changes in the adult. These changes are the structural variations by which natural selection has evolved new species. The genes of a modern animal, therefore, include those that formed it by mutation, and hence they can reproduce its present structure.

We should very much like to understand how the chemical DNA, whether of the genes or the chromosome molecules, or both, can influence the proliferating cells to build up an embryo and finally an adult of the parent species. The geneticists and biochemists tell us that on the chromosomes of the cell nucleus is encoded the entire plan for the development of the embryo, which serves as a working blueprint for the developing cells. To clarify this somewhat anthropomorphic statement, it must be explained that the language of the code is that of molecular chemistry, which the biochemists are industriously trying to interpret. (See numerous papers in the *Scientific American* during the past 10 years.) The code characters are said to be different combinations of the component elements of the DNA molecules. The message is delivered in the form of enzymes, but the language of enzymes has not been fully translated.

Though the fact of embryonic development from a single cell is commonplace knowledge, that it is done by the chemically guided interaction of cell molecules is almost unbelievable. Yet no other power can be invoked, no outside force normally affects the embryo. Though the chemical basis of embryogeny may be a mystery beyond our comprehension, we have to accept it as a fact. It makes us one with the physical universe. Without DNA we might still be one-celled animals.

When the embryo is once established, DNA seems to delegate its authority largely to *organizers*. An organizer is any part of the embryo that induces a neighboring part to develop in a particular way. The effective chemical substance emitted by an organizer is called an *evocator*. That chemicals can produce specific forms of growth in living tissue is clearly demonstrated in the formation of plant galls by insects. Something injected into the plant by the female insect when she inserts her eggs, or something excreted by the larvae, causes an abnormal growth of the plant tissue into a gall specific of the insect species that caused it.

CELL MOVEMENTS

The free-living Protozoa are one-celled motile animals; in fact it is because of their movements that we recognize them as living things. Simplest of them is the amoeba, a minute shapeless mass of protoplasm, and yet it moves, ingests particles from the water, digests and assimilates those of food value, ejects the others, reacts to external stimuli, and reproduces itself. The amoeba thus performs all the essential functions of the higher animals, but does them in a very much simpler manner.

The amoeba moves in any direction by throwing out fingerlike processes of its body called pseudopodia. Since it can project pseudopods from any part of its body, it has no permanent anterior or posterior end. If it comes into contact with a solid object, it turns one way or another, just as would any other living animal. But what is life in such a simple creature? The experimentalists tell us (see Meier and Schneirla, 1935, pp. 14–23) that in response to the stimulus of touch on the amoeba a chemical reaction is produced that sets up currents in the body protoplasm resulting in the extension of a pseudopod and movement of the body. According to the strength of the stimulus, movement may be toward or away from the point of stimulation. Forward movement is explained by Allen (1962) as due to contraction of the pseudopods. If this is animal life in its simplest manifestation, it is little more than chemical and physical reactions induced in a plastic substance by external stimuli. Other protozoa have become more complex in structure and have developed specific motor organs in the form of vibratile cilia or flagella.

The protozoa all move by some visible motor mechanism, but some cells in the tissue of plants or animals have been described as simply moving in a purposeful direction without giving any evidence of how they do it. Several examples of this are given by Lewis (1940). One is that of spicule-carrying cells in sponges, described by Schröder (1936). The primary spicule is formed as an axial filament in the cytoplasm of a cell, which then dies. Another silica-containing cell now comes up and discharges its silica on the young spicule, which is thus increased in thickness. Other cells then attach themselves to the spicule and transport it to its proper place in the sponge body. It would be useless to ask what motivates or operates these transporting cells.

A still more remarkable example of activity in tissue cells has been ascribed to the flatworm *Microstomum*, described by Lewis from the studies of Kepner, Gregory, and Porter (1938). The worm eats the green fresh-water hydra and ingests its nematocysts (epidermal cells with projectile threads). The hydra possesses four kinds of nematocysts, in two of which the threads are stinging, a third kind adhesive, and the fourth grasping. All four kinds of nematocysts are taken into the stomach of the worm and penetrate through the stomach wall into the parenchyma. Here the non-stinging nematocysts are digested and absorbed as being of no use to the worm. The stinging nematocysts, however, are transported by certain parenchyma cells to the epidermis, where they are oriented with the threads directed outward. At the point of contact of each nematocyst with an epidermal cell, the latter becomes pitted internally and externally to allow the discharge of the nematocyst thread. Thus *Microstomum* arms itself with the stinging nematocysts of the hydra as weapons for its own defense. After 100 hours all ingested nematocysts are ready for action, but when the epidermis is fully loaded, the superfluous nematocysts are retained in the stomach and thrown out of the mouth.

"Thus it becomes evident," the authors point out, "that endoderm, parenchyma, and epidermis of microstomum cooperate in the manipulation of hydra's nematocysts." "In all this conduct," according to the senior author, "physical and chemical factors are involved, but some organizer appears to be directing these factors." The "organizer," however, does not visibly appear, nor is it evident what the motor force of the transporting cells may be, even if their activities are directed by an organizer. A further mystery is: how did these coordinated activities originate in the evolutionary history of *Microstomum*, and then become transmitted by heredity? Some zoologists are reluctant to accept this story of *Microstomum* and the nematocysts of hydra, but Lewis (1940) and Tinbergen (1951) quote it without comment.

INSTINCT

A primarily distinctive quality of animals is mobility, only a few having adopted secondarily a sedentary life by attachment to a support. A moving animal encounters differences in the environment, some of which are advantageous to it and others harmful. Movement, therefore, must be capable of regulation. In some way the animal must be sensitive to environmental conditions, and its sensory impressions must be transmitted to the motor system.

The simplest animal movements are those of the Protozoa. They include avoiding reactions to obstructions, the avoidance of unfavorable chemical conditions in the water, and in some cases reaction to light. The protozoa move either by changes in the shape of the body or by the action of external cilia or flagella. Yet they have no specific sense organs, nervous system, or muscles; the one-celled body evidently acts in all three capacities.

The many-celled animals have a great advantage in the potentiality for cell differentiation. This has enabled them to develop specific sensory, conductive, and motor tissues along with efficient organs of locomotion. Their capacity for varied movements, therefore, is practically unlimited. In the lower Metazoa, probably including all the invertebrates, the sensory-nervous-muscular circuit works automatically in response to a sensory stimulus. The resulting behavior of the animal is called *instinct*. Instincts, thus, having a purely physical basis, are acquired by structural inheritance, are not learned, and require no act of consciousness on the part of the animal. Instincts are present also in all the higher animals, but in the vertebrates, with the development of the forebrain, the faculty of consciousness appears, leading to intelligence, and instincts become of less and less importance, until in man they are all but suppressed. Animals guided by instinct seldom make mistakes, but they cannot adjust their actions to changed conditions. Animals with intelligence, on the other hand, are prone to make mistakes or to do the wrong thing, but they *can* correct their errors and adjust their actions to circumstances.

Tinbergen (1951) in his book on "instinct" discusses animal behavior that subserves the individual, such as locomotion, feeding, avoidance of danger, fighting, and reproduction. Activities of this nature are mostly direct reflexes to stimuli and might be termed *instincts of intrinsic behavior* because they have to do with the welfare and life of the individual. On the other hand, many animals have constructive instincts for nest-building, cocoon-spinning, web-making, etc. Such instincts may be distinguished as *instincts of extrinsic behavior*. They are comparable to tool-making, house-building, and the manufacture of mechanical appliances by the human species. As a third class of instincts we might include the migratory drive of some animals, such as that of the eels, the salmon, many birds, and some insects.

Intrinsic behavior is common to all animals, varying according to the habits, structure, and sensory equipment of each species. Extrinsic instincts are most highly developed in the insects, spiders, birds, and some mammals. It is of particular interest because the constructural procedure of the animal often closely resembles human workmanship, and yet is unlearned and acquired by heredity.

Examples of extrinsic instinct among the insects are so well known they scarcely need to be cited. They include the familiar cocoon-spinning of the caterpillars, nest-building by the wasps, comb-making by the honey bees, and the construction of above-ground nests by some termites.

The spiders have long been famous for their spinning of silken webs. The types of webs vary from the too familiar formless mass of threads spun by the house spider to the flat orbs of the outdoor garden spiders. Each species of the latter, as noted by Crompton (1950), builds one fixed pattern of web, but the talents of the different species vary. A relatively simple example of a flat web is that of *Hyptiotes paradoxus*, which is a triangle with two inner radii diverging from the apex, and the interradial spaces filled with cross-threads. The spider's method of making this web is described in detail by Peters (1938), who shows that the spider follows a complex but entirely orderly plan of construction. Clearly she "knows" in advance what the completed web must be like and exactly how to make it. As many separate acts are involved as there are threads in the web, and yet the spider goes from one to the next as if she carries the whole plan in her mind. Still more elaborate and complex are the orb webs of *Aranea*, but even in the spinning of these webs the spider is just as competent and methodical as *Hyptiotes*.

A human workman making a fabric as intricate as a spider's web would have to learn in advance how to do the job, or he first would work out a plan in his mind or on paper. Then he would consciously direct the action of his arms and fingers for each phase of the work. The spider, on the other hand, never learned how to spin a web, or how to make one of the particular pattern characteristics of her species. Yet to all appearances she regulates her actions just as does the human workman. She is assumed to work automatically like a machine, with no consciousness to direct her operations. Yet at the end of one act something shifts her nerve impulses to the muscles proper for the next act in the series that leads to the completed web.

In some ways other than web-spinning *Aranea* seems to show something resembling intelligence. When an insect lands in the web, the spider comes out of her retreat to inspect it and takes action according to the nature of the captive or its display of activity. An ordinary fly she carries off at once and makes quick work of it. In the case of a grasshopper she is more cautious and deliberates before acting. Then, according to Crompton (1950), she directs the end of her abdomen toward the grasshopper and throws out a mass of silk, not in the form of threads but as a sheet that completely enswathes the victim, which now bound and helpless the spider drags to her retreat and leisurely feeds on its blood. A wasp or a bee is first examined with suspicious caution. The wasp, evidently recognized as dangerous, is either cut out of the web or allowed to escape by its own efforts; a bee may be successfully wrapped up and carried off. Such acts on the part of the spider look like reasoned judgment, but since the spider is not supposed to have reason, her behavior must be merely reactions according to the nature of the visual stimulus. The spider presumably receives a different ocular stimulus from the fly, the grasshopper, or the wasp, each of which activates an appropriate set of muscles. If we accept this explanation we are faced with the question as to how the nerve connections are prearranged in advance to give the proper response. Either the spider deceives us in appearing to act as if she has some slight degree of intelligence, or we deceive ourselves in thinking that she has none.

The ground-living wolf spider, *Lycosa*, spins no web to entangle her prey, but she encloses her eggs in a silken cocoon, which she attaches to her body and drags with her wherever she goes until the young hatch. As observed by Crompton (1950) the mother *Lycosa* now appears to have such a sentimental attachment to her ball of eggs that she will fight to the death to retain it. Yet she does not know her own cocoon from that of another spider, since she will readily accept a substitute, or even an artificial cocoon made of cork. Clearly the female *Lycosa* does not know that the cocoon she so sedulously guards contains the eggs that will guarantee the perpetuation of her species. Her apparent emotional attachment to the cocoon is merely a temporary physiological condition necessary for the security of the eggs during the incubation period, comparable to the development of the milk glands and the physical modification of the uterus during pregnancy in a mammal. In neither case is "maternal instinct" involved.

The moth caterpillar is another noted silk-spinner. Its spinning apparatus is operative from the time it leaves the egg, but only when the caterpillar comes to the end of its feeding life does some internal condition dictate the spinning of a cocoon. Now, without any preliminary practice, each caterpillar knows just how to construct a cocoon like that of its predecessors in which to await its dissolution in the pupa. The cocoon is for the protection of the pupa in which the adult moth will be formed.

Notwithstanding all that has been written on the subject of animal instinct, the physical mechanism of instinctive behavior is still unknown. Simple instincts may be mere reflexes to stimuli, but complex instincts of action and construction, involving a series of coordinated reflexes, are not easily explainable. A single neuromuscular arc may serve for a simple reflex, but it is hardly to be supposed that a complex instinct involves the presence of as many preformed circuits as there are separate acts in the performance. The spinning spider, then, would have to be a complete, automatic web-making machine constructed to run through the whole series of acts involved in spinning the web. Yet the spider has only one set of muscles, and a different action of the same muscles would have to be stimulated for each act. It would seem, therefore, that there must be some mechanism in the central nervous system that determines the muscular reaction for each stimulus. This may be what has been called the "innate releasing mechanism," but giving something a name does not explain what it is.

Some biologists do not like the term "instinct" because it cannot be defined and is often used to mean some mysterious inner sense of the animal. Yet the word is indispensable for convenience in writing about animal behavior; at least it stands for visible facts.

As we ascend the ranks of the animal kingdom instinct plays an ever-decreasing role until in man it is almost abolished, except for a few acts such as grasping and sucking during infancy. Among the birds, however, instincts for nest-building are equal to anything in the insect world or the web-spinning of the spiders. Many of the smaller rodents dig burrows that are specific of their kind, and the beaver is noted for the construction of dams and the building of houses. The house cat, though she has no idea of sanitation, carefully covers her voided feces when out of doors, and will go through the motions even on a wooden floor. Kittens in their play stalk each other and crouch for a final spring, just as did their unknown ancestors hunting prey in the wild.

Finally there is the seeming mystery of instinct inheritance. If, however, instinct depends, as it somehow must, on physical structure and organization, it is no more inherited as such than are physiological activities, which are functions of inheritable physical organs.

CONSCIOUSNESS

The spoken pronoun "I" usually does not refer to the physical body of the speaker, but to an abstract feeling of conscious individuality that is he himself. Yet no amount of introspection will reveal to us what our consciousness is. Small wonder then that the concept of human duality has long prevailed, that a nonmaterial spirit, soul, or *psyche* resides within our physical bodies, which receives sensations from the outer world, is master of the body, thinks, and gives orders to our muscles. All this, however, from a strictly scientific viewpoint is a creation of the imagination; "spirit" and "soul" are mere words without intelligible definitions. Biologically, we might ask how could an immaterial nothing be duplicated from generation to generation? If the mind is not a function of something material, there is no known mechanism of psychic inheritance, or of mental evolution from ape to man.

Since even the strongest advocates of duality of mind and body cannot explain what they mean by consciousness, some psychologists, as Watson (1930), practically deny the existence of consciousness, and hence that it can dictate our actions. The creed of the behaviorists is "Every human action is a mechanical reflex response to a stimulus." Physiology, according to Mitchell (1923), has for its final goal "nothing less than a complete interpretation of life phenomena in terms applicable to nonliving mechanisms — in short, a physico-chemical explanation of life." He admits, however, the goal is yet far away and dim. Lashley (1923) points out that the mechanistic view of human behavior conforms with the general principles of physical mechanics, and makes the animal no exception. The human body, it is argued, is a physical mechanism and must be subject to the laws of mechanics. Therefore, according to this view an immaterial "mind" or "consciousness" cannot modify or guide the actions of the body.

This argument does not seem to negate the existence of consciousness; it simply denies that consciousness has any activating function, and reduces it to brain action accompanying physical activities. According to Herrick (1924) disembodied functions are not recognized in biology as causes of anything. "It is the functioning organ which is the cause, and it seems to be at least a plausible inference that the observed effects of mind on body are in reality effects of one functioning organ (the brain thinking) on other parts of the body." "Consciousness, then, is a factor in behavior, a real cause of human conduct, and probably to some extent in that of other animals."

There can be no doubt that the seat of consciousness is the brain. Consciousness is totally abolished by serious injury to the brain, or by shutting off the blood supply to it. Consciousness is aroused, except by abnormal conditions in the brain itself, only by the discharge of sensory nerve impulses into the brain cortex. Troland (1926) believes that consciousness is generated in the nerve association centers (synapses) that occupy most of the cortex. However, we do not locate our feeling of consciousness in the brain. A pain, for example, is felt at the point of physical injury, but if the nerves to the brain are deadened by an anesthetic we do not feel a surgical operation or the pulling of a tooth. In the same way our other sensory perceptions are projected to the objects or conditions that stimulate the sense organs. Consciousness is the perception of what we see, hear, or feel. Yet the brain action, whatever it may be, is essential to the conscious sensation.

Human consciousness, then, is merely a mental experience generated in the brain by nerve impulses from the sense organs. A nerve impulse is a wave of metabolism propagated through the nerve, accompanied by an electrical disturbance, and is the same from whatever sense organ it is engendered. The nerve structure may be adapted to its function, but the resulting form of consciousness depends on the particular brain center to which the nerve goes. Our conscious perceptions correspond with the varieties of sense organs we possess.

Our ordinary state of consciousness, when nothing disturbs us, is the sum of all sensory impressions external and internal received at any one time. If the sensory nerves gradually cease to convey messages, we fall asleep and consciousness disappears.

With most of us awareness of our surroundings seems so real that we cannot doubt the reality of consciousness, if only as a sensation. Surely, pain, fear, anger, pleasure are states of consciousness that may induce muscular movements, but few of us can be convinced that our everyday acts are not consciously dictated. Yet we do not know how we perform actions that we ascribe to intent. Picking up a pencil from the table, for example, seems to be a perfectly simple voluntary act, but the human arm, shoulder, hand, and fingers contain more than 40 muscles, and we do not know what muscles we use, or how they are stimulated and coordinated in action to carry out the dictates of our "will."

Though we must admit, then, that consciousness is real and is somehow a product of brain activity, by no effort of the imagination can we understand it. As said by Sperry (1952): "Despite steady advancement in our knowledge of the brain, the intrinsic nature of mind and its relation to cerebral excitation remains as much an enigma today as it was a hundred years ago." The histologists have found no correlation between the histological structure of the brain centers and the conscious sensations aroused in them. As noted by Sperry, "Present-day science is quite at a loss even to begin to describe the neural events involved in the simplest forms of mental activity." The physiologists know what goes on in our visceral organs; they have not yet been able to fully explore the secrets of the brain.

It must be noted that our forms of consciousness resulting from sensory stimuli give us little or no information about the nature of the stimuli. From our sensation of illumination and color, for example, we should never know that physical light is vibrations of something traversing space that impinge on the eye. What we call sound is a form of consciousness generated by propagated waves of air. Some people, therefore, cannot understand that there is no sound without an ear to hear it. So with odor and taste, which in consciousness are sensations produced by chemical substances.

Truly, in our consciousness we live in a world that does not conform with reality. Only the primitive sense of touch gives us some
information about the nature of the object felt, its shape, size, and
whether it is hard, soft, smooth, or rough.

Consciousness in ourselves has come to be more than the regis-
tration of sensory stimuli. It is also the medium of imagination,
memory, and reason. This group of faculties constitutes intelligence, and greatly complicates the efforts of the psychologists to
rationalize our mental life according to any theory. It is much
easier to understand how we see than how we think. There is no
doubt that intelligence has developed with the evolution of the
vertebrate forebrain, but it is scarcely perceptible below the mammals. The higher mammals can learn by "trial and error," and they
exhibit many human emotions, but it is highly doubtful that any
but the human species is capable of abstract reasoning.

It is a long-disputed and still unanswered question as to where
consciousness begins in the animal kingdom. Since pain is a most
acute form of consciousness, it would seem reasonable to believe
that any animal that gives vocal evidence of feeling pain must
have consciousness. This would include the mammals and birds
and perhaps the frogs, but lack of a voice can hardly be taken as
evidence of insensitivity to pain. We cannot positively assert that
the higher invertebrates do not have some dim awareness of their
surroundings or of their actions. It is hard to imagine that an insect or a spider, for example, is merely a mechanism responding
automatically to stimuli that in us generate consciousness. Consciousness in other animals, however, is beyond experimental investigation, and probably will long remain a secret of the animals
themselves.

The greatest literary crime that can be brought against a writer
on animal behavior is indulgence in anthropomorphism — the at-
tributing to animals of human motives and reason. Yet there is
plenty of animalism in the human species, and some recent accounts of animals in nature, such as that of the African lioness by
Adamson (1960, 1961) and of the otter by Maxwell (1961), suggest
that animals may be more human than we have been willing to
admit. After all, we have a common ancestry.

Since most of our body structures and our mental faculties have been evolved from our animal progenitors, it is reasonable to suppose that the sensation of awareness arose in some form of life much lower in the scale of evolution than ourselves. Perhaps consciousness began as an adjunct to instinct, but having a high survival value of its own, it underwent evolutionary improvement, gradually eliminating the need of instinct. Finally, consciousness became the basis of the higher mental faculties, and set us apart, at least some of us, from all the other animals.

REFERENCES

ADAMSON, JOY. 1960. Born free. A lioness of two worlds. 220 pp., numerous photographs. New York.
    1961. Living free. The story of *Elsa* and her cubs. 161 pp., numerous photographs. New York.
ADLER, I. 1957. How life began. 128 pp., ills. New York.
ALLEN, R. D. 1962. Amoeboid movement. Scientific American, February 1962, pp. 112–122.
BONNER, D. M. 1962. Heredity. 112 pp., 41 figs. Englewood Cliffs, N.J.
CROMPTON, J. 1950. The life of the spider. 192 pp., 23 figs. New York.
FISCHBERG, M., and BLACKLER, A. W. 1961. How cells specialize. Scientific American, September 1961, pp. 124–140.
GAMOW, G. 1952. The creation of the universe. 147 pp., 40 text figs., 11 pls. New York.
HERRICK, C. J. 1924. Neurological foundations of animal behavior. 334 pp., 131 figs. New York.
JACOB, F., and WOLLMAN, E. L. 1961. Viruses and genes. Scientific American, June 1961.
JEANS, J. 1929. The universe around us. 341 pp., 24 pls., 24 figs. New York and Cambridge.
KEPNER, W. A., GREGORY, W. C., and PORTER, R. J. 1938. The manipulation of the nematocysts of Chlorohydra by microstomum. Zool. Anz., vol. 121, pp. 114–124, 4 figs.
LASHLEY, K. S. 1923. The behavioristic interpretation of consciousness I, II. Psychol. Rev., vol. 30, No. 4, pp. 237–277; No. 5, pp. 329–355.
LEHRMAN, R. L. 1961. The long road to man. 192 pp., 53 figs.
LEWIS, I. F. 1940. Cell reactions. Amer. Naturalist, vol. 74, pp. 97–106.
MAXWELL, G. 1961. Ring of bright water. 211 pp., numerous illustrations. New York.
MAZIA, D. 1953. Cell division. Scientific American, August 1953.
MEIER, N. R. F., and SCHNEIRLA, T. C. 1935. Principles of animal psychology. 529 pp., 107 figs. New York and London.
MITCHELL, P. H. 1923. A text book of general physiology. 748 pp., 174 figs. New York.
MOSKIN, J. R. 1962. In the next twenty-five years, man will master the secret of creation. Look, special issue, January 1962, pp. 44, 46.

NEEDHAM, J. 1942. Biochemistry and morphogenesis. xvi+787 pp., 328 figs. Cambridge Univ. Press.

OPARIN, A. I. 1938. The origin of life. 270 pp., 8 figs. New York.

1961. Life, origin of. The Encyclopedia of the Biological Sciences (ed., Peter Gray), pp. 561–563.

PETERS, H. 1938. Über das Netz der Dreickspinne, *Hyptiotcs paradoxus*. Zool. Anz., vol. 121, pp. 49–59, 5 figs.

PLATT, R. 1961. When life on earth began. Reader's Digest, December 1961, pp. 194–200.

SCHRÖDER, K. 1936. Beiträge zur Kenntnis der Spicularbildung, der Larven-spiculation und der Variationsbreite der Gerüstnadeln von Süsswasser-schwämmen. Zeitschr. Morph. Ökol. Tiere, vol. 31, pp. 245–267, 24 figs.

SPERRY, R. W. 1952. Neurology and the mind-brain problem. Amer. Scientist, vol. 40, No. 2, pp. 291–311.

TINBERGEN, N. 1951. The study of instinct. 228 pp., 130 figs. Oxford.

TROLAND, L. T. 1926. The mystery of mind. 253 pp., 22 figs. New York.

UREY, H. C. 1952. The planets: their origin and development, xvii+245 pp., 16 figs., photograph of the moon. Yale Univ. Press.

WALD, G. 1954. The origin of life. Scientific American, vol. 191, August 1954, pp. 44–53.

WATSON, J. B. 1930. Behaviorism. 308 pp., 23 figs. New York.

DONALD M. MacKAY

What Is Cybernetics?

[FROM THE SMITHSONIAN REPORT FOR 1963]

CYBERNETICS *is one of the new sciences to appear during the 20th century. It was defined a few years after the close of World War II as the science of control and communication in the animal and the machine, thus relating it closely to engineering. In both animal (including man) and machine, the method of obtaining effective action depends basically upon the "feedback" principle. The essence of this principle is simply a link which will reduce the supply when an indicator reads "excess" and vice versa. Of course, for complex electronic applications such as the automatic guidance of a missile, only an electronic computer possesses sufficient flexibility and speed to replace the human brain. The author of this article, Donald M. MacKay, is a physicist who began his career in radar research with the British Admiralty during World War II. Between 1946 and 1950 he was concerned with the early development of Information Theory and of high-speed analog computing techniques, which led to his present interest in the information-processing mechanisms of the nervous system, and the theory of automata with comparable functions. Since 1960 he has been Professor of Communication in the University of Keele, Staffordshire, England. He points out that the very exacting function of com-*

puters, particularly in space vehicles, is bringing about the development of machines that can upon occasion change their own connections or instructions. Such automatic action can be compared to the work of the human brain, and Dr. MacKay concludes with a discussion of the propriety (or impropriety) of regarding human beings as "cybernetic mechanisms."

A RAILWAY TRAIN needs no steering gear. The forces required to correct for the buffetings of wind and way are supplied automatically, by the sideways reaction of the rails against the wheel flanges. A ship, lacking such implicit means of guidance, requires a helm, normally controlled by a *helmsman*. The Latin for helmsman is *gubernator;* the Greek, *kybernētēs*. From the first comes our word *governor*. From the second, in 1843, André Ampère derived the term *cybernetics (la cybernétique)*, to denote the *science of government*.

In 1948, Norbert Wiener of the Massachusetts Institute of Technology independently proposed the same term for *The Science of Control and Communication in the Animal and the Machine*, as the title of a book whose repercussions are among the remarkable scientific phenomena of our century. Just as it appeared, the war-born art of eliminating the human element in military missiles was being rapidly adapted to peaceful applications in all manner of industrial fields, aided by the explosive postwar development of electronic computing techniques. At the same time the physiologists and students of animal behavior, many of them fresh from wartime experience in radar and electronics, were alive as never before to the possibilities of explaining all bodily activity – even at the human level – in terms of hierarchies of "self-guided" mechanisms. In the ferment of ideas thus generated, the growing realization that scientists in these widely separated areas had a common problem was due in no small measure to Wiener's book.

What, then, is this common problem? In brief, it is to understand (or procure) the organization of effective action – of all processes, whether artificial or natural, in which goals, ends, standards are sought or maintained, and unacceptable states or events avoided. As a discipline, cybernetics thus belongs to the same family as engineering, and no sharp lines can be drawn between the two.

What characterizes cybernetics, however, is the generality of its ideas. Whereas much of engineering, or cell biology, or neurophysiology, or economics, is necessarily concerned with particular problems of energy-transport, or biochemistry, or finance, the cyberneticist is concerned only with those abstract features, common to systems in all fields, by virtue of which effective action is organized.

To bring out some of these essential features, let us first look at our helmsman. Basically, the chain of events by which the ship's course is governed has three stages, which we may call *indication* (of disparity between actual and desired course), *calculation* (of form of action required to diminish disparity), and *selection* (of the helm-position calculated to be appropriate). As a result of his action, the indication will generally alter, so that we have here a "closed loop" of cause and effect — the so-called "feedback loop" which is a feature of all self-regulating, as distinct from merely physically constrained, mechanisms.

Cybernetics is built upon the realization that each of the foregoing stages can in principle be mechanized. The compass, the ball-float, the centrifugal governor, and the bimetallic thermometer are long-familiar examples of sensitive devices whose mechanical output can indicate the disparity between the present state of some quantity (direction, water level, speed, or temperature) and some preset "goal state." Rudders, water cocks, steam valves, and furnace regulators are even older examples of the third stage in the regulative chain.

What is new in scale (though not so new in principle) is the mechanization of the second stage — the process of calculation. Although a mechanical general-purpose computer was devised by Charles Babbage in the middle of the 19th century, it was only the advent of electronics that gave such devices the speed and capacity needed to replace the human brain in organizing complex regulative actions. For the simplest type of ball-cock, steam-governor, or thermostat, the only "calculator" required is a simple mechanical link between indicator and control, so that supply is reduced when the indicator reads "excess."

For a self-guided missile, or a "self-optimizing" chemical process-controller, on the other hand, the calculating mechanism must continually modify and supplement the link between the indicator and the selector of action, in accordance with a multitude of other data from auxiliary receptor-organs and from the past as recorded in its storage devices.

In still more complex automata now envisaged, the repertoire of action includes means of changing the pattern of instructions or connections within the automaton itself — a kind of gear-changing operation on its own logical machinery. In this way by "trial and error" (a form of intelligent natural selection), as well as by calculation, it develops within itself the organizing routines and "conditioned reflexes" found necessary in the course of past interaction with its field of activity. The scope of "artificial intelligence" along these lines is virtually unlimited in principle. It is thus hardly surprising that cybernetics in popular thought is so closely identified today with the theory of computers.

The earliest and most characteristic mathematical developments in cybernetics, however (in a paper by J. Clerk Maxwell in 1868), were concerned with a more central problem — that of warding off *instability.* In any closed cycle of control, if the response to control is too sluggish or too violent, it is fatally easy for the system to become unstable, overcorrecting itself in a series of wild swings in opposite directions, called "hunting." Although the mathematics of unstable behavior has mostly been developed for "linear" systems (those whose responses change in strict proportion to changes in input), there are a number of general principles and rules of thumb which invite application in a wide range of fields at present plagued by instability. These include, for example, keeping the *number* of stages in a chain as small as possible; reducing *sensitivity* to the minimum acceptable; and combatting sluggishness by taking *rates of change* of indication as a guide to action.

The second great area of mathematical development specific to cybernetics has become known as Information Theory. To control a task of a given complexity to a given accuracy, in an environment with given statistical features, how much information does a cybernetic governor need? The theory of information sets out to make such questions precise, and to give mathematical answers to them. Thanks largely to the work of C. E. Shannon, it has been generalized to enable communication engineers to evaluate and compare the channel capacities of different encoding or transmitting systems, and to take precise account of the effects of random disturbance, or "noise." Even more important, it has shown how statistical correlation between different elements of a signal ("redundancy") can be used to enable random errors in transmission to be detected and corrected, so that a "noisy" channel can — in principle, and given a long enough run for statistical purposes — transmit up to a definite rate with arbitrarily little error.

Once again it should be added, however, that in the bulk of cybernetic investigations to date it is the *qualitative* notions of information theory — information, encoding, noise, redundancy, channel capacity, error-correction — rather than its mathematical apparatus, which have so far found illuminating uses. No one interested in the cybernetic approach should be frightened off, or unduly impressed, by sprinkled references to unfamiliar mathematics in the somewhat uneven literature of the field. With few exceptions to date, their function will turn out to be decorative rather than pivotal.

We have confined discussion thus far to examples of natural and artificial helmsmanship — control under the guidance of information. This is what the term "cybernetics" was coined to denote, in contradistinction to the older method of physical constraint typified by our railway example. Unfortunately the popularity of the term has led to its being used in some quarters to include situations of the opposite sort — those where no element of information-guided selection is present, but (as with the railway) the necessary corrective forces depend wholly on the inertial reaction of the situation where they are required. Thus a pendulum, or a ball at the bottom of a bowl, is described by some writers as a cybernetic system under "feedback," because it automatically suffers a force opposed to its displacement from equilibrium. Even such lowly forms as the reaction of a floor to the weight of an object placed on it cannot then be excluded. It is gradually being realized that such usage trivializes the term; but for the present at least the reader must expect to find it sometimes used in confusing and even contradictory senses.

Behind the confusion there is in fact an interesting ambiguity in the cybernetic approach — in the very nature of control itself. The cybernetician seeking to understand a complex system begins by trying to discern the "pattern of subordination" — asking "which controls what?" The difficulty is to define "control." Everyone would agree that a watercock controls the flow of water into a cistern; but if two cisterns are connected together, so that the level in each affects the level in the other, can we say that one controls the other? However we decide, there is obviously an important difference between the two cases. The second shows no more than a passive tendency to equilibrium between action and reaction; but the first includes an "active" element (the cock plus water supply) whose control lever determines the flow of water without itself suffering appreciable reaction.

Suppose now that we link the cock lever to a ball floating on the water, as in the familiar ball-cock. What now controls the level of the water? In one sense, we may still say "the cock"; but in another and more important sense, it is not now the cock per se, but its height above tank bottom, which (other things being equal) governs the final water level. If we had means of raising and lowering the whole watercock-and-ball assembly, this would enable us to select the water level at which the cock would turn itself off.

What this example makes clear, I think, is the subtle and arbitrary human element that underlies many cybernetic notions. Basically, by saying that A controls B we mean that if *we* could control A then *we* could control B. In a strictly physical sense, divorced from the human notion of "purpose," the notion of control tends to be ambiguous or meaningless. The only objective physical distinction we can firmly draw is between (1) devices, such as watercocks, steamvalves, transistors, and rudders, where the input, A, determines the form of the output, B, without supplying all the energy of B; and (2) devices such as transmission lines, levers, springs and gear trains, where the energy of B is totally provided from the energy of A. In the first case, the energy of A is at least partly devoted to altering the structure through which the energy for B is channeled — altering the coupling between the output, B, and its internal energy supply. In the second, no analogous process occurs. In the first case a cybernetician would say that A exerts "active control" over B. In the second (if we wish) we may speak of "passive control"; though to some of us it would here seem clearer to speak simply of action and reaction.

The important point is that in cybernetics we are concerned with the action of *form* upon *form* rather than of *force* upon *force*. The rigorous theory of such processes is still in its infancy, and a good deal of what is offered today under the aegis of cybernetics necessarily has little behind it but sanctified common sense (and not always that!).

What light do all these developments throw on our understanding of biological processes? As current scientific literature shows, they have suggested fruitful questions right down to the level of the components and chemistry of the individual cell, where both informational and cybernetic notions crop up. With the still more complex structure of the brain, our problem is to find any set of manageable abstractions whose interaction may be studied with profit.

Here the role of cybernetic models is often misunderstood. It is not a question of finding some artificial system that will behave externally in the same way as the brain. Superficial resemblances of this sort can be a curse to the theoretical neurologist. As in all scientific research, the role of a model is to serve as a kind of template, which we hold up against the real thing in order that any discrepancies may stand out more clearly, and guide us toward the making of a better one. We judge a model to be useful, therefore, not merely by its predictive successes, but also by the clarity with which its failures can be interpreted, and lead to its refinement. Only the unexpected yields fresh information; and even this is informative only when we know what to make of it — hence the crucial importance of disciplining our models as far as possible by the structural realities of the system we want to understand. The so-called "black box" approach may serve well enough in "human engineering"; but, especially if we want our models to account for pathological as well as normal conditions, our progress in science is soon halted, if not totally misdirected, unless we work hand-in-hand with those who lift the lids and peer inside.

Finally, what of the future of "cybernetic machinery"? Already, we know enough to say that any pattern of behavior which can be precisely specified — including the sorts of behavior that we would normally classify as "intelligent," "insightful," "recognitive," "purposeful" and so forth — can in principle be shown by an artificial mechanism, embodying only known processes. Some of us are developing ways of enabling such mechanisms to grow and modify parts of their own internal wiring as a result of experience. The design of artificial limbs, speech organs, and mechanisms of visual and auditory form-perception are all likely to make rapid progress in the next decade. Many of these and other developments will be linked with prosthetics — the effort to replace human faculties lost by disease or damage.

This prospect, though (like that of space travel 20 years ago) it may savor of science fiction, inevitably raises two serious questions. The first is whether we are now in a position (in principle — blessed phrase!) to synthesize fully human behavior. The answer, quite shortly, is "no." Those aspects of human behavior that we understand well enough to specify exactly can indeed be mechanized, given enough time and space and computer capacity. But mechanization, impracticably complex though it would be, is not the real problem. The fundamental limit to our power of synthesizing human behavior is precisely in our own understanding of what it is to be human. That this is incomplete at present needs no demonstration. That it could ever be otherwise — even in principle —I personally take leave to doubt.

The second question is whether by implication we are now entitled to regard natural human beings as "no more than" cybernetic mechanisms. This question is ambiguous. It may be asking whether the human brain-plus-body can be regarded as no more than a cybernetic mechanism. In that case, although our ignorance of brain mechanisms still far exceeds our knowledge, most scientists today would, I think, answer with a cautious affirmative. What they would emphasize is the astronomical complexity of any mechanism (whether we call it cybernetic or not) embodying 10,000 million cells, each of which is itself bafflingly complex.

There is, however, a quite different idea which is so often ex-

ILLUS. 75—*Common features of the "effective actions" shown here and in Illus. 77 illustrate the generality of the cybernetic approach. Both involve "indication, calculation and selection," though in contrast to missile, chameleon's action is largely precomputed. Precomputed guidance is also used in mechanical systems. (Photos from* Zoo Quest to Madagascar, *Lutterworth Press.)*

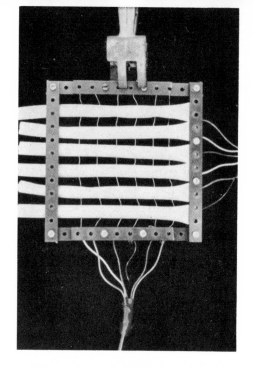

ILLUS. 76—*These photos symbolize three stages in the advance of control systems.* BOTTOM, RIGHT: *This steam-engine governor, photographed in motion at the Science Museum, London, is one of the*

earliest examples of a practical automatic control system. Using the engine's output (speed) to control the energy input to the engine, it foreshadows the use of the feedback, so fundamental to modern control systems and to cybernetics. (Photo Patrick Thurston.) FAR LEFT: *Modern test vehicle used for guidance and control experiments—sensing device at left, control devices at right. Much of remaining space is taken up by calculating devices—it is this stage of control that has developed so remarkably in modern systems. (Crown Copyright.)* TOP, RIGHT: *A look into the future of control systems. Picture of an experimental arrangement enabling an automaton to change its own pattern of connections. Vertical tubes are filled with electrolyte and serve also as "bus bars." Insulating film of oxide can be formed electrolytically on horizontal wires at points of intersection by currents passed through them, thus altering input-output relations of the network so as to match changing patterns of demand. (MacKay and Ainsworth, Brit. Pat. App. 12887/61.)*

---

pressed by asking the same question. This is the fear (or the hope, according to taste) that a complete cybernetic explanation of human bodily activity, if once we had it, would debunk any higher view of human nature, in moral or religious terms. This idea, I think, is based on a philosophical mistake — the mistaking of these higher accounts of human action and the scientific, mechanistic account as mutually exclusive *rivals,* so that if one of them were complete and correct, it would leave no room for the other. The truth seems to be that when theologians speak about moral and religious factors in human behavior, they are not talking about quasi-physical (and scientifically inexplicable) *forces* at work on the mechanism of the brain. They are referring rather to the personal significance — the point — of the activity whose mechanical aspect the scientist may successfully explain. Thus the religious account not only leaves room for the mechanistic — it leaves a need for it (and vice versa) if justice is to be done to all aspects of the human being. To rest content with the mechanistic explanation would be to miss the point, rather in the way that an electronic explanation of the activity of a computing machine (though complete in itself) would miss the point that an equation was being solved.

In this sense man remains, indeed, a mystery; but that mystery stands wholly apart from any puzzlement we feel about the mechanism of his brain.

ILLUS. 77—*These three stages of flight of three missiles show some common features with Illus. 75. But here guidance action is continually computed, controlled mainly by the error between the paths of the missile and its target. This guidance action is very similar to that of a tennis player returning a ball. (Photos: top, Crown Copyright; center, Bristol Siddeley; bottom, Bristol Aircraft.)*

GEORGE F. BASS

The Promise of Underwater Archeology

[FROM THE SMITHSONIAN REPORT FOR 1963[1]]

THE ARCHEOLOGY *of the sea bottom is strictly a 20th century branch of science. Actually only some 20 years have elapsed since the first attempt to adapt the scientific methods of field archeology to underwater sites. The invention of the aqualung turned archeologists into divers and gave them the underwater time and mobility necessary for the delicate work of mapping and salvaging ancient wrecks and their cargoes. The author, George F. Bass, Research Associate of the University Museum, University of Pennsylvania, directed the Museum's program of underwater archeology in the Mediterranean off the southwest coast of Turkey. Here a preliminary survey had revealed some 30 sunken wrecks estimated to cover a time period of about 2,000 years. Dr. Bass gives a fascinating account of the intricate methods worked out to record details of the ancient ships themselves and to salvage and preserve the cargo, including such delicate objects as pottery vessels and knife blades. He gives a complete account of the first ancient wreck thus researched, which turned out to date from around 1200 B.C.*

---

[1] Revised as of February 1965 by the insertion of an addendum at end of article. Drawings are by Eric J. Ryan of Colgate University.

Because of the intact condition of the cargo in such wrecks, it will often be possible to date them more exactly than sites excavated on land, where weathering and human interference may obliterate vital evidence.

The great historical wealth lying on the bottom of the Mediterranean has been known to archeologists only since the turn of the century. At that time a group of Greek spongedivers stumbled onto a wreck at Antikythera that yielded quantities of marble and bronze statues, pottery, glass, and a remarkable astronomical computer that has greatly increased our respect for Greek technology. After the addition of the magnificent *Antikythera Youth* to the Athens Museum, sculptures continued to come from the sea: the *Marathon Boy*, the marbles from the Piraeus harbor, the jockey and horse from Artemision, and above all the *Artemision Zeus*.

These were chance finds and, while important in themselves, their excavation can hardly be called scientific. Only with the invention of the aqualung by Cousteau and Gagnan in 1943 did divers gain the mobility necessary for the delicate work demanded by systematic archeology. Soon after, notably along the French and Italian coasts, expeditions were able to concern themselves with hull construction, methods of lading and even the daily life on ancient ships. These excavations used the technique of sketching underwater on frosted plastic, and established the airlift, a type of suction hose, as the primary excavating tool of the marine archeologist. Unfortunately, however, the supervision usually came from nondiving archeologists who could follow the work only through sketches, photographs, and, occasionally, underwater television.

The primary duty of the field archeologist is to record and present the smallest details of his excavation so that the proof of his interpretation is readily available to other scholars. At least one ancient wreck has puzzled some experts on ancient pottery who claim that various pieces of the cargo are divided by more than a century. Their thesis, that two wrecks were involved, may be denied by the excavators of the wreck, but the proof of the denial is not to be found in the excavation report since it contains not a plan or section of the material as it lay on the seabed. That two ships could fall in the same spot is not at all improbable. On the treacherous reef at Yassi Island, near ancient Halicarnassus in western Turkey, wreck is piled upon wreck, and, nearby, two marvelously preserved wrecks lie within 75 feet of each other. Methods of making accurate plans and sections under water became the pressing need.

With the development of various sounding devices, metal detectors, and small, inexpensive submarines, there can be no doubt that wrecks of all periods of antiquity will be discovered and excavated in the Mediterranean. Neolithic and early Bronze Age ships may settle forever the question of early migration routes. If middle Bronze Age peoples came to Greece by sea, we should find ships carrying the typical gray "Minyan" pottery so closely associated with them. One or two Iron Age ships may solve the problem of the ivory trade of that period, or answer the puzzle of whence came the bronze griffin heads found from Turkey to the Etruscan tombs of Italy. And, if precise methods of excavation are followed, we will learn exactly how triremes were rowed.

The University Museum of the University of Pennsylvania in 1960 undertook a program to develop the means of recording and preserving the data from such wrecks. The first step in the program was to staff the Museum's marine expeditions with the proper personnel; it was realized at once that weekend skindivers and helmeted spongedivers, who had done so much of the previous work, had no more place in such operations than they would have on land digs. The present staff consists of archeologists and archeology students, draftsmen, photographers, an architect, a marine biologist, and a medical doctor, all of whom dive and most of whom learned to dive specifically for underwater archeology. Rounding out the staff are a number of carefully selected experienced divers and mechanics. Such a staff must of necessity be larger than most found on land, for its members do the actual digging and cleaning. On land one archeologist may direct a vast crew of skilled and unskilled laborers. Underwater, however, each worker must be able to supervise himself and make sudden decisions that may radically affect the interpretation of the finds.

The areas chosen for study, along the coasts of Lycia and Caria in southwest Turkey, were charted by Peter Throckmorton. Gathering his leads while working and diving with Turkish sponge-divers, Mr. Throckmorton was able to locate about 30 wrecks covering a span of over two millennia. The first of these wrecks to be excavated was dated to the late Bronze Age by a study of the finds raised upon its discovery. It lay in 90 feet of water just off Cape Gelidonya.

A preliminary survey revealed that the wreck rested on a rocky bottom with almost no covering of sand to preserve wood and other organic material. The metal cargo was still *in situ,* but it was covered with a lime sea deposit up to 8 inches thick, and hard as concrete. The concretion presented a double problem: how to make an accurate plan of the objects imbedded in it, and how to remove and preserve fragile artifacts such as bronze knife blades and spearpoints without breaking them.

On land such problems could have been easily overcome, but on land there is not the all-important time limitation. Underwater, a diver must breathe air at the same pressure as the pressure of the water surrounding him. The deeper he goes and the longer he remains at any depth, the more pressurized nitrogen will be absorbed by his body. If the diver ascends too rapidly, the nitrogen will come out of solution with much the same effect as bubbles appearing in a bottle of champagne when it is uncorked. Such bubbles in the body may block the bloodstream in various areas, causing the crippling and often fatal divers' disease known as the bends. The only precaution is strict adherence to diving tables giving the rate of ascent following dives of various depths and duration. At Gelidonya the practical limit was only 1 hour and 8 minutes for each diver to work each day.

In order to save these precious minutes on the bottom, it was decided to cut loose lumps of concreted cargo, weighing up to 300 pounds apiece, and to raise these intact. Before being cut free with hammer and chisel, each lump was marked in several spots. These spots were triangulated with horizontal metertapes running from fixed reference points driven into the rock around the site. The triangulated points were put onto a plan and the lumps were raised to the surface with a winch and cable. In one instance wood was seen protruding from beneath a heap of concreted cargo. Winching from a small boat in a rough sea presented the real danger that this fragile evidence might be crushed. The mass of concretion was, therefore, attached to a large plastic balloon with a lifting force of 400 pounds; the balloon was inflated on the bottom from a diver's mouthpiece and carried the cargo gently to the surface.

The lumps of concretion were carried to the expedition camp and reassembled exactly as they had appeared on the seabed. Then they were cleaned with chisels so that the cargo finally lay free and could be drawn and photographed in detail. Using the points triangulated on the bottom, the architect was able to add the details to his over-all plan which now showed the position of each object as it had rested in the ancient ship. A record of the work in progress was also kept in a number of "aerial surveys." These were made by a photographer, with plumb line and level attached to his camera, swimming at a fixed distance above the wreck. The resultant series of photographs were enlarged to a set scale and glued together to form montages showing the entire site.

Such work was exceedingly slow. The jumble of wood that had been crushed beneath the cargo was the only well-preserved portion of the ship's hull. Although this covered an area of little more than a square meter, it took the entire team of divers 3 weeks to cut behind the solid rock on which it rested so that the wood fragments could be raised together and studied on land.

These fragments matched the elements used by Odysseus in making a small boat (not, it would seem, a raft) with the aid of Calypso (*Odyssey* 5.233–261). There were planks with bored holes and dowels, and at least two of the planks were joined together at their ends. On board, perhaps only as part of the cargo, were the main tools used by Odysseus: axes and adzes. Homer also tells how Odysseus made a wattle fence around his ship to keep out the waves, and then "spread out a great deal of brushwood." Because this last phrase has made little sense to classical scholars, it has been variously translated and interpreted as a brushwood bed, as part of the wattle fence or a backing for it, and even as ballast.

It would now seem that a literal translation of the passage is all that is needed. Over the planks of the Gelidonya wreck was spread a layer of brushwood, with the bark still well preserved, which served as a cushion between the heavy metal cargo and the thin hull planks.

Not enough wood was preserved to give an accurate idea of the size of the ship, but the distribution of the cargo suggests a length of not much more than 8 or 9 meters. This would easily have handled the cargo and ballast stones that were collected from the site. The cargo was almost completely of metal. More than a ton of copper and bronze objects was preserved, making this by far the largest hoard of such implements yet found by preclassical archeologists.

Forty ingots of almost pure copper, in the so-called "oxhide" shape and averaging 45 pounds apiece in weight, were found piled neatly on the site. Traces of matting indicate that these may have been wrapped together in small stacks. Over 90 of these ingots had been known previously from the late Bronze Age, appearing in Cyprus, Crete, Greece, and Sardinia, and many numismatists considered them a premonetary form of currency. Their superficial resemblance to dried oxhides had even led to the conclusion that one ingot was worth one ox. Careful study of the Gelidonya group, however, has revealed that the ingots were merely convenient forms for transporting raw copper. They have no standard weight (variations in weight among those from different sites had been attributed by some archeologists to local standards in use), and their resemblance to dried skins has been shown to be completely fortuitous. Their "legs," previously known as rather late developments in the evolution of the ingot shape, were merely handles for ease of porterage; the faces, one rough and "hairy," and the other with a rolled rim seemingly representing the curling of a dried skin are simply the result of the method of casting and the type of mold used. Dozens of ingot fragments, in small groups on the wreck, have proved by weight not to be fractional parts of whole ingots, as might be expected if the ingots were truly currency.

The use of these ingots is seen in a wall painting in the Tomb of Rekh-mi-rēʿ at Thebes. Egyptian smiths are shown melting down "oxhide" ingots to be cast with square white ingots. The obvious conclusion from this scene, that copper and tin were being mixed to form bronze, has been contested by some authorities who have thought that the white ingots must be lead. This is not as arbitrary as it might seem, for only two or three items of pure tin have been found from this early date. The Gelidonya wreck, however, yielded a number of piles of white powdery material that, after being carefully collected in plastic bags and analyzed, proved to be pure tin oxide. This proves that the previous lack of evidence of industrial tin had been due only to the fortunes of excavation. Not only may we now feel sure that the white ingots of the Egyptian tomb paintings are tin, but this discovery also adds an argument for the identification of *anāku* in the old Assyrian documents from Cappadocia as tin rather than lead.

Most of the ingots are stamped with Cypro-Minoan signs. The meaning of these letters might add greatly to our understanding of this still-undeciphered script. Only after careful analysis of each ingot will it be possible to say if the marks refer to different mines, foundries, destinations, or metal quality. Careful excavation again plays an important role. Stratigraphy, so essential for chronological conclusions in the excavation of land sites, might seem to be of little value in the study of an ancient wreck; most of the objects on a ship are contemporary. Even here, however, the general rule that "higher means later" has validity. If all of the ingots (or, in the case of other ships, wine jars or tiles) were not put on board at the same place, those lowest in the hold would have come from the earliest ports of call. Thus, if we find by analysis that the lower ingots from the Bronze Age ship seem to come from different mines than those above, it may some day be possible to trace the route of the vessel. This information, together with a study of ancient place names, might offer still another clue to the meaning of the ingot signs.

With the ingot fragments, often packed together in the same baskets, were hundreds of bronze tools, weapons, and household utensils. These included picks, hoes, axes, adzes, mirrors, bowls, chisels, knives, a hammer, a spade, and a spit. Some were complete and may have been used by the crew of the ship, but the vast majority were broken before being stored on board. One perfectly preserved wicker basket bottom was found still holding tightly packed scraps of metal. Similar founder's hoards have been found on land and it was known from these that old utensils were commonly melted and recast in Mycenaean times. A swage block and a possible stone anvil make it almost certain that a smith traveled on board the ship. Numerous whetstones, found in the "cabin" area, would have been used to sharpen newly made tools.

From the area assumed to be the cabin of the ship came such personal possessions as scarabs, weights, pottery, stone maceheads, pieces of crystal, a cylinder seal, an oil lamp, and even traces of a meal: olive pits and fish bones were found imbedded in concretion. An astragal was probably only for playing the popular ancient game of knucklebones. The only nonmetallic objects certainly not from the cabin area were two stone mortars and a jar of glass beads.

A study of the ship and its cargo allows us to reconstruct something of its history. The bits of broken pottery give a date of around 1200 B.C., when the entire eastern Mediterranean was in a state of upheaval. The main part of the cargo was certainly from Cyprus, known as the copper center of the late Bronze Age; not only the ingots, but 232 of 302 bronze objects found on board find their closest parallels on Cyprus.

Although the ship loaded its cargo in Cyprus, there is no reason to assume that it was Cypriot. Egyptian tomb paintings show both Cretan Minoans and Syrians bringing copper "oxhide" ingots to the pharaoh as tribute. The pottery seems to have a mixed background, but the lamp — the most likely of the terra cotta objects to have been a permanent item in the ship — is Syrian. Some of the weights are of a type and standard used in Egypt, Syria, and Cyprus, and tell us little. The scarabs and cylinder seal, while possibly trinkets picked up en route, seem also to be Syrian. There is also a possibility that the tin originated in Syria. Such evidence, although not conclusive, led the author to believe that we were dealing with a Syrian merchantman that had picked up its cargo in Cyprus. Since that time an analysis of the wood has shown that the hull was probably made with Syrian wood, while the brushwood, surely picked up with the metal cargo, may be Cypriot.

With the lessons learned at Gelidonya it was possible to devise more efficient methods of working underwater for the next project.

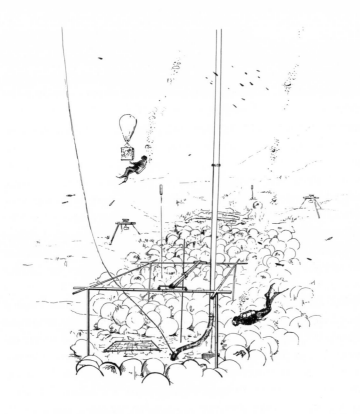

ILLUS. 78—*Mapping devices, suction hose, and lifting balloon used in excavation of Byzantine shipwreck during 1961.*

This was a Byzantine wreck lying on a slope in 100 to 130 feet of water just off Yassi Island near Bodrum. The greater depth limited daily diving times to the extent that mechanical aids, offering both speed and accuracy, became essential to the architect. Three new devices were tried (Illus. 78). The first was a pair of plane tables set on opposite sides of the wreck. Two divers, sighting through simple alidades, could record vectors and elevations on a surveying pole held by a third diver. This proved successful for over-all measurements, but demanded great clarity of the water and the use of three divers. A 5-meter square mapping frame was then placed over part of the wreck; this was leveled on its telescopic legs and positioned by the plane tables. A horizontal beam rode across the top of the frame, using two sides of the frame as tracks.

Yoked to this beam was a vertical pole that could be moved back and forth on the beam as well as up and down. The sides of the frame, the horizontal beam and the vertical pole were all calibrated in centimeters. By placing the bottom of the pole on an object, therefore, it was possible to read both coordinates and an elevation for its position. Again, too much time was taken in recording each point, so a movable, 2-meter square grid was placed on the wreck. Detailed drawings, photographs, and elevations could be made through the wires of the grid, making it necessary to record only the four corners of the grid with the mapping frame.

These aids were excellent for a beginning, but all needed refinement before being used on a detailed plan of the wooden hull that came to light under the cargo. In the second season on the Byzantine wreck a variation of the mapping frame was used (Illus. 79 and 80). This is essentially a combination of nine frames, each 2 meters by 6 meters, assembled like steps over the entire length of the wreck. Each step is horizontal and may be moved down independently of the others on its legs as the excavation goes deeper into the sand; this insures that the frames are always level and are always near the objects to be plotted beneath. A number of 2-meter square grids ride over the frames, each having three positions on each step. Thus the wreck is broken into 27 squares that can be independently excavated, drawn, and photographed. Photographic towers of light metal are bolted to the grids to insure perfect grid pictures of each area. Objects are identified in the photographs by numbered plastic tags attached to the objects on the wreck as they appear in the course of excavation. Distortion caused by the slope of the ground, which puts some objects at an appreciably lower level than the grid, must be corrected by the architect before he can use these grid photographs in making his plans and sections; lens distortion has not been significant when using the proper cameras.

Improvements in the airlift were also made. The airlift is no more than a large, vertical pipe with a flexible lower end. Air is sent to the lower end of the pipe through a hose. This air rises through the pipe, pulling water, sand, and mud with it. The airlift should be used only for removing loose sand and not, as is common, for actual excavating. Wood can be easily broken by it, and

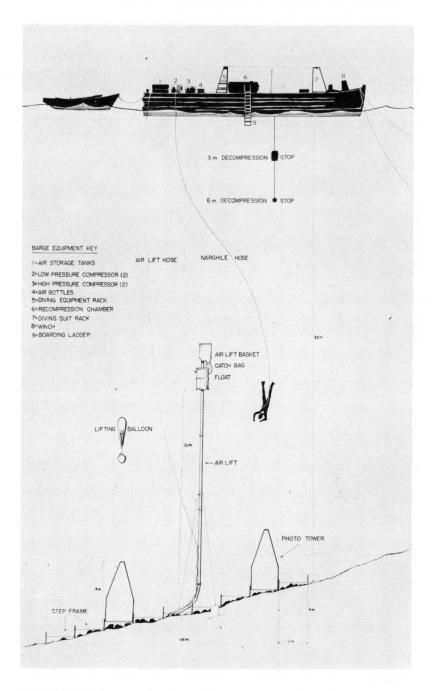

ILLUS. 79—Diagram of excavation of Byzantine shipwreck in 1962.

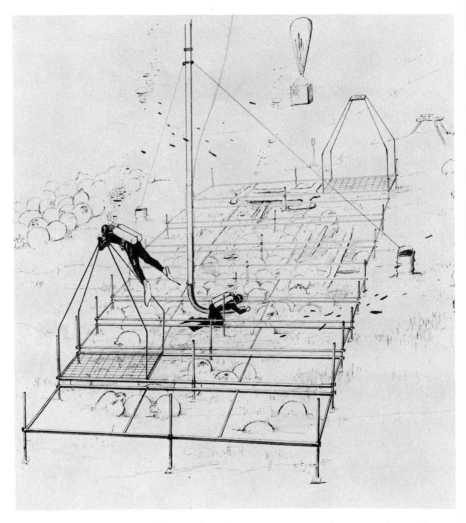

ILLUS. 80—Divers photograph and excavate seventeenth-century shipwreck at depth of 120 feet.

the original location of small objects sucked up by it is never known. Tiny pieces from time to time do enter the pipe, so at Yassi Island a wire basket was bolted to the top of the pipe. The mesh of the wire allows most of the sand to be carried away by the current, but coarse sand and small objects are trapped and fall into a bag attached beneath the basket. The bag is raised whenever full and the sand within is carefully inspected on land.

The Byzantine wreck is still being excavated, but already much has been learned. The hull was filled with a cargo of nearly 1,000 wine jars, mostly large globular amphoras, stacked in several layers. Across the bow lay six iron anchors with a seventh just off the starboard side. Toward the stern of the ship was found a flat, depressed area with scattered roof tiles that had covered the ship's cabin, and just aft of this was the crew's large water jar. Beneath the tiles were found the personal belongings of the captain. A small hoard of gold coins, all dated to the reign of the Emperor Heraclius (610–641), gives us a fairly solid date for the sinking of the ship and, therefore, dates the objects found in it. This would make the tableware from the cabin, including plates, pitchers, cups, bowls, jars, and cooking pots, probably the best-dated collection of pottery from that century. A set of silver-inlaid bronze weights, a whetstone and a stone mortar show how little the belongings of a sea merchant had changed in nearly two millennia. Thirteen terra cotta lamps, in a style often dated two centuries earlier, now provide a fixed date for others of their type. A censer and cross in bronze and a caldron and tray in copper also came to light. Two bronze steelyards for weighing cargo were found with chains and hooks in perfect condition. The bar of the larger was decorated at its ends with bronze animal heads, and its counterweight was a lead-filled bronze bust of Athena. A Greek inscription on this steelyard gives us the name of its owner: George Senior Sea Captain. A small glass medallion, with a cruciform monogram of the name Theodore, suggests the name of a second member of the crew.

All of these finds could have been turned up quickly by any diver, but much information would have been lost. The wood of the hull and scattered traces of wood from the rigging are now pinned in place on the packed sand of the seabed with thousands of sharpened bicycle spokes. A restoration, based on plans and sections of these pieces, will give the first information regarding the details of Byzantine ship construction. Because the positions of the fallen roof tiles had been plotted to the centimeter, and the angle at which the keel lies had been measured, it will even be possible to estimate the height and position of the cabin by measuring the distance between the tiles and the keel; the tiles themselves will give us the size of the cabin. All of the iron nails and

ILLUS. 81—Diver takes series of photographs from floating bar to form stereo-pairs.

spikes have long since disappeared, but iron-oxide shells remain; plaster casts taken of the hollow interiors, when the shells are sawed in half, reproduce perfectly the original shapes and sizes of the missing iron pieces.

Such work is slow and laborious, but well worth the effort. Almost any object made by ancient man was likely to have been

ILLUS. 82—Two-man submarine Asherah *maps wreck photogrammetrically with pair of cameras at 150 feet.*

transported by sea. Even the architectural members of temples and churches have been found as cargo on sunken ships. Seldom are archeologists offered material in such perfectly dated contexts on land, and seldom has the material been so well preserved against the destruction of men themselves. It is hoped that patience and care will be used in bringing these findings to light.

ADDENDUM

Since the above was written, the excavation of the Byzantine ship-wreck has been completed. The careful methods of excavation and mapping allowed a reconstruction of much of the ancient hull up to the level of its deck beams. At the same time, even more efficient methods of making plans underwater were devised. Attempts to map parts of the wreck photogrammetrically, with stereophoto-graphs, were promising during the third season at Yassi Island: a bar was floated horizontally over the site (Illus. 81) and a camera, weighted so that it hung always level from gimbals, was slid along it by a diver who snapped a picture at each of a series of marks 1.20 meters apart on the bar. The resultant photographs could be matched as stereo-pairs and when their parallax differences were measured with a micrometer, the distance of any object under the bar could be calculated. Thus both planimetric and elevation mea-surements were quickly provided without time-consuming hand measurements underwater.

This new method of mapping showed so much promise that in 1964 a two-man submarine, the *Asherah,* was built for underwater "aerial surveys" by the University Museum, aided especially by the National Geographic Society and the National Science Founda-tion. The 16-foot, 4½-ton craft can descend to depths of 600 feet and remain for as long as 10 hours. Excellent maneuverability is provided by two side-mounted, electrically powered propellers which can be rotated separately or together; thus the vehicle can go straight up, down, backward, forward, or hover like a helicopter.

A pair of modified aerial-survey cameras were mounted in un-derwater housings about 6 feet apart on a bracket attached to the front of the submarine (Illus. 82). Specially ground correcting lenses prevented the distortion normally caused underwater by the index of refraction of water. The cameras were fired electrically from within the submarine, and then advanced their own film and re-cocked their shutters automatically.

In one short dive the *Asherah* was "flown" twice over a late Roman wreck lying in 150 feet of water. The stereo-photographs taken by the two cameras during the dive provided material for an accurate three-dimensional model of the site. Fifty-six hours of laboratory work were needed for the analysis of the photographs and the calculation of elevation measurements, but the underwater work had taken two men less than a month of diving.

Plans are now under way to search for wrecks with underwater television, a proton magnetometer, and newly developed sonic devices. Sites found hundreds of feet deep will be viewed and mapped from the *Asherah*, but for proper excavation archeologists will have to rely on special gas mixtures for breathing, or will be forced to live on the sites in underwater houses. One thing is certain: no matter where wrecks are found, the means will be found to excavate them.

FRANK H. H. ROBERTS, JR.

The Carbon-14 Method of
Age Determination

[FROM THE SMITHSONIAN REPORT FOR 1951[1]]

ONE OF THE FIRST *questions asked by museum visitors regarding an antiquity of any kind is, "How old is it?" The same question, although for scientific reasons, faces archeologists excavating ancient various types of geological evidence. These were not too reliable 20 years ago, the answers had to be in tree-ring correlations and in various types of geological evidence. These were not too reliable and applied only to restricted areas, but the new approach discussed in this article can provide accurate dates for materials coming from any part of the world. The author, Dr. Frank H. H. Roberts, Jr., was a member of the staff of the Smithsonian's Bureau of American Ethnology for over 37 years. He was its Associate Director from 1948 to 1957 and its Director from 1958 until his retirement in June 1964. He did a large amount of archeological research, chiefly in the western United States, and is a leading authority on the earliest inhabitants of the American continent, the so-called Paleo-Indians. In this article Dr. Roberts explains the complex chemical and physical basis of the carbon-14 method of determining very precise ages of materials up to a present maxi-*

───

[1] Revised as of February 1965 by the addition of a supplementary note at end of article.

mum of some 30,000 to 45,000 years. He gives actual dates obtained by this method for ancient sites — not only in many parts of America — but also in Europe, Asia, and Africa.

During the period immediately following World War II an important byproduct of research on cosmic rays was the development of a method whereby the age of certain objects can be determined by laboratory tests. The latter are based on the carbon-14 content of the objects, and their results undoubtedly will be extremely useful in archeology, several branches of geology, oceanography, meteorology, and related fields where chronology is essential to the solving of many problems. Previous types of "calendars," such as tree-ring dating, pollen analysis, and glacial varves, were helpful in restricted areas but were not universally applicable. This latest method of age determination does not suffer from that handicap. For the first time it now appears that prehistoric dates that are virtually precise can be obtained from samples from any region in the world. The method has some limitations and an occasional test goes awry, but as the techniques are improved the age determinations unquestionably will become more accurate.

Carbon 14, a radioactive heavy form of carbon with an atomic weight of 14 in contrast to the normal, stable carbon atomic weight of 12, is continually being formed in the upper atmosphere of the earth. It results from the bombardment of nitrogen-14 atoms by cosmic rays, streams of neutrons flowing toward the earth from outer space. The new carbon-14 atoms thus formed, commonly called radiocarbon, begin an immediate spontaneous disintegration but enough remain to combine with oxygen to form carbon dioxide which eventually mixes, in the air that surrounds the earth, with the much larger proportion of carbon dioxide containing ordinary carbon. All living things which absorb carbon dioxide from the atmosphere take in some of the carbon 14 as well as the carbon 12. The proportions between the two have been shown experimentally to be constant in all living matter. The radiocarbon con-

448 SMITHSONIAN *Treasury of Twentieth-Century Science*

stantly disintegrates, but it is continually replaced through the life processes which are in exchange with the atmosphere. When an animal or a plant dies there is no further replacement of carbon 14. That remaining, however, continues to disintegrate at a rate that is the same everywhere. For that reason the amount of radiocarbon still present is in direct proportion to the time that has elapsed since death occurred, and by measuring the constantly diminishing rate of disintegration it is possible to calculate the age of an organic sample.

It is not possible in an article of this nature to explain and discuss in detail the scientific processes involved in radiocarbon dating, but the main features in the development of the method should be mentioned. In 1934, not long after the discovery of artificial radio-activity, Dr. A. V. Grosse suggested that the existence of radio-active elements produced by cosmic rays would be established (Grosse, 1934). Some 10 years later Dr. W. F. Libby, of the Institute of Nuclear Studies of the University of Chicago, predicted that living matter would be found to contain natural or "cosmic" carbon 14 (Libby, 1946). The next year he and Dr. Grosse tested methane gas derived from sewage and found the expected amount of carbon 14 (Grosse and Libby, 1947). Dr. Libby and his associates then proceeded to demonstrate experimentally that carbon 14 occurs in the same concentration in all living matter. In doing this they tested living material from many parts of the world — from different latitudes, altitudes, and different geographical situations (Libby, Anderson, and Arnold, 1949). The materials consisted of wood from Chicago, Mount Wilson, New Mexico, Bolivia, Ceylon, Tierra del Fuego, Panama, Palestine, Sweden, New South Wales, and North Africa; sea shells from Florida; and seal oil from the Antarctic.

In the course of the various studies it had been determined that the half-life of carbon 14 is about 5,568 ± 30 years, which means that one ounce of the material is reduced by decay to half an ounce during the 5,568-year period and that half of the remainder decays during the next 5,568 years leaving a quarter of an ounce, etc. (Engelkemeir and Libby, 1950; Jones, 1948; Miller et al., 1950). Because of this, Dr. Libby was convinced that the amount of carbon 14 present in any particular object would be an indication of the age of that object and proceeded to develop a method for measuring it. This involved the perfection of a specially constructed and extremely sensitive screen wall counter, a form of Geiger counter, which would measure the rate of atomic disintegration of natural carbon 14 without the use of a thermal diffusion column. The problem also included the development of a complicated chemical separation unit to reduce the carbon 14 to its purest form. In running tests the samples to be dated are burned, treated in the separation unit, and then measured in the radiation counter. The measurements are given on the basis of the carbon-14 disintegrations per minute per gram of carbon. For present-day living samples the specific activity is 15.3, for samples 5,568 years old it is 7.65, and for samples 11,136 years old it is 3.83. The disintegration rate is such, however, that the proportion of radiocarbon remaining after 20,000 years is so small that accurate counting is very difficult and the effective range may be considered somewhat less than that age. There is a method for enriching samples which may make possible the obtaining of dates as far back as 30,000 years, but that at present appears to be the maximum. The errors in the dates now being obtained are considered to range from 5 to 10 percent.

When the laboratory equipment was ready Dr. Libby and his associate, Dr. James R. Arnold, ran a series of tests on samples whose ages had been fairly accurately established by other means but which were unknown to them. Material, ranging in age from 1,300 to 4,600 years, from Egyptian tombs, from archeological sites in our own southwest, and from redwood trees was provided by different museums, and it was found that the carbon-14 dates obtained for them agreed with the known ages within the calculated error of the method. In making the preliminary tests it was found that the most useful materials are plant fibers and wood, charcoal, antler, burned bone, shell, dung, and peat.

Arrangements were then made with a committee representing the American Anthropological Association and the Geological Society of America to obtain samples for testing and a grant was made by the Wenner-Gren Foundation for Anthropological Research (the Viking Fund) to assist in the support of the program. Archeologists and geologists began sending in the necessary materials and the series of tests got under way in the spring of 1949. Announcements of the dates obtained were made informally from time to time, but it was not until October 1950 that a lengthy series was made public. That list was printed in February 1951 in *Science*, vol. 113, No. 2927, pp. 111–120. An additional list appeared in the same journal, vol. 114, No. 2960, pp. 291–296 in September of that year. Most of the information contained in those articles was also published, with discussions of its significance, in the Memoirs of the Society for American Archeology, *American Antiquity*, vol. 17, No. 1, pt. 2, 1951.

The method developed by Dr. Libby and the results obtained indicated so many potential applications for radiocarbon dating that new laboratories for making carbon-14 measurements have been established at Yale University, the University of Michigan, Columbia University, and the United States Geological Survey. Others are contemplated and perhaps even now are under way. The first series of measurements by the Lamont Geological Observatory at Columbia University was announced in *Science*, vol. 114, No. 2970, in November 1951.

From the standpoint of archeology, most of the dates reported thus far have been fairly satisfactory, but in a number of instances there appears to be a contradiction between the archeological evidence and the age obtained from the carbon-14 tests. One factor to be considered in this connection is that the older material appears to be more consistent than that of relatively recent times, and even though the error in the method may make a difference of several hundred years in the actual chronology, the results are very helpful and will aid materially in making the syntheses of cultural relationships and developments that are essential to an understanding of past history. For many people greatest interest probably attaches to the archeological remains that fall within what may be called geologic time. The results in this Early Man category are in some respects as surprising as a few of those in other fields, but on the whole they are reasonably satisfactory.

In the United States the age of the well-known Folsom complex caused considerable comment when the figure pertaining to the type site was released. As a matter of fact, that discussion has continued actively to the present. Unfortunately many of the arguments it produced were not necessary because the announced date was not that of the culture-bearing horizon of the Folsom complex but that of a fire pit in the fill of a secondary channel that had cut through the original deposit of bison bones and artifacts. Such was known at the time when the first announcement was made, but unfortunately the explanation accompanying the date was not clear. If, as the geologists who have examined this site maintained, the cultural stratum was of very late Pleistocene or early Recent Age (Brown, 1929; Bryan, 1937), the date of $4,283 \pm 250$[2] years obviously was wrong or else the geologists were greatly mistaken in their identification of the deposits. Subsequently material from a Folsom horizon at Lubbock, Tex., was tested and a carbon-14 date of $9,883 \pm 350$ years was obtained. The latter more closely approximates the magnitude estimated for Folsom on geologic evidence. The deposits at Lubbock, in the opinion of Dr. E. H. Sellards of the Texas Memorial Museum and his associates, correlate closely with those at the site in the Black Water Draw near Clovis, N. Mex., which Dr. Ernst Antevs has identified as belonging to a pluvial period which he believes corresponds to the end of the Pleistocene and has estimated the age as being from 10,000 to 13,000 years (Antevs, 1949). It is possible, of course, that some of the material at Clovis is older than the Lubbock site, because the Folsom culture undoubtedly lasted over a reasonably long period. Also, certain faunal differences suggest a greater age for some of the Clovis manifestations. The difference between the carbon-14 date and Dr. Antevs' estimate is not too great, however, and it seems a fair assumption that the general idea that the Folsom complex is about 10,000 years old is not far out of line.

The late Dr. Kirk Bryan and Dr. Louis L. Ray, after completing their studies at the Lindenmeier site in northern Colorado, another Folsom location, estimated its age as from 10,000 to 25,000 years, with the statement that they believed it nearer the latter than the former (Bryan and Ray, 1940). Thus far it has not been possible to obtain charcoal or other material suitable for carbon-14 tests from the cultural level at that location and it is not known if the esti-

---

[2] The errors indicated for all dates are standard deviations based solely on the error of counting random events. Other errors probably are involved and the true error will be somewhat greater.

mate is too great or if perhaps the occupation there was earlier than at the similar sites farther south. Geologically the age appears to be somewhat older. Bryan and Ray concluded that the occupation at the Lindenmeier site was in Wisconsin III times or late Mankato. Of interest in this connection is the fact that some early sites on Lime Creek in western Nebraska have been correlated with the Mankato (Schultz and Frankfurter, 1949) and carbon-14 dates of 9,524 ± 450, and 10,493 ± 1,500 have been announced for them. The cultural material is not Folsom, but projectile points of the types found there have been collected elsewhere at sites where the characteristically fluted Folsom type occurs in a lower and older stratum. Dates for the Mankato, based on materials from other localities, have consistently run between 11,000 and 12,000, or an average age of 11,400 years before the present.

Other archeological remains of about the same age on the basis of carbon-14 dates are Gypsum Cave in Nevada, with an average of 10,455 ± 340 for the 6-foot 4-inch level and an average of 8,527 ± 250 for the 2-foot 6-inch level; the Fort Rock Cave in Oregon, 9,053 ± 350; and Palli Aike Cave at the tip of South America, with 8,639 ± 450. The deposits in Gypsum Cave where the oldest artifacts were found have been correlated with a dry period immediately following the Provo Pluvial and the age estimate was placed from 7,000 to 9,000 years ago (Antevs, 1948). In that particular case it appears that the estimated and the carbon-14 dates are in fairly close agreement. Archeologically such an age would not be unreasonable, although there is still some question as to the contemporaneity of the associated wooden objects and the sloth dung from which the date was obtained. In connection with the Gypsum Cave dates it might be noted that the accumulation of material between the 6-foot 4-inch level and the 2-foot 6-inch level, a depth of a little less than 4 feet, represents approximately 2,300 years.

The Fort Rock Cave in Oregon is particularly interesting as well as somewhat puzzling. At that location a large number of fiber sandals and some basketry were recovered from beneath a layer of pumice which has been identified with the Newberry eruption that presumably followed that of the Mount Mazama eruption which produced Crater Lake (Cressman, Williams, and Krieger, 1940).

The sandals were tested and were found to have an average age of 9,053 ± 350, the oldest actual artifacts thus far dated. If the assumption that the Newberry eruption followed that of Mount Mazama is correct, it appears that there was a considerable interval between the time the sandals were left on the floor of the cave and when they were covered by the pumice. The Mount Mazama eruption has been dated by a carbon-14 test of charcoal from a tree killed by the eruption and the age 6,453 ± 250 was obtained. Williams (1942) had previously estimated it to be between 4,000 and 7,000, Allison (1946) had placed it at 12,000 to 14,000 and Hansen (1946), on the basis of pollen stratigraphy, suggested 12,500 or somewhat later. The maximum, under the circumstances, for the Newberry would appear to be somewhat less than the 6,453 ± 250 of the Mount Mazama and it may well have been considerably later. The date for the sandals, of course, is not that for the overlying pumice but it is rather difficult to explain how they remained on the surface of a cave floor for several millennia without alteration and then were charred by the heat from the Newberry pumice (Cressman et al., 1940, p. 68; Cressman, 1942, p. 52; 1943, p. 239). When first announced, the date for the sandals was thought to indicate a reverse order for the volcanic eruptions. That is not now considered to be the case however. A subsequent statement to the effect that the dated sandals came from some distance below the pumice (Cressman, 1951, p. 308) bolsters that opinion. Archeologically, as well as geologically, the Mount Mazama pumice is an important feature in Oregon in that it forms a line of demarcation for dating deposits occurring beneath and above it. Once the age of the Newberry pumice, or pumices (since the presence of four cones in the crater and others along the eastern base of the volcano suggest there may have been several eruptions), has been established it also will be equally helpful. Hansen estimates the Newberry eruption at between 7,500 and 9,500 and Allison places it at from 11,000 to 12,000, but in view of the Mount Mazama results it would seem that the carbon-14 date will prove to be considerably less. If the date for the sandals is correct, it is extremely significant because it shows that the inhabitants of North America at that time had not only developed a fine technique in the manufacture of protection for the feet but that they also were making a highly artistic form of basketry decorated with a false embroidery. It is possible, of course, that when perishable materials belonging in the complex of some of the other cultures of this period are found an equally high kind of industry will be revealed.

What may well prove to be one of the most important archeological sites thus far found in North America from the standpoint of the sequence and dating of cultures, as well as geologic data, is Danger Cave near Wendover, Utah. The cultural debris there reaches a depth of about 14 feet. The midden rests on an old beach of glacial Lake Stansbury. The beach consists of two feet of sand deposited on cemented gravels. Charcoal, wood, and mountain-sheep dung were found in the sand layer. Radiocarbon tests of the dung gave an age of $11,453 \pm 600$, while the wood ran $11,151 \pm 570$. Thus far no results have been announced for the cultural material and it must be considered as being an unknown number of years later than the beach, although the initial occupation may not have been long delayed after the receding water opened the cave to habitation. The date of the latter, however, will be extremely useful in geologic studies of the area. This is particularly so in view of the fact that bat guano mixed with the gravels of an old beach of Lake Lahontan in the Leonard rock shelter near Lovelock, Nev., gave a carbon-14 date of $11,199 \pm 570$.

The close correlation between the beach levels in the two caves is important in showing that climatic conditions then were such that there was a pronounced shrinkage in the two lakes. A similar phenomenon is noted for ancient Lake Texcoco in Mexico where radiocarbon tests indicate that the late Pleistocene shrinkage apparently started approximately $11,003 \pm 500$ years before the present.

In South America two caves in Tierra del Fuego near the eastern end of the Strait of Magellan yielded material that has given dates of $10,832 \pm 400$ and $8,639 \pm 450$ years. The older of the two dates was obtained from sloth dung and there apparently were no cultural associations. The date is important, however, because it has a bearing on the last ice advance in the area and also the survival of the giant sloth. It is interesting to note that the date agrees very closely with the $10,455 \pm 340$ obtained from similar material from Gypsum Cave in Nevada. The date for the other cave, called

Palli Aike, which contained archeological deposits, was obtained from charred sloth, horse, and guanaco bones. It is not only important in indicating that man was present there at a reasonably early time but is also significant because the material came from hearths on the surface of a layer of volcanic ash, and as the occupation of the cave apparently followed closely after the eruption which deposited the ash the date probably is approximately that for the last major eruption in the adjacent group of small volcanoes along the Chilean-Argentine boundary. Furthermore, it helps to place a land rise of 42½ feet east of the first narrows of the Strait and recession of a large glacial lake which exposed the rock shelters that were soon occupied by people. In addition, the date substantiates an estimated age for volcanic ash distributions in Tierra del Fuego and Patagonia based on pollen analysis (Bird, 1951).

As is to be expected, dates for archeological sites attributable to prehistoric man in the Old World are somewhat older than those in the Western Hemisphere. Charcoal from the famous Lascaux Cave, considered one of the world's oldest and most remarkable art galleries, on the Vézère River near Montignac (Dordogne), France, tested 15,516 ± 900. The charcoal came from occupational deposits in the northwestern portion of the cave and is thought to represent a Magdalenian level. Thus far, however, it has not been possible to correlate the radiocarbon date with any of the seven or eight art styles in the magnificent murals on the wall of the cave (Movius, 1951). Another upper Paleolithic site of Magdalenian times at La Garenne, St. Marcel (Indre), France, has an interesting series of dates. One sample consisting of an ashy material mixed with sand, charcoal, and burned bones tested 15,847 ± 1,200, burned bone collected in and around a hearth dated 11,109 ± 480, while burned bone from the same horizon but outside the hearth gave 12,986 ± 560. Of comparable antiquity is a site at Mufo, Angola, Portuguese West Africa, where a stone blade associated with carbonized wood was found in a late upper Pleistocene deposit. Tests made on the wood yielded 11,189 ± 490 years. Not quite so old, but still of considerable age, are two dwellings in Denmark belonging to the late boreal, pollen zone VI. Hazelnuts from one of them gave an average of 9,929 ± 350 years, while birchwood from the other tested 9,425 ± 540. Materials from a cave located five miles west of Behshahr at the southeast corner of the Caspian Sea, in Iran, show dates ranging from $8,545 \pm 500$ to $10,560 \pm 1,200$. The deposits in the cave contain Bronze Age, late Neolithic, Neolithic, late Mesolithic, and Mesolithic. The earlier date presumably is that of the Mesolithic, while the later was from a zone containing upper Mesolithic artifacts.

In the United States there is a somewhat younger group of cultures which are represented at various places in the West and Southwest. They may represent developments out of the older remains previously mentioned, but on the other hand they may indicate subsequent migrations to the area. That is a problem which still needs to be solved by the archeologists. Nevertheless there is some significance in the carbon-14 indications.

Associated with Folsom materials at sites where artifacts were picked up from the surface were types of points which were given the name Yuma. The latter became somewhat of a catch-all designation for points that could not otherwise be identified and has more or less been replaced by specific site names. The first points of this type were believed to be contemporaneous with Folsom, but subsequent work showed that their contemporaneity at best was a very late one and that they more likely actually represented a subsequent horizon. In this category are specimens such as those found by Dr. G. L. Jepsen, of Princeton University, at Sage Creek in Wyoming. The average date for that material, derived from partially burned bison bones, is $6,876 \pm 250$. Other specimens falling in the same category were found in a site at the Angostura Reservoir in South Dakota. Charcoal found at the occupation level tested $7,715 \pm 740$, while similar material taken from an oval-shaped unprepared hearth dated $7,073 \pm 300$. Geologic studies at both of those locations have not yet been completed so it is not known what the conclusions are with respect to their geologic age.

Caves in the Humboldt Valley in Nevada have furnished specimens that have been dated $7,038 \pm 350$ years, $5,737 \pm 250$ years, and $2,482 \pm 260$ years. These dates were obtained from bat guano and archeological artifacts. In the cave containing the oldest objects, the guano layer below the artifact-bearing stratum rested on Pleistocene gravels and, as previously mentioned, material from the contact tested $11,199 \pm 570$. Briefly, the evidence there shows that man was present in that district by 5000 B.C. and that the region was occupied during the dry Altithermal Period of 4000 B.C. After approximately 1,500 years' occupation the region apparently was abandoned until about 500 B.C. from which time there is an unbroken archeological record to the present day. The oldest date thus far for California is 4,052 ± 160, but since *Olivella biplicata* shell beads were found at the 7,000-year-old level in one of the caves in Nevada, it seems evident that there must have been people along the Pacific coast at that time (Heizer, 1951).

In southeastern Arizona a series of cultural horizons designated the Cochise yielded carbon-14 dates of 7,756 ± 370 and 6,210 ± 450 for the oldest stage. The next or second stage yielded dates from 4,508 ± 680 to 4,006 ± 270, while the third stage gave 2,463 ± 310. From these dates it is obvious that the sequence of the three stages which was established on geologic and typological evidence was sound. The dates themselves, however, are somewhat lower than previous estimates based on climatological studies, particularly in the case of the first period which is about 2,000 years younger (Sayles and Antevs, 1941). The carbon-14 figures indicate that, contrary to the opinion of many, the Cochise peoples had not moved into that area prior to the appearance of hunting peoples of the Folsom type in the region immediately to the east. In that connection it may be pointed out that the fire pit with a date of 4,283 ± 250 years at Folsom was roughly contemporaneous with the second stage of the Cochise in Arizona and the Early Horizon culture in California. In the same category is a fire pit in the secondary channel fill at the Lindenmeier site with its 5,020 ± 300. Furthermore, the date falls in the same general horizon as some of the Archaic remains in the eastern part of the United States, as that of the site of the much-debated Tepexpán Man in Mexico with its 4,118 ± 300, and of the Huaca Prieta Mound No. 3 in Peru with 4,044 ± 300.

Bat Cave in Catron County, N. Mex., with dates from 5,931 ± 310 to 1,752 ± 250, falls into this same general period. In some ways the archeological material from it may not be as important as that found at other sites, but there is an excellent sequence of artifact types characteristic of different geographical areas and several projectile points similar to the second stage of the Cochise were found there. The main significance of Bat Cave is in the light that it throws on the botanical problem of the development of maize or Indian corn. From the six feet of accumulated refuse in the cave a series of shelled cobs, loose kernels, and various fragments of husks, leaf sheaths, and tassels was recovered. The specimens from the bottom level to the top show a distinct evolutionary sequence. The corn from the bottom level is a primitive variety which was both a popcorn and a form of pod corn, while that at the top is an essentially modern form. The evolutionary period required for such changes thus appears to be far shorter than previously supposed. The sequence also indicates that there were important factors bearing on the evolutionary process; namely, that there was a marked reduction in the pressure of natural selection, that there were mutations from the more to the less extreme forms of pod corn, that contamination by teosinte modified the corn, and that crossing produced a high degree of hybridity (Mangelsdorf, 1950).

In the eastern United States the Archaic at Frontenac Island, N. Y., gave a date of $4,930 \pm 260$. A site at Lamoka Lake, N. Y., produced charcoal which tested $5,383 \pm 250$, while shell mounds in Kentucky yielded dates from $4,900 \pm 250$ to $5,149 \pm 300$. Geological determinations have not played a particularly important part in the studies of those sites, although such investigations as were made there would indicate that there was some expectation of reasonable antiquity. Probably somewhat younger but still falling within that period is the fishweir at Boston where peat from the Boylston Street site gave a carbon-14 date of $5,717 \pm 500$ for the lower peat underlying the weir. A second date was obtained from a fragment of coniferous wood which was taken from marine silt overlying the lower peat and the weir. It was $3,851 \pm 390$. The weir itself presumably should be younger than the oldest date but older than the later one. On the basis of climatological evidence it had been estimated that the weir was in use just prior to 2000 B.C. (Antevs, 1943). Hence it appears that the people who built and used the weir may have been contemporaneous with those who lived at the Frontenac Lake, Lamoka, and Kentucky sites. These dates from the eastern United States are somewhat older than had been anticipated and show that migration to that area was relatively early.

There are some generally comparable dates for the Old World

and as the testing continues there undoubtedly will be more. Wheat and barley grain from a pit in the Neolithic Fayum A Period in Egypt gave the age $6,095 \pm 250$, which is about 1,000 years later than originally estimated by archeologists for the remains found there. Charcoal from house floors at El-Omari, near Cairo, Egypt, tested $5,256 \pm 230$, the period represented being tentatively identified as Middle Predynastic. A slab of wood from a roof beam of the tomb of Vizier Hemaka of the First Dynasty, at Sakkara, Egypt, ran an average of $4,883 \pm 200$ which is in the previously accepted range of 4,700 to 5,100 years for that dynasty. A cypress beam from the tomb of Sneferu at Meydum, Egypt, tested an average $4,802 \pm 210$ which is within the range of error for the age determined from archeological evidence and the Egyptian calendar. There are other dates of lesser magnitude for Egypt as well and they agree rather closely with the radiocarbon results (Braidwood et al., 1951). Fairly well-preserved land-snail shells from basal levels at Jarmo, Iraq, a Kurdish hill-country site lying on the flanks of the "Fertile Crescent" north and east of classic Mesopotamia, tested $6,707 \pm 320$ years. That site has been considered, on typological grounds, to be the earliest village remains thus far excavated in western Asia. The carbon-14 age is about 2,000 years younger than had been estimated by archeological reasoning. A piece of charred wood from a Neolithic lakeside settlement at Ehenside Tarn, England, showed a carbon-14 age of $4,964 \pm 300$. The conventional dating for such remains has been 4,000 years. Charcoal from a feature considered to be late Neolithic and to belong to the first phase of the monument at Stonehenge, England, tested $3,798 \pm 275$. On the other side of the world charcoal from part of the structural remains of a house found in the bottom levels of the Ubayama shell mound, about 10 miles west of Tokyo, Japan, had an average age of $4,564 \pm 220$. That is supposed to be the oldest house site in Japan. Charcoal from a higher level at the same mound showed $4,513 \pm 300$.

Curiously enough, Alaska, which should give the oldest archeological dates in the Western Hemisphere if the migration theory for the populating of the New World from northeast Asia is correct, thus far has shown nothing older than $5,993 \pm 280$ for a habitation site. That date was obtained from charcoal and willows from the bottom level of a cave containing evidence of at least two different cultures. Artifacts from the same level consist of diagonally chipped blades, stone and bone arrow points, microlithic side-blades, and decorated and slotted bone. The side-blades and the bone suggest a Mesolithic tradition. The other cultural materials, separated from the former by more than a meter of debris, are of a type that elsewhere in Alaska has been found to be approximately 1,000 years old. A base log from a Paleo-Eskimo house at Cape Denbigh tested 2,016 ± 250, while charred wood from the middle levels of the same site showed 1,460 ± 200. Spruce wood from a site at Gambell, St. Lawrence Island, yielded 2,258 ± 230. The dates for the Alaskan remains, however, do differ from archeological conceptions as to their age and as yet there is no satisfactory explanation for the discrepancy.

There is one interesting series of dates covering a long sequence of cultures in the Chicama Valley, Peru (Bird, 1951). The range is from 4,424 ± 104 to 2,211 ± 200 and so far as the archeological evidence is concerned there is nothing which would throw doubt on the validity of the radiocarbon determinations. The same cannot be said, however, for dates for certain remains in the United States. The latter are much younger than many of those in Peru and involve the so-called Hopewell and Adena cultures. Archeologists had generally agreed that the Adena and its typologically related cultures preceded the Hopewell. When three different kinds of organic material comprising six samples from Hopewell sites were tested they were found to be 1,951 ± 200, 2,044 ± 250, 2,285 ± 210, and 2,336 ± 250. The Adena materials, on the other hand, range from 1,168 ± 150 to 1,509 ± 250, and the related cultures from 633 ± 150 to 1,233 ± 250, and 1,158 ± 250 to 1,276 ± 150. Generally speaking radiocarbon shows that Hopewell is not only older than Adena but antedates it by 1,000 years (Griffin, 1951). Since this is so contrary to the accepted archeological chronology, the results have been sharply questioned. The discrepancy probably cannot be attributed to the method itself because all the dates are within the range of carbon-14 determinations that were checked by samples of known age. Consequently it would seem that either the archeological concepts need to be changed or the specimens used in the tests were contaminated.

There are various other dates of anthropological significance now available but space will permit the consideration of only two more. They are of particular interest for other than strictly archeological reasons. A test was made of a sample from a carved wooden lintel from a building at the ruined Mayan city of Tikal in northern Gautemala. The building is believed to have been the sacerdotal palace or residence for the priests serving a nearby temple. The lintel in question formerly spanned an interior doorway and was composed of five sapote beams. The complete lintel was decorated with an inscription giving the Maya date 9.15.10.0.0 3 Ahau 3 Mol. The correlation of the Mayan and Gregorian calendars has long been a source of dispute and there have been two principal schools of thought in the matter with a difference of about 260 years in the results obtained. According to the Goodman-Martínez Hernández-Thompson correlation the date was June 30, A.D. 741, while in the Spinden correlation it was August 30, A.D. 481. The radiocarbon age based on the average of two runs was $1,470 \pm 120$. The expected result on the basis of the first correlation method should have been 1,210–1,240. For the second it should have been 1,470–1,500. As far as this particular sample is concerned, it appears that the Spinden correlation is the correct one (Kulp et al., 1951). The other object of special interest to many people that was subjected to the carbon-14 method was the Book of Isaiah, the Dead Sea scrolls found in a cave near Ain Fashkha in Palestine. History and tradition placed the age of the book in the first or second century before Christ. The linen wrappings that enclosed the scrolls were used for the radiocarbon sample and gave $1,917 \pm 200$ as their age. The scrolls probably are somewhat older and the date of their wrappings may well be that of the time when they were cached in the cave.

The results from carbon 14 as far as geology is concerned are spotty because of the difficulty in obtaining suitable material for testing and because in many instances their stratigraphic position is questionable. However, certain things are apparent from the work done thus far. The dates do fall roughly into the same order as the stratigraphic sequence of the deposits from which the specimens for testing were collected and their relative chronology is acceptable. On the other hand, they are for the most part more recent than many geologists believed would be the case. For example, the Mankato substage of the Wisconsin glaciation is shown to have gotten under way about 11,400 years ago with the maximum being reached at approximately 11,000. This is somewhat less than half the age previously assumed for the Mankato and if correct will require considerable revision of ideas on the part of some students of geochronology. It is interesting to note that radiocarbon dating has confirmed the conclusion, based on pollen studies, that a series of deposits in Germany, England, and Ireland were correlated and belonged to the same interval, the Alleröd. Furthermore, they appear to be correlatives of the Two Creeks bog in Wisconsin and to show that there was contemporaneous climatic fluctuation in Europe and North America (Flint, 1951, a, b). The European dates are: Peat from Wallensen im Hills, northwest Germany, 11,044 ± 500; lake mud from Neasham, near Darlington in the extreme north of England, 10,851 ± 630; peat from Hawks Tor, Cornwall, England, 9,861 ± 500; and lake mud from Knocknacran, County Monaghan, Ireland, 11,310 ± 720.

There are older dates for geologic material than those above. Wood from a peat bed in the Dranse Valley, south of Lake Geneva in France, is reported as at least 19,000 years old. Wood and peat samples collected between Chambéry and Grenoble in southeastern France are considered at least 21,000. Wood samples from the Lake Kickapoo deposits at Wedron, Ill., from the Camden Moraine south of Dayton, Ohio, from a bank of Skunk Creek in Polk County, Iowa, and from Vermilion County, Ill., have been reported as older than 17,000 years. Coaly peat from an exposure along Eagle River north of Anchorage, Alaska, ran 14,300 ± 600. Partially lignitized wood from the shore of Tustermana Lake, Kenai Peninsula, Alaska, gave the date 15,800 ± 400. Wood from a depth of 30 to 60 feet along Fairbanks Creek, Alaska, and associated with extinct mammal bones, dated 12,622 ± 750. A fossil cedar log dredged from St. Georges Harbor, Bermuda, and representative of the extensive forest that once flourished there but has long been extinct, tested 11,500 ± 700.

Dates derived from pollen analysis and the radiocarbon determinations show a general consistency, but there are some disagreements which suggest that the stratigraphic position of some of the samples was not determined properly. Also it seems that there may be a possible source of error in a postdepositional replacement of carbon 14 by carbon 12. Several dates from bogs were mentioned in a previous paragraph. The results from a series of samples reflecting tree growth in the eastern United States are interesting in that they show that the pine phase was reached in West Virginia 9,423 ± 840 years ago at a time when that region was definitely outside the glaciated area. The same stage was reached at 8,323 ± 400 in Connecticut, and 7,988 ± 420 in Minnesota in the region south of the limits reached by the ice sheet during the Mankato substage. In northern Minnesota the phase dated 7,128 ± 300. It was still later when similar conditions prevailed in northern Maine, as the radiocarbon test on material from Plissey Pond gave the result 5,962 ± 320 (Deevey, 1951). On the basis of these figures it is easy to visualize the slow spread of pine growth from south to north during the relatively dry climatic conditions following the retreating ice sheet.

Work on ocean samples has not progressed as far as that in other lines of research, but what has been done indicates that useful information will be forthcoming not only with respect to deposits at the bottom of the sea but also pertaining to the age and movements of subsurface currents. Unquestionably as more laboratories are established and the techniques are perfected other fields will be found where radiocarbon age determinations will have a definite place. There are, of course, various aspects of the problem that still need clarification. For example, it is not known what effect different climatic conditions may have on samples, whether the carbon-14 content is consistent in wet and dry areas, or if perhaps the rate of disintegration may be accelerated or decreased by the nature of the deposits where the object to be tested was found. However, the results thus far indicate that the carbon-14 method is valid and, bearing in mind the expectable error, that a majority of the dates obtained are reasonably accurate. Improved methods for collecting samples and greater care in avoiding subsequent contamination probably will sharply reduce the number of unacceptable determinations.

REFERENCES

ALLISON, I. S. 1946. Early man in Oregon: Pluvial lakes and pumice. Sci. Month., vol. 62, pp. 63–65.

ANDERSON, E. C., and LIBBY, W. F. 1951. World-wide distribution of natural radiocarbon. Phys. Rev., vol. 81, No. 1, pp. 64–69.

ANTEVS, ERNST. 1943. Review of the Bolyston Street fishweir by Frederick Johnson et al. Amer. Antiq., vol. 8, No. 3, p. 304.

1948. The Great Basin, with emphasis on glacial and post-glacial times; climatic changes and pre-white man. Univ. Utah Bull., vol. 33, No. 20, pp. 168–181.

1949. Geology of the Clovis sites. Appendix to Ancient man in North America, by H. M. Wormington. Denver Mus. Nat. Hist., pop. ser. No. 4, 3d ed., revised.

ARNOLD, J. R., and LIBBY, W. F. 1951. Radiocarbon dates. Science, vol. 113, No. 2927, pp. 111–120.

BIRD, JUNIUS. 1951. South American radiocarbon dates. Amer. Antiq., vol. 17, No. 1, pt. 2, pp. 37–49.

BRAIDWOOD, ROBERT J., JACOBSEN, T., PARKER, R. A., and WEINBERG, S. 1951. Radiocarbon dates and their implications in the near and middle eastern areas. Amer. Antiq., vol. 17, No. 1, pt. 2, pp. 52–53.

BROWN, BARNUM. 1929. Folsom culture and its age, with discussion by Kirk Bryan. Geol. Soc. Amer. Bull. 40, pp. 128–129.

BRYAN, KIRK. 1937. Geology of the Folsom deposits, *in* Early Man, pp. 140–143. Philadelphia.

BRYAN, KIRK, and RAY, LOUIS L. 1940. Geologic antiquity of the Lindenmeier site in Colorado. Smithsonian Misc. Coll., vol. 99, No. 2.

CRESSMAN, L. S. 1942. Archaeological researches in the northern Great Basin. Carnegie Inst. Washington Publ. 538.

1943. Results of recent archaeological research in the northern Great Basin region of south central Oregon. Proc. Amer. Philos. Soc., vol. 86, No. 2, pp. 236–246.

1951. Western prehistory in the light of carbon 14 dating. Southwestern Journ. Anthrop., vol. 7, No. 3, pp. 289–313.

CRESSMAN, L. S., WILLIAMS, H., and KRIEGER, A. D. 1940. Early man in Oregon: Archaeological studies in the northern Great Basin. Univ. Oregon Monogr., Studies in Anthropology, No. 3.

DEEVEY, EDWARD S., JR. 1951. Discussion of the relation of some radiocarbon dates to pollen chronology. Amer. Antiq., vol. 17, No. 1, pt. 2, pp. 56–57.

ENGELKEMEIR, A. G., and LIBBY, W. F. 1950. End and wall corrections for absolute beta counting in gas counters. Rev. Sci. Instr., vol. 21, p. 550.

FLINT, RICHARD FOSTER. 1951a. Discussion of the geologic material dated by radiocarbon, a brief. Amer. Antiq., vol. 17, No. 1, pt. 2, pp. 54–55.

1951b. Pin-pointing the past with the cosmic clock. Nat. Hist., vol. 60, No. 5, pp. 200–206.

GRIFFIN, JAMES B. 1951. Some Adena and Hopewell radiocarbon dates. Amer. Antiq., vol. 17, No. 1, pt. 2, pp. 26–29.

GROSSE, A. V. 1934. An unknown radioactivity. Journ. Amer. Chem. Soc., vol. 56, No. 9, pp. 1922–24.

GROSSE, A. V., and LIBBY, W. F. 1947. Cosmic radiocarbon and natural radio-activity of living matter. Science, vol. 106, No. 2743, pp. 88–89.

HANSEN, H. P. 1946. Early man in Oregon: Stratigraphic evidence. Sci. Month., vol. 62, pp. 43–51.

HEIZER, ROBERT F. 1951. An assessment of certain Nevada, California, and Oregon radiocarbon dates. Amer. Antiq., vol. 17, No. 1, pt. 2, pp. 23–25.

JONES, W. M. 1948. A determination of the half-life of carbon 14. Phys. Rev., vol. 76, p. 885.

KULP, J. LAWRENCE, FEELEY, H. W., and TRYON, LANSING E. 1951. Lamont natural radiocarbon measurements, I. Science, vol. 114, No. 2970, pp. 565–568.

LIBBY, W. F. 1946. Atmospheric helium 3 and radiocarbon from cosmic radiation. Phys. Rev., vol. 69, Nos. 11–12, pp. 671–72.

LIBBY, W. F., ANDERSON, E. C., and ARNOLD, J. R. 1949. Age determination by radiocarbon content: World-wide assay of natural radiocarbon. Science, vol. 109, No. 2827, pp. 227–228.

MANGELSDORF, PAUL C. 1950. The mystery of corn. Sci. Amer., vol. 183, No. 1, pp. 20–24, July.

MILLER, W. W., BALLENTINE, R., BERNSTEIN, W., FRIEDMAN, L., NIER, A. O., and EVANS, R. D. 1950. The half-life of carbon 14 and a comparison of gas phase counter methods. Phys. Rev., vol. 77, p. 714.

MOVIUS, HALLAM L. 1951. The Lascaux Cave. Amer. Antiq., vol. 17, No. 1, pt. 2, pp. 50–51.

SAYLES, E. B., and ANTEVS, ERNST. 1941. The Cochise Culture. Medallion Pap. No. 24, Gila Pueblo, Globe, Ariz.

SCHULTZ, C. BERTRAND, and FRANKFURTER, W. D. 1949. The Lime Creek sites, in Proc. 5th Plains Conference for Archaeology, pp. 132–34. Lincoln.

WILLIAMS, H. 1942. The geology of Crater Lake National Forest, Oregon. Carnegie Inst. Washington Publ. No. 540.

SUPPLEMENTARY NOTE

Since the foregoing article first appeared, great progress has been made in the field of radiocarbon dating. Numerous laboratories, including one at the Smithsonian Institution, have been established throughout the United States, in Canada, Venezuela, Argentina, England, Ireland, Denmark, Sweden, Germany, West Germany, the Netherlands, Belgium, France, Switzerland, Monaco, Finland, Poland, Czechoslovakia, the USSR, Italy, Southern Rhodesia, India, Japan, New Zealand and Australia. While much of the work has been concerned mainly with the dating of samples, a number of the laboratories have devoted considerable time to research on the problem of carbon-14 and its related elements. There have been improvements in the techniques of testing samples. Equipment and instruments now being used are vastly superior to those employed earlier. Whereas in the beginning solid carbon, after having been properly prepared, was placed in the Geiger counters, samples to be dated now are converted to a gas which is circulated through the counters. This method is much more efficient, more accurate, and provides less likelihood for contamination. The dating limit has been extended until an age of 45,000 years can be determined with reasonable accuracy. Some laboratories claim 60,000 years but consensus is that such would only be under very exceptional circumstances.

Investigations have shown that radiocarbon concentration in the atmosphere varies from time to time and place to place. The Industrial Revolution with the subsequent growth in factories, smelters, etc., and the contamination of the air with their outpourings of smoke and fumes, is believed to have had a definite effect in that respect. Also, there are certain natural phenomena which play a part. Allowance must be made for those factors. Furthermore, it has been established that the half-life of carbon-14 is greater than had been supposed, although the new figure has not yet been definitely established. The mean of three new determinations by laboratories working on that problem is $5,730 \pm 40$, and that is regarded as the best value now obtainable. However, for dating purposes the original Libby value of $5,568 \pm 30$ (5,570, for convenience) is still employed by all the laboratories. On the basis of the new half-life the determined dates would be somewhat older, and an approximate conversion may be accomplished by multiplying them by 1.03.

During the years since radiocarbon dating became such a valuable assistant in various fields of research, several thousand samples have been tested and their ages announced. For the earlier years the matter of obtaining that information is difficult because the data are scattered through some hundred separate papers. For a time extensive lists were printed in *Science* and the *New Zealand Journal of Science and Technology,* but with the ever-growing amount of such material it became evident that special provision should be made for its publication. In January 1959 the *American Journal of Science,* vol. 257, No. 1, published a major list of dates and issued a reprint designated *American Journal of Science Radiocarbon Supplement*, vol. 1. Volume 2 of the supplement appeared the following year and in 1961 the name was changed to *Radiocarbon*. The latter appears annually and contains dates submitted by most of the laboratories. Thus far there is no complete index to the radiocarbon dates which have been announced through the years. *Radiocarbon* plans to issue a comprehensive index after an agreement has been reached on the half-life years for carbon-14 and all the previous dates have been recalculated. A useful index for archeological dates was published in *Current Anthropology*, vol. 3, No. 5, pp. 451–477, December 1962.

There has been some confusion with respect to the use of the B.P. which has been an integral part of carbon-14 dates. It signifies Before the Present and means that the number of years indicated was before the year that the date was determined or announced. Some preferred to convert the B.P. to A.D./B.C. To simplify matters and assure consistency, it has been agreed that 1950 will be accepted as the standard reference year.

Dates recently have been obtained for the Clovis and Folsom type materials discussed in the original article. Samples from several Clovis sites give ages closely clustered around 9,200 ± 500 B.C. Charcoal collected at the Lindenmeier site in northern Colorado, the best example of a Folsom phase camp site known thus far, yielded the date 8,830 ± 135 B.C. Considerably older dates have been announced for other archeological materials in the United States, but they have not stood up under rigorous checking.

R. LEE

Jet Streams

[FROM THE SMITHSONIAN REPORT FOR 1957[1]]

IT IS ALMOST *a rule of scientific and technological investigation that the solution of one problem leads to the appearance of other problems that require urgent attention. With the advent of jet aircraft which fly at great speeds and high altitudes, the importance of studying the so-called jet streams in the upper atmosphere became of vital importance. These high-level air currents moving at very great velocities had first been noted some 30 years ago, but little attention was given them until the latter years of World War II. The author, R. Lee, of the Meteorological Service of Canada, describes the surprising features of jet streams as disclosed by flying specially equipped planes through these "above the weather" air currents. In this way were learned their heights, directions of flow, and their relationships with temperature. One unexpected finding was the severe turbulence encountered at heights above 30,000 feet where it had been supposed there would be none. Through the continuing meteorological research on these strange upper-atmosphere rivers of air, jet aircraft pilots are learning how to take advantage of them in increasing speed and avoiding turbulence.*

[1] Revised as of February 1965.

INTRODUCTION

O<small>N</small> A<small>PRIL</small> 1, 1954, three United States Navy F–9F fighters streaked across the United States on a cross-country flight. The lead plane of the trio unofficially broke the existing speed record with a flight time of 3 hours and 45 minutes, assisted by tailwinds as high as 170 m.p.h. Spectacular as the flight was, an even more remarkable aspect of it remained unpublicized for, before the flight took off, Lieutenant Dickson, Navy meteorologist, estimated the flight time to be 3 hours and 41 minutes! The take-off time and route were deliberately planned to take advantage of the jet stream high in the upper troposphere. About 15 years ago, the possibility of such a flight would have belonged to the realm of fancy, yet today such feats of planning and flying are accepted as commonplace by the men who fly our modern jet aircraft.

Let us look for a moment at the phenomenon which made this flight possible — the jet stream. In a sense, the accumulation of knowledge leading up to this successful forecast began as early as 1933, when V. Bjerknes, J. Bjerknes, H. Solberg, and T. Bergeron first gave evidence for the existence of jet streams in their classic textbook, *Physikalische Hydrodynamik*. Eleven years later, in 1944, Professor Willett of the Massachusetts Institute of Technology published a paper showing a jet stream, but it was not until the closing phases of World War II in the Pacific that its practical importance became widely recognized. As the scene of operations in the Pacific Theater shifted northward in 1944 and 1945, United States high-altitude bombers began to report westerly winds of up to 250 knots over Japan. The air speeds at that time were such that a high-level bombing run from east to west under such conditions meant that an aircraft would present a stationary target for the antiaircraft batteries below. Here, then, was a meteorological phenomenon whose military significance could not be ignored.

The impact of this discovery on the meteorological world left little time for serious reflection on the nature of these strong, high-level air currents, which were later to be named "jet streams." Many questions remained unanswered. For instance, where are jet streams found? What is their structure? How do they behave?

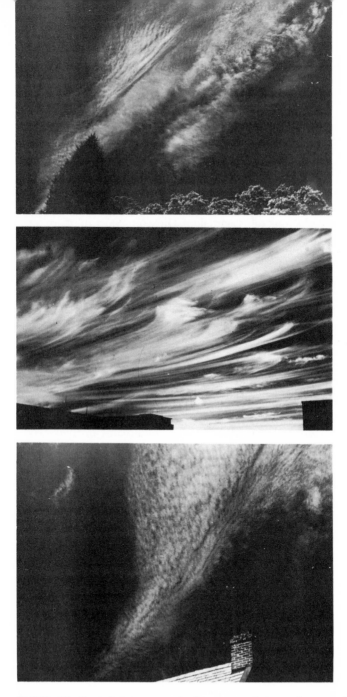

ILLUS. 83—*Typical jet-stream clouds as viewed from the ground. (Photographs courtesy of Dr. Vincent J. Schaefer, Munitalp Foundation, Inc.)*

To answer these and other questions, the Office of Naval Research of the United States Navy sponsored a general atmospheric circulation project at the University of Chicago in 1946. Dr. C.-G. Rossby, one of the world's leading meteorologists, was called upon to direct the project. His colleagues were Palmén, Riehl, and many other outstanding meteorologists. Since then, research activities related to jet streams have spread to all parts of the world.

For a period of time, attention was focused on meteorological analyses of upper winds and temperatures obtained by radiosondes, which consist of meteorological instruments coupled with a small transmitter carried aloft by hydrogen- or helium-filled balloons. Winds were obtained by tracking the balloons with radar equipment. Out of these studies emerged a fairly complete large-scale picture of jet streams which has remained substantially unchanged in the light of subsequent research. In more recent years, research has been directed to the finer details of the tropospheric wind field and to winds in the stratosphere and mesosphere. A large part of jet-stream research is still being conducted by the United States Navy, Bureau of Aeronautics Project AROWA (Applied Research Operational Weather Analysis), at various locations in the United States and other regions of the world. Also actively engaged in this field is the Geophysics Research Directorate, Air Force Cambridge Research Center, which is sponsoring Project Jet Stream. The main task is to determine precisely the horizontal and vertical distribution of wind in jet streams in a large number of cases. For this purpose, specially instrumented aircraft are flown through jet streams, taking continuous observations whose analyses will yield details unobtainable in any other way.

STRUCTURE OF TROPOSPHERIC JET STREAMS

As a result of the intensive preliminary studies at the University of Chicago and other institutions throughout the world, a relatively clear picture of the jet stream began to emerge. It was found that jet streams are worldwide features of the atmosphere. That is, they are essentially high-speed rivers of air that encircle the earth in the middle latitudes of each hemisphere. Air motion is generally from west to east; however, on any individual day, a jet stream may follow a meandering course that dips in some regions into the Tropics and extends north of the Arctic Circle in others. A schematic diagram showing a single jet stream is presented in Illus. 84. The heavy continuous line defines the axis of the jet stream along which the wind speed attains its maximum values in the horizontal. One can usually find the axis of a jet stream encircling the globe on any given occasion.

Illus. 85 shows a view of a jet stream as seen by an observer looking downstream from a point along the axis. The numbers along the bottom of the diagram are the International Station Numbers which identify five stations in Alaska and one in the Yukon, lying approximately in a line oriented from northwest to southeast. From right to left, they are named, respectively, Kotzebu (133), McGrath (231), Fairbanks (261), Big Delta (263), Northway (291), and Whitehorse (964). The distance between Kotzebu and Whitehorse is 735 nautical miles. The ordinate is pressure in millibars (mb.) plotted on a logarithmic scale; 500 mb. corresponds very nearly to 18,000 feet, 200 mb. to 39,000 feet, and 100 mb. to 53,000 feet. Lines of equal wind speed in knots, called isotachs, are used to portray the wind field. Thus, within the central isotach around the main jet axis, labeled J, above 400 mb., the wind speed is in excess of 90 knots.

If we consider the horizontal width of that band of winds in excess of a given value, say 80 knots, we would find it to be surprisingly narrow — of the order of 100 miles in this example, but generally about 300 nautical miles. The vertical depth of the winds greater than 80 knots in Illus. 85 is less than 2 miles. A comparison of the horizontal width of this jet core with the depth would lead us to the conclusion that the jet stream can be represented fairly accurately in shape by a flat ribbon parallel to the earth's surface. Other features on the cross section are the tropopause, indicated by the discontinuous heavy line around the 300–400-mb. levels, and the continental arctic frontal surface separating the relatively warm maritime arctic air mass on the right of the diagram from the cold continental arctic air to its left. The broken lines are isotherms labeled in degrees Centigrade.

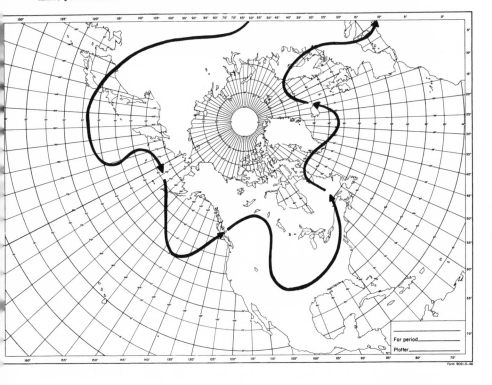

ILLUS. 84—Typical path of the polar jet stream in the Northern hemisphere.

RELATIONSHIP BETWEEN JET STREAMS AND FRONTS

This particular cross section is typical of the northernmost jet stream which has been encountered by R.C.A.F. flights many times in the past. Further studies of jet streams have revealed that, on the average, four main tropospheric jet streams are present over North America during the winter months. Except for the southernmost subtropical jet stream which usually appears in the vicinity of Florida and Cuba, each of the other three is closely associated with one of the three main frontal surfaces over North America in winter. These three frontal surfaces are respectively called the polar front, the maritime arctic front, and the continental arctic front, found in this order from south to north. The polar and maritime arctic jet streams have structures very similar to the continental arctic jet stream in Illus. 85. There is one fundamental difference between them, namely, the height of maximum wind speed is found at higher altitudes as one proceeds southward. For instance, the axis of the continental arctic jet stream is normally found between 25,000 and 30,000 feet, the maritime arctic jet stream between 32,000 and 36,000 feet, and the polar front jet stream between 35,000 and 40,000 feet. These jet streams are also found over Japan in winter. Thus we can see why the strong winds were not encountered by the high-altitude bombers of World War II until the scene of operations moved sufficiently far north in the western Pacific.

Another notable fact about the three northernmost jet streams is that the axis of each jet stream is always found in the warm air above its respective frontal surface and most often above the 500-mb. (18,000 feet, very nearly) position of the front. This relationship has immediate value to the meteorologist, for, by means of it, he is able to estimate the location of a high-level jet stream from temperature data at the relatively low level of 500 mb., even in the absence of high-level wind observations. Furthermore, knowing which front he is dealing with, he can provide a reasonable estimate of the height of the axis. One other feature brought out by extensive cross-section studies is that the strongest winds at any level below the axis are invariably found in the warmer air.

JET STREAM WINDS

The wind speeds in the jet-stream cross section shown in Illus. 85 are not particularly high compared with those found at lower latitudes. Both the maritime arctic and polar jet streams consistently exhibit stronger winds on any given occasion. In fact, the strongest winds are found where two or more jet streams move closely to one another. Although this can occur anywhere, the preferred locations for such intense jet streams are the eastern coastlines of the Asian and North American Continents.

What are the highest wind speeds likely to be found in jet

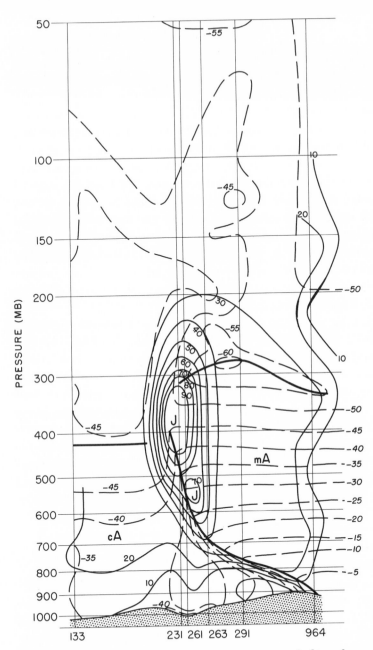

ILLUS. 85—View of continental-arctic jet stream seen looking downwind. Lower numbers identify Alaskan and Yukon stations. Ordinate is pressure in mb. Solid lines are isotachs in knots. Broken lines are isotherms in °C. Heavy solid lines show frontal surface and tropopause. (After McIntyre and Lee, 1954.)

streams? In the past, wind-speed measurements as high as 400 knots have frequently been reported in weather messages. However, when the original observations, which are obtained by balloon-tracking methods, are carefully checked, they are invariably found to be in error. For example, a reported 400-knot wind over Philadelphia late in January 1955 was checked and found to be incorrect on account of instrumental difficulties. The revised estimate of the maximum wind was around 270 knots. Recently a number of accurate wind measurements have been made by aircraft flying across selected jet streams. The highest reliable measurement made by this method up to November 1955 is 290 knots. However, it must be stressed that this figure does not necessarily belie the accuracy of winds reported by other aircraft not similarly equipped. A case in point is the encounter by a *Comet* of a 350-knot wind over Tokyo.

Another significant feature of jet streams is brought out by the vertical cross section in Illus. 85 — the asymmetry of the wind distribution about the axis. The speeds decrease more slowly with distance on the right side of the axis than on the left side, facing downstream. Thus, a pilot wishing to maintain strong tailwinds would find it advantageous to stay to the right of the jet-stream axis, where a slight shift in location relative to it will produce little change in the tailwind component. A corresponding shift on the left side of the axis will result in a considerably larger decrease in the tailwind. Now, on the right side of the jet stream, the wind can drop off at a rate as high as 35 knots per 100 nautical miles. On the left side, however, there can be a much greater rate of decrease in wind speed with distance; actual measurements have shown rates as high as 100 knots per 100 nautical miles.

It is also important to know the wind-speed variations in the vertical, or vertical wind shear. Above and below the jet axis, the wind speed decreases at an average rate of 10 to 15 knots per 1,000 feet. Extreme values of the vertical wind shear have been found to be as high as 30 to 35 knots per 1,000 feet by B–47 flights. Generally speaking, it is only necessary to fly at right angles to the wind for a short distance at the same height, simultaneously taking frequent observations of air temperature, to find whether one is above or below the axis. If the temperature changes very little, one will know the flight level is near the level of maximum wind speed. If the temperature increases while flying to the left of the wind, one can conclude that the flight level is above the level of maximum wind. Finally, if the temperature decreases while flying to the left, the flight level will be below the level of maximum wind. This association of the vertical wind shear with the horizontal temperature field is known to meteorologists as the "thermal-wind relationship." It has been exploited by many commercial airline pilots to locate high winds on long flights across the Atlantic and Pacific Oceans. By way of example, Capt. Bernard C. Frost of B.O.A.C., in flying the North Atlantic routes between 15,000 and 25,000 feet, found that the outside air thermometer was a very valuable guide to the location of jet-stream winds. Once in a strong wind at a certain altitude, he found that the strong wind could be maintained by flying along the same isotherm. He further states:

> An amazingly accurate guide for calculation of wind strength on either side of the jet stream (within altitude limits normally flown; viz. 15,000–25,000 ft.) was that the wind decreased some 8 knots for every degree Centigrade drop in temperature on the polar (or cold) side; and it decreased some 16 knots for every degree Centigrade rise on the equatorial (or warm) side.

N. E. Davis, writing in the September 1954 issue of the *Meteorological Magazine,* described a successful transatlantic crossing in a jet stream by a B.O.A.C. *Stratocruiser,* under Capt. L. V. Messenger and Navigating Officer M. H. Sutcliff, on August 2–3, 1953. By the judicious use of their outside air thermometer, they were able to locate and fly for three hours (about 1,000 miles) in the strong winds below a jet stream. The penetration of the jet stream from the cold side was indicated by a sudden rise in air temperature.

Therefore, to maintain strong tailwinds when flying below the jet axis, one should endeavor to stay in the warm air. Above the jet stream, one should try to stay in the colder air to the right of the jet axis. In a similar manner, the temperature field can be used to detect and maintain a track along which the headwinds will be more favorable, if one is flying into the wind.

Research flights across jet streams have revealed some interesting details of the wind field in the vicinity of their axes. The results of several such flights under project AROWA have recently been published. They have shown that the wind speed is rather variable within a jet-stream core. Winds have also been found to vary considerably with time at a fixed point. For instance, Lt. Col. R. C. Bundgaard, U.S.A.F., reported that the wind speed changed from 120 knots to 60 knots, and again to 120 knots, within 4 hours at 34,000 feet over Dayton, Ohio, on March 5, 1954. On another occasion, five B–47's observed a wind change from 200 to 72 knots at 40,000 feet over Alabama during a 3-hour period on April 14, 1953. Such variations are impossible to forecast at the present state of knowledge. It is hoped that further research into the mechanics of air motion will provide answers in the future.

CLOUD FORMS OF THE JET STREAM

Through the work of Dr. Vincent J. Schaefer, of the Munitalp Foundation, Inc., and many military as well as commercial pilots, there has now been gathered considerable information on cloud forms associated with jet streams. This knowledge can be used as an auxiliary tool to locate jet streams.

Dr. Schaefer has found four main cloud types associated with jet streams. They are cirrus, cirrocumulus, lenticular altocumulus, and altocumulus, extending from horizon to horizon, and having waves at right angles to the air flow. From the ground, these clouds can be observed to move at great speeds, often resulting in rapid local changes in cloud cover during short intervals of time. Illus. 83 shows three of Dr. Schaefer's remarkable photographs of typical jet-stream clouds as observed from the ground.[2]

Aloft, cloud formations at various levels can often give indications of the wind direction. Under conditions of high winds, an upper cloud surface will show streaks in the direction of the wind and a billow structure at right angles to these streaks, in a manner analogous to wind lanes on a sea surface with a superimposed transverse wave pattern.

---

[2] The writer wishes to express his gratitude to Dr. Schaefer for permission to publish these photographs.

CLEAR-AIR TURBULENCE

It was once thought that aviation hazards, such as icing and turbulence, were confined to the lower troposphere, and that, once aircraft could fly "above the weather," all problems of flight comfort would be solved. This myth exploded when high-altitude aircraft encountered turbulence as violent as that encountered at low levels. The bumpiness, or turbulence, is described by those who have experienced it to be like the pounding of a fast speedboat racing across a very choppy sea surface. Since there is no visual warning, it has been called clear-air turbulence.

In order to ascertain the nature of this phenomenon, many special research flights have been carried out over the British Isles, Europe, and the United States. Through the kind cooperation of R.C.A.F. personnel, the Meteorological Service of Canada has also acquired and studied numerous turbulence reports. The conclusions reached by various investigators are largely in agreement, but there are also contradictions which will only be resolved by further research.

Clear-air turbulence can occur at any level of the atmosphere flown thus far. It is generally found in isolated patches 50 to 100 miles in length and width. These patches consist of one or more layers, the vertical thicknesses of which are generally not great, being of the order of 500 to 3,000 feet. On occasion, thicknesses of 6,000 feet or more have been reported. Because clear-air turbulence occurs in layers, a satisfactory method of moving out of turbulent air is to change altitude by 1,500 to 2,000 feet.

Clear-air turbulence has been found to occur in the vicinity of jet streams where the wind speed varies greatly with distance in the horizontal or vertical. Thus, the regions above, below, and to the left of the jet axis, facing downstream, are the preferred locations of turbulence. The air in the core of the jet stream and to its right is smooth by comparison. If an aircraft is flying parallel to a jet stream, an attempt should be made to fly on the right side of the jet axis, because not only would there be a smaller chance of encountering turbulence, but also there would be the added advantage of maintaining strong tailwinds.

The frequency of various intensities of turbulence has been studied by J. Clodman, of the Meteorological Division. Analysis of more than 500 reports of aircraft turbulence over a height range of 18,000 to 45,000 feet revealed the following results. For three stations where reports of nonoccurrences were also made, about a quarter of all flights encountered turbulence. Fifty-two percent of these occurrences were classed as light, 25 percent as moderate, 5 percent as heavy, and 3 percent as severe. The remainder were classified as light to moderate or moderate to heavy. Hence the majority of these occurrences were in the light or moderate range. The few cases of moderate and heavy turbulence occurred in layers not greater than 3,500 feet in depth, in agreement with the results obtained in Britain.

A comparison of the frequency of turbulence reports at each level with the frequency of time flown at each level showed that they were almost identical, from which it is inferred that the probability of encountering turbulence at any level from 18,000 to 45,000 feet is approximately the same.

A study of turbulence reports collected on *Canberra* test flights over Britain was described by Eric Hyde, test pilot of Short Bros. and Harland Ltd., of Belfast, in the April 1954 issue of *Flight*. The general conclusions are similar to those reached elsewhere. However, they do report that the intensity of turbulence decreased with increasing height. For example, all cases of severe and violent turbulence were encountered below 30,000 feet, the area most affected being around 25,000 to 29,000 feet. The highest recorded altitude of turbulence was 49,000 feet, where only light turbulence was felt. Only rarely was turbulence encountered above the tropopause, and it was never greater than moderate. In contrast to experience elsewhere, there were many flights through well-documented jet streams which yielded no trace of turbulence at all.

THE ARCTIC STRATOSPHERIC JET STREAM

Just as the decade following the end of World War II saw the growth and consolidation of our knowledge about tropospheric jet streams, so did the next few years see the direction of research turn to the virtually unknown stratosphere and mesosphere. The

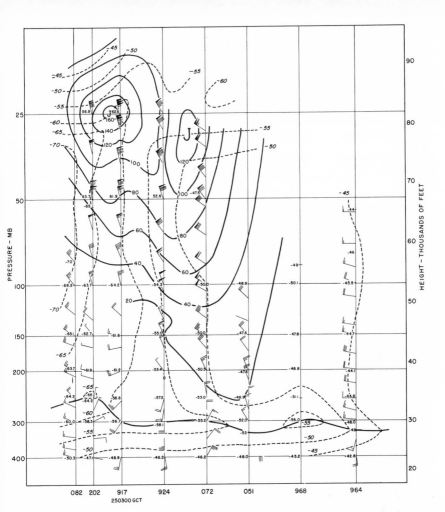

ILLUS. 86—Vertical cross section of the Arctic stratospheric jet stream, 1500
GCT, February 26, 1956. Tropopause is indicated by thick solid
line, isotherms (C) by broken lines, and isotachs of observed northwesterly winds in the stratosphere by thin solid lines (knots).
(After Lee and Godson, Journal of Meteorology.)

development of vastly improved balloon-borne sensing instruments capable of reaching 100,000 feet made possible the systematic exploration of the middle stratosphere, while rocket probes
permitted pioneering studies of the higher levels.

One of the early successes of stratospheric research was the factual verification of a well-defined winter westerly jet stream in the
stratosphere at high latitudes, now called the Arctic stratospheric
jet stream or polar-night maximum. As in the case of tropospheric

jet streams, indirect evidence implying its existence appeared as early as 1934 in a report by Palmén, who presented a mean meridional vertical cross section of temperature showing a circumpolar warm belt in the stratosphere at approximately 55° N. in winter, to the north of which temperatures decreased rapidly to about 75° N. This zone of strong horizontal temperature gradient was then known to extend to at least 70,000 feet above sea level. Moreover, the near coincidence of this zone with the intersection of the earth's shadow cone and the ozone layer strongly suggested that it owed its existence to differential solar radiational heating of the ozonosphere across the boundary of polar darkness. A concerted effort to synthesize the prevailing sparse upper wind data in the polar regions by Canadian meteorologists gradually unfolded the grand pattern of the Arctic stratosphere at high latitudes. While the behavior of the Arctic stratosphere appears to vary in detail from year to year, it is nevertheless possible to describe in general terms its more striking aspects which seem to recur with rhythmic regularity.

To grasp in outline a typical annual cycle of events, consider the spherical shell of ozone surrounding the earth concentrated in the layer 40,000 to 150,000 feet above mean sea level, coincident with the stratosphere and commonly called the ozonosphere. Although ozone appears in minute quantities, it plays an important role in filtering out the ultraviolet radiation from the incoming solar beam. It responds strongly to ultraviolet solar heating and reradiates in several infrared bands. During the Northern Hemisphere summer, continuous daylight at the Pole results in higher temperatures near the Pole than in middle latitudes. The summer wind pattern corresponding to this temperature field consists of a broad easterly current from equator to Pole between April and September. Following the autumnal equinox, the radiation pattern reverses in the sense that the stratosphere near the Pole cools more rapidly relative to the middle latitudes which still receive some sunlight. Simultaneously, the summer easterlies weaken and gradually give way to westerly winds at high latitudes, which subsequently increase in speed and spread southward, more or less in unison with the southward advance of polar darkness. Curiously enough, a meandering horizontal wave pattern develops in the westerly current, too, similar to that found in tropospheric jet streams as illustrated in Illustration 84, except that there seems to be a preference for one or two waves. Hence, once the jet stream becomes established, it moves away from the earth's shadow at certain longitudes as a result of the wave motion, so that it is often found far south in middle latitudes.

The disappearance of the Arctic stratospheric jet stream in the late winter or early spring is a much more spectacular event than its origin. In contrast to the slow, gradual process of transition from stratospheric easterlies to westerlies in the fall, the end is markedly abrupt, often occurring within a matter of four weeks. It is manifested by intense warming of the entire polar stratosphere to temperatures as high as 0° Centigrade, and the warming pattern apparently propagates downward from the mesosphere. This phenomenon, called by Godson "the final warming," is accompanied by the breakdown of the cold stratospheric mass of air over the pole into isolated cells at lower latitudes, the disappearance of the Arctic stratospheric jet stream, and a gradual return to summertime stratospheric easterlies. The "final warming" phenomenon normally occurs in the late winter but is known to have taken place as early as January. When it happens this early, there is a return to weak westerly winds followed by a transition to stratospheric easterlies in the spring.

The typical structure of the Arctic stratospheric jet stream is illustrated by a vertical cross section for the winter of 1955–56 shown in Illus. 86. The plane of the cross section extends from Alert near northern Greenland on the left to Whitehorse in the Yukon, on the right. Data for the cross section were obtained from the following stations shown in Illus. 87: Alert (082), Thule (202), Eureka (917), Resolute (924), Mould Bay (072), Sachs Harbour (051), Aklavik (968), and Whitehorse (964). The northwesterly winds at and above the 100 mb. level shown by the wind arrows are nearly at right angles to the plane of the cross section, so that this would be the view as seen by an observer in the polar basin looking toward the southeast. The highest reported wind on the cross section is 160 knots at around 80,000 feet at Eureka (917), not unlike the 200-knot winds often found at these levels in midwinter, when the atmosphere over the Pole is in complete darkness

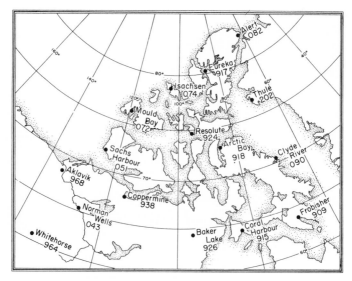

ILLUS. 87—*Upper-air stations in the Canadian Arctic. (After Lee and Godson,* Journal of Meteorology.)

to a height of several hundreds of miles. The intense horizontal temperature gradient is clearly evident from the temperature field below the jet stream which shows an increase from $-70°$ to $-50°$ Centigrade in a distance of 800 miles. Owing to some irregularity in the orientation of the cross section, there is some uncertainty in the reality of the double wind maximum.

The winter stratospheric jet stream and its cyclical pattern of events is not confined to the northern hemisphere — it has been found to have a counterpart in the Antarctic as well. The annual cycle in the southern hemisphere is also similar except for a phase difference of around six months.

The discovery of this radiationally induced monsoonal pattern in the high-latitude stratospheric wind and temperature fields is one of the exciting developments of the mid-20th century. Its role in the general circulation of the atmosphere is only partially understood. Nevertheless, it is possible to anticipate in some measure its impact on supersonic jet transports planned to cruise between 65,000 and 75,000 feet. Hopefully, too, we can look forward to the day when scientists will succeed in unifying the phenomenon of jet streams with the myriad facets of our endlessly fascinating atmosphere.

HENRY G. HOUGHTON

An Appraisal of Cloud Seeding as a Means of Increasing Precipitation

[FROM THE SMITHSONIAN REPORT FOR 1951[1]]

ONE OF THE *greatest challenges facing the scientists of the world today is to determine the possibility of controlling the weather. Hurricanes, tornadoes and prolonged drought pose the most serious atmospheric threats to mankind and these phenomena are under intensive study by meteorologists. The first serious scientific effort to modify the weather has been the seeding of clouds in an effort to increase rainfall. In this article and the supplementary note that follows it, Prof. Henry G. Houghton, Head of the Department of Meteorology at the Massachusetts Institute of Technology, reviews the efforts made to date to increase precipitation by cloud seeding and views them in the light of the available knowledge of atmospheric processes. He warns against accepting at face value some of the overoptimistic claims made by nonscientists and news writers. Although he is forced to conclude that there is as yet no convincing evidence that cloud seeding can lead to substantial increases in precipitation, this does not mean that he is pessimistic*

---

[1] Revised as of February 1965 by the addition of a supplementary note at end of article.

about the long-term prospects of weather modification. He simply feels that we do not yet know enough about the complex factors involved in the precipitation process to devise the crucial experiments that may lead to effective means for supplementary natural rainfall. The present disagreements between meteorologists and potential water users on premature exploitation must not be permitted to interfere with a broad and continuing program of research that offers the best hope for ultimate success in achieving some useful control of weather.

THE TREMENDOUS economic implications of the artificial control of rainfall have led to overoptimistic statements in the public press and to ill-advised commercial applications of rain-making techniques by persons who do not possess the necessary technical qualifications. These events have been viewed with concern by all responsible meteorologists. It is unfortunate that much of the money which has been spent by public and private agencies in an effort to increase precipitation in specific areas has contributed so little to our scientific understanding of the processes involved. Without adequate scientific information it is impossible to determine, with any assurance, the economic value of cloud seeding or to prescribe the most favorable conditions and procedures.

As in the case of all scientific research, the several groups and individuals who are working in this field have criticized one another's experiments and interpretations. This normal scientific interchange has been unduly accentuated by the glare of publicity which has caused some of those concerned to be more dogmatic than is justifiable in view of the present incomplete information. In the view of the public the meteorological world has been divided into believers and nonbelievers. This is an unfortunate and ridiculous concept. The fact is simply that the information at hand is not sufficient to permit an unequivocal conclusion regarding the possibilities of the artificial control of precipitation.

It is the purpose of this paper to assess the seeding techniques for stimulating precipitation on the basis of present scientific information and to point out the more significant gaps in our knowledge. The writer has not been associated with any of the research groups in this field but has kept himself informed through the literature and personal contact with many of the active investigators. For the sake of brevity and continuity no specific references will be made to papers and reports describing the results of seeding experiments. The summary of the results as required for the present discussion is well known to most readers. Those who wish to read the original accounts are referred to the excellent bibliography recently published (1).[2] It is not the intent of the writer to attempt to refute or support specific claims of individuals; rather it is proposed to survey the subject as impersonally as possible. Lack of complete information makes the inclusion of certain personal opinions of the writer inevitable.

METHODS AND RESULTS

Modern rain making owes its origin to the discovery by Schaefer (2) that the insertion of dry ice or any object colder than about $-40°$ C. into a supercooled water-drop cloud converts the cloud to ice crystals. Later Vonnegut (3) showed that the same result could be obtained by introducing tiny crystals of silver iodide, which are presumed to act as sublimation nuclei because of the dimensional similarity of the crystal lattices of silver iodide and ice. The mechanism by which dry ice forms ice crystals is still in debate, as is the whole problem of sublimation nuclei, but it is a demonstrable fact that either agent will convert a supercooled cloud to an ice cloud. Knowledge of the mechanism of ice-crystal formation is desirable, however, for an estimate of the number of ice crystals created by a known amount of the nucleating agent.

The application of the nucleating agents to rain making is based on the Bergeron-Findeisen ice-crystal theory of precipitation. According to this theory, all moderate to heavy precipitation is initiated by the appearance of a few ice crystals in a supercooled cloud. By virtue of the fact that the vapor pressure over ice is less

---

[2] Numbers in parentheses refer to bibliography at end of this article.

than that over water at temperatures below freezing, the ice crystals grow by sublimation at the expense of the supercooled water drops. If the number of ice crystals is very small compared to the number of water drops, the ice crystals will become large enough to fall. After further growth by sublimation and collision they leave the cloud as precipitation elements. It was suggested that many natural supercooled clouds do not release precipitation because of a failure by nature to provide ice crystals. The use of the newly discovered methods for producing ice crystals in a supercooled cloud to initiate precipitation in such clouds was a logical step.

The reported results of cloud-seeding experiments have been quite diverse. In a vast majority of the tests there had been visible evidence of the transformation of supercooled clouds to ice crystals. It seems safe to conclude that the occasional absence of such effects has been due to poor observing conditions or to the choice of a cloud which either was not sufficiently supercooled or was already composed of ice crystals. Nucleation of stratiform clouds often leads to the production of "valleys" or "canyons" and occasionally to the formation of holes through which the ground may be seen. Holes seem to occur most often when the cloud deck is relatively thin. The effect of the seeding is observed to progress laterally from the seeding line, often reaching a width of 1 to 2 miles in 30 to 50 minutes. Precipitation in the form of virga is a common observation, but only rarely does any precipitation reach the surface from stratiform clouds.

The observational evidence on the effects of seeding cumulus clouds is extremely varied. Again there is evidence that seeding converts the supercooled portions to ice crystals, but observation is much more difficult. It appears that some cumulus clouds dissipate when seeded, some are little affected, and, occasionally, accelerated vertical development results. Reports on precipitation range from none to very heavy. It is extremely difficult to say whether the precipitation results from seeding or from natural processes independent of the seeding. Observations made in a few cases of the elapsed time between seeding and the appearance of the precipitation are reasonably consistent, suggesting a cause-and-effect relationship. The data suggest that small cumulus clouds are usually partially or completely dissipated by seeding. It appears that the seeding of more active cumulus clouds often results in virga or light precipitation and, very occasionally, in heavier precipitation. Claims have been made that the seeding of large cumulus clouds under proper conditions may lead to the development of widespread precipitation. Very few cases of this type have been reported.

Langmuir (4) has suggested that "warm" clouds, in which the ice nuclei can have no effect, may be induced to precipitate by seeding them with water. The injected water drops grow as they fall by colliding with the cloud drops. If the cloud is deep and wet with strong updrafts the drops may grow to such size that they will rupture. The broken portions might then be carried up in the updraft so that the process would become self-sustaining. The conditions requisite for the operation of this process are likely to be those that lead to natural precipitation. A few tests of water seeding have been made but results are still inconclusive. There is little question that injected water drops will grow by collision and fall out as rain but there is reason to doubt that the continuing process visualized by Langmuir can operate except in clouds that are ready to release precipitation from natural causes. Because of the lack of adequate tests of this method and the more widespread interest in seeding with ice nuclei, no further discussion of the water-seeding process will be undertaken here.

ARTIFICIAL NUCLEI

Taken by itself the observational evidence, reviewed very briefly above, does not constitute an adequate basis for a sound appraisal of the potentialities of the cloud-seeding techniques. It is the purpose of this paper to amplify and supplement the observational evidence with the aid of existing knowledge of cloud physics and synoptic meteorology. It is considered that both the laboratory and flight experiments prove beyond any reasonable doubt that dry ice and silver iodide will both convert a supercooled water cloud to an ice-crystal cloud. The only necessary condition is that the cloud temperature be a few degrees below the freezing point. For silver iodide, Vonnegut (5) states that the maximum temperature is near $-4°$ C.; dry ice has been shown to cause ice crystals to appear at $-0.7°$ C. (6), but the temperature should be low enough to allow an appreciable difference between the vapor pressures over water and ice. There is no reason to doubt that ice crystals will grow in a supercooled cloud. The size attained by the crystals is dependent on their number, the initial liquid water content of the cloud, the temperature and the depth of the supercooled portion of the cloud. It is an essential feature of the Bergeron-Findeisen precipitation theory that the number of ice crystals be small compared to the number of supercooled drops; otherwise the terminal size of the ice crystals would be of the same order as that of the cloud drops and no precipitation would ensue. There is no satisfactory information on the number of ice crystals produced by dry ice. The estimate of Langmuir (7) that one pellet of dry ice forms 10^{16} ice nuclei would imply concentrations of the order of 10^3 nuclei/cm.^{3} even if the nuclei produced by a few pounds of dry ice were distributed through several cubic miles of cloud. Quantitative estimates of the number of nuclei produced by silver-iodide generators have been made, but it is nearly impossible to estimate their concentration in the cloud after release. Atmospheric seeding experiments have resulted in the formation of precipitation elements with a wide range of seeding rates. The inference is either that a much smaller number of nuclei is formed than has been estimated or that there is a marked selective action such that only a small fraction of the nuclei become ice crystals. If the latter is true, the situation would be analogous to natural condensation in which only a small fraction of the total number of condensation nuclei become cloud drops. It is not intended to imply that overseeding is impossible, but it appears that this has seldom been an important factor in the seeding experiments which have been reported. When dry-ice pellets are dropped the initial seeding is in a vertical plane from which the ice crystals appear to diffuse laterally. It would be expected that the concentration of "seeds" would be a maximum at the center and would decrease rapidly on either side. If overseeding occurs anywhere it should be found along the seeding line. There is no convincing evidence of overseeding in this region.

It may be concluded that it is often possible to release some precipitation from supercooled clouds by seeding them. The pertinent question is how much precipitation can be released in this way which would not fall from natural causes. If the answer to this is unfavorable, it is still important to know whether the time of release of precipitation and the total precipitation can be altered by seeding.

Unless the seeded cloud is replenished, the upper limit to the precipitation is determined by the total liquid water contained in a vertical column through the cloud. Measurements indicate that a liquid water content of 1 g/m³ is rather a high value. If all the water in a cloud 10,000 feet deep of this water content were deposited as rain, the total rainfall would be about one-eighth of an inch. This is clearly an overestimate, since it is not likely that all the water could be precipitated and some would evaporate before reaching the ground. Most clouds would contain less water than has been assumed in this example. It is concluded that, unless the cloud is continuously replenished, the precipitation released by seeding will be very light and the cloud will be partially or completely dissipated by the removal of its water. Stratiform clouds have released practically no precipitation when seeded, as would be expected in view of their small total water content.

THERMODYNAMIC EFFECTS

It is next in order to consider the ways in which seeding might stimulate the growth and replenishment of the cloud. The phase transformation induced by the seeding releases the latent heat of fusion and the latent heat of sublimation of the water vapor which sublimes as a result of the lower equilibrium vapor pressure over ice. The exact value of the resultant temperature rise of the air depends on the initial temperature, the air density, and the liquid water content, but for a typical case it is of the order of 1° C. It is important to note that this heating occurs only in the supercooled portion of the cloud and that the temperature rise ordinarily increases with elevation. To be really effective the heating should occur in the lower part of the cloud and below the cloud base. Unless there is a temperature inversion of $1°$ C. or more, the heating will produce accelerated vertical motion in the supercooled portion with a maximum near the cloud top. As a consequence, there will be horizontal inflow above the freezing level. It is probable that a small pressure fall will ensue with a correspondingly small horizontal inflow into the column below the freezing level. None of these effects will induce additional vertical motion below the freezing level since they do not provide buoyancy forces in the lower levels. Air cannot be "sucked" up but must be driven up by a force applied to each element of the air column. There will be a tendency for the supercooled portion of the cloud to separate from the portion below the freezing level. Unless the environment above this level is very moist and the lapse rate steep, it is doubtful that there will be any marked growth of the upper portion of the cloud. If there is to be an acceleration of the cloud development as a result of the heat released by seeding, a natural convective circulation must be active in the lower layers. If this natural convection has been terminated somewhere above the freezing level by a small inversion or a slightly stable lapse rate, the heat released by seeding may extend the convective activity upward. This requires rather special conditions. It may be remarked that a temperature rise of $1°$ C. in the upper portion of a cloud is not very impressive when viewed on an adiabatic chart. The evaporation of the solid carbon-dioxide pellets will cause the cooling of the air through which they pass. This will cause localized subsidence, but in view of the small amounts of carbon dioxide used this cooling will have little effect after the first few seconds.

An effect similar to the heating discussed above will result if the liquid water of the supercooled cloud is caused to precipitate. This removal of mass will result in an upward acceleration. It is easy to show that the removal of 1 g of water per cubic meter will cause the same vertical acceleration as a temperature rise of about $0.3°$ C. Note, however, that the falling precipitation will impose a downward acceleration on the lower levels of the cloud. This downward acceleration will increase as the precipitation elements grow in their fall through the cloud. It is believed that this downward force of the precipitation is partly responsible for the downdraft in a mature thunderstorm. The convective circulation in a thunderstorm is strong enough to maintain an upward motion in part of the cloud in spite of the downdraft. It is hard to see how the release of precipitation from a seeded cloud can increase the convective circulation.

It is reasonable to conclude that seeding only rarely will stimulate the vertical development of a cloud. In the vast majority of cases dissipative effects are to be expected. These conclusions seem to be borne out by the results of cloud-seeding tests.

ARTIFICIAL VERSUS NATURAL NUCLEI

The basic premise of the method for the release of precipitation by seeding is that there is often an insufficient number of natural nuclei of sublimation or crystallization present in supercooled clouds to initiate precipitation by the Bergeron-Findeisen mechanism. The regular existence of supercooled clouds in the atmosphere supports this assumption. Present knowledge of the concentration and properties of natural nuclei of crystallization and sublimation is incomplete. Supercooled clouds are much more frequent than ice-crystal clouds down to about $-10°$ to $-15°$ C. At lower temperature ice-crystal clouds become more and more frequent although supercooled clouds have been reported at temperatures at least as low as $-35°$ C. Measurements of the number of ice crystals appearing in an expansion chamber by Findeisen and Schultz (8) have indicated that the first crystals appear in the neighborhood of $-7°$ C. The number of crystals formed was found to increase slowly as the temperature was lowered. At a temperature variously reported to be from $-32°$ to $-42°$ C. a very large increase in the number of crystals occurs. Thus, this experimental evidence is in general accordance with the observed temperature distribution of supercooled clouds. The nuclei introduced by seeding are active at temperatures of about $-5°$ C. and below. It is well to point out here that it is not at all certain that ice crystals are a necessary prerequisite for natural precipitation. Moderate rain often falls from tropical clouds that do not extend to the freezing level. The mechanism responsible for such precipitation presumably can operate also in a supercooled cloud although the ice-crystal mechanism is more effective if the ice crystals are present.

The vertical development of convective clouds is often terminated by an inversion. If the temperature at the top of such a cloud were below $-5°$ C. but still not low enough to activate the natural ice nuclei, seeding might release rain that otherwise would not fall. From the prior discussion it is evident that the precipitation could be substantial only if the cloud were also deep and in active development. This is the most interesting case considered so far. It is difficult to estimate the frequency of occurrence of the requisite combination of conditions from the data that are available. Certainly many convective clouds are topped by inversions at a temperature level of between, say, $-5°$ and $-20°$ C. but how many of them remain in active development after they reach the inversion and in how many cases is there a lack of natural freezing nuclei? Even though it might not be possible to secure data on the freezing nuclei, a well-designed observational program should help to answer these questions.

It is of interest to consider whether continuous seeding would be required to maintain precipitation in the case discussed above. It has been suggested that when snow crystals are once formed they shed tiny splinters as they fall, which then serve as very effective sublimation nuclei. If this happens, the process would tend to be self-perpetuating, after the initial seeding, as long as the circulation was such as to carry the splinters into the updrafts. Information on splintering is very incomplete and no definite conclusions can be drawn. It seems probable that the effectiveness of this process depends on the form of the snow crystals; the dendritic (feathery) type would appear to be a much better source of splinters than the columnar and tabular forms. It has been stated that natural snow often appears to fall from below the $-10°$ C. level, thus suggesting that something like the splintering process is active. A more careful study of this might yield some useful clues, particularly if samples of the snow crystals could be obtained. If splintering does not occur, continuous seeding would be required.

SEEDING OF PRECIPITATING CLOUDS

It is next in order to consider the possibility that seeding will alter the timing or the total amount of precipitation that falls from a cloud which is about to release precipitation from natural causes. It is almost impossible to answer this by means of individual seeding experiments. An objective answer might be obtained by seeding all potential rain clouds over a well-defined area for a long period of time (a year or more) and then comparing the precipitation in the area to that in similar control areas. Even here, there are pitfalls and the experiment should be very carefully designed in advance by a competent statistician-meteorologist team.

Evidence has been presented above that the activation temperatures of the artificially introduced ice nuclei are higher than those of most of the natural ice nuclei. If an active cloud, which is about to release precipitation by natural processes, is seeded, the onset of precipitation may be advanced by the time interval which would be required for the cloud to grow from the temperature level corresponding to the activation of the artificial seeds to that of the natural ice nuclei. The vertical distance between these levels might be of the order of 2 km. The corresponding time interval might range from, say, 20 minutes for an active cumulus to a few hours for frontal cloud systems. This might provide a means for increasing the precipitation in a selected area from a given cloud even though the total precipitation from the cloud were not changed. The net increase of precipitation in a given area from a large number of clouds would be small because only a few of them would be in the proper stage of development as they approached the area. It is possible that the seeding would decrease the precipitation from the cloud by causing the precipitation elements to form at a lower level, thus decreasing the total water condensed in the cloud. It may be concluded that although the time of precipitation may be advanced, it would be difficult to obtain any practical advantage from this prospect except under very special circumstances.

Because of inadequate knowledge of natural precipitation processes it is not possible to make an unequivocal statement as to whether or not it is possible to increase the rainfall from a precipitating cloud by seeding it. Precipitation requires vertical motion and the consequent condensation of water vapor followed by a process which converts the condensed water vapor into larger elements which can fall to the ground. A "precipitation efficiency" might be defined as the ratio of the rainfall to the mass of water vapor in the rising current. An efficiency of 100 percent could be achieved only if all the water vapor were condensed and all the condensate were converted to precipitation. The "precipitation efficiency" can be considered as the product of a "condensation efficiency" and the efficiency with which the condensate is converted to precipitation elements. The condensation efficiency is determined primarily by how far the water vapor is lifted. The efficiency of conversion of the condensate to precipitation depends on the temperature at which the ice nuclei operate and on their number. The condensate which is not converted to precipitation finds its way into the downward circulation required by continuity and is evaporated. Seeding provides ice nuclei which are active at a lower elevation (higher temperature) than the natural ice nuclei. If there is an insufficient number of natural ice nuclei which are active at or above the lowest temperature in the cloud, seeding might increase the precipitation by reducing the amount of condensate which would otherwise be lost in the descending branch of the circulation (increase in the efficiency or conversion). On the other hand, if there is a sufficient number of natural ice nuclei which are active at temperatures found within the cloud, seeding may reduce the precipitation by causing the precipitation mechanism to operate at a lower level in the cloud where less of the water vapor will have been condensed (decrease of the condensation efficiency). Finally, if the splintering mechanism is a regular and effective natural means of nucleating clouds once precipitation has started, seeding will have no effect since splinters of ice are the best possible ice nuclei. Lack of knowledge on the number and type of natural ice nuclei and on the importance of the splintering effect leaves the answer in doubt. It is the opinion of the writer that a significant fraction of the condensed cloud water is often lost by evaporation in the downward branches of the circulation. If true, this suggests that the precipitation can be increased by seeding if the proper number of nuclei can be introduced in the right place.

It has been suggested that silver-iodide nuclei may be effective at a considerable distance from the point of release. There is no doubt that the particles can be transported for considerable distances by the winds. The particles will diffuse laterally and vertically, thus infecting an increasing volume of air with a corresponding decrease in concentration. It is not known with certainty how long the silver-iodide particles will retain their nucleating ability. The chance that the nuclei will encounter the proper conditions is evidently increased by permitting them to diffuse and cover considerable areas. On the other hand, this makes the task of assessing the results exceedingly difficult. There is little to gain from this technique at least until more adequate information is available on the effects of seeding individual clouds under carefully determined meteorological conditions.

LARGE-SCALE EFFECTS

The general conclusion reached so far is that seeding may induce significant amounts of precipitation only under rather special conditions which are very close to or identical with those that lead to natural precipitation. Suppose that these conditions are met and the cloud or clouds are seeded. Under the most ideal conditions the seeding may result in enhanced convective activity and the release of precipitation. The amount of precipitation is limited by the large-scale horizontal transport of water vapor into the area. This can be increased only by the creation or intensification of a circulation the size of a cyclone. There is no evidence that local convective activity will lead to cyclogenesis. In fact, widespread convective activity often breaks out in an area characterized by flat pressure gradients without any subsequent effect on the pressure distribution. It must be admitted that knowledge of the causes and mechanism of cyclogenesis is incomplete but there is evidence that changes in the upper troposphere and stratosphere are important. It is difficult to imagine any influence of seeding at these heights. This is consistent with other evidence which strongly suggests that the location of cyclogenetical areas is largely determined by the large-scale hemispheric circulation patterns rather than by local effects. If seeding increases the amount of precipitation it will also result in a proportionate increase in the latent heat released. If a substantial increase in precipitation could be produced over a large area the latent energy released would doubtless have an effect on the circulation pattern though not necessarily in the region of increased rainfall. Natural precipitation anomalies are much larger than those which might conceivably be produced by seeding, but even in such cases the effect of the release of latent energy on the circulation is not clear. In any discussion of a net increase of rainfall over large areas it is important to remember that precipitation is only one segment of the hydrologic cycle. An increase in rainfall requires increased evaporation and a greater transport of water vapor. It may be concluded that there is little prospect that cloud seeding will produce large-scale effects in the atmosphere.

The hope that large-scale effects might result from seeding is based in part on the assumption that large segments of the atmosphere are often in a metastable condition such that a small impulse will suffice to release the instability. A logical corollary of this theory is that the point at which the activity will start spontaneously is indeterminate, but that a small artificial impulse may be sufficient to initiate the release of the instability at a predetermined point. If this principle of indeterminacy is correct, it sets a basic limit on the precision with which it is possible to forecast weather. Most meteorologists will agree that this principle often seems to hold in the development of such small-scale phenomena as thunderstorms and tornadoes. This may be due, of course, to the fact that the scale of these phenomena is small compared to the spacing of the observations. In the case of large-scale phenomena there is no real evidence in favor of the indeterminacy principle. To be sure, many errors are made in forecasts, but these appear to be explicable in retrospect when adequate data are available. The motion of such disturbances seems to be continuous without the erratic behavior to be expected from the indeterminacy principle. Studies of the motion and development of cyclones strongly suggest a dependence on the large-scale fields of motion and temperature. These large-scale variations appear to be of much more importance than any small-scale, accidental differences.

SUMMARY AND CONCLUSIONS

The principal conclusions reached in this paper may be summarized as follows:

1. Seeding of supercooled clouds with dry ice or silver iodide will convert the clouds to ice-crystal clouds if the temperature is below about $-5°C$.

2. Seeding of an inactive cloud will not induce an important amount of precipitation.

3. Seeding a cloud will not accelerate the growth of the cloud unless there is active vertical motion below the freezing level and the environment above the freezing level is moist and only slightly stable. Partial or complete dissipation is more likely due to the lifting-off and drying-out of the top of the cloud and the downward force exerted by the falling hydrometeors.

4. Seeding of an active cloud which does not quite reach the activation temperature of the natural ice nuclei may release useful precipitation.

5. It appears possible to advance the onset of precipitation from a cloud that is about to precipitate from natural causes by seeding it.

6. The possibility of increasing precipitation initiated by natural processes by seeding cannot be determined because of incomplete information about natural precipitation processes. There is at least some possibility that the precipitation can be increased in certain cases.

7. The conditions under which it appears possible that seeding might cause, or increase, precipitation are almost or exactly the same as those required for the natural release of precipitation.

8. Inasmuch as the most favorable conditions for the augmenta-

tion of precipitation by seeding are almost or exactly the same as those requisite for natural precipitation, definitive results cannot be expected from isolated seeding experiments.

9. On the basis of present physical knowledge and synoptic experience there appears to be no prospect that large-scale effects can be produced by seeding.

In view of the above conclusions, it is considered that attempts at the practical application of cloud-seeding techniques to increase natural rainfall are premature. The entire problem is still in the research stage, and any funds available should be devoted to research on the basic mechanisms involved. Useful research results cannot be expected from personnel without extensive training and experience in cloud physics and synoptic meteorology.

It is the opinion of the writer that not enough attention has been paid to the meteorological factors in most of the past cloud-seeding experiments. It is believed that this omission is in large part responsible for some of the diametrically opposed conclusions of certain workers in this field.

There are two general approaches to further research in this field: full-scale experimentation with a properly designed experimental plan and adequate meteorological data; and detailed studies of cloud physics, both in the laboratory and in the free atmosphere. If possible, both approaches should be prosecuted simultaneously. The second plan is less expensive than the first and promises more fundamental results. However, the full-scale experimental trials must be made in the end since a complete knowledge of cloud physics would still leave out some important meteorological factors.

In some quarters it is argued that cloud seeding has been a failure and that further experimentation is unwarranted in view of the high cost. It must be admitted that the high hopes of weather control proclaimed by the popular press have not been realized. Nevertheless, the demonstration that several cubic miles of supercooled cloud can be converted to ice crystals with a few ounces or pounds of suitable material is extremely spectacular in the light of previous efforts to control meteorological processes. This should be sufficient to stimulate further investigation. It is quite possible that further fundamental discoveries lie ahead which will not be uncovered unless the research is allowed to proceed. It is indeed unfortunate that publicity and argument have clouded the immediate issue, but this must not be allowed to obscure the long-range scientific view.

REFERENCES

1. METEOROLOGICAL ABSTRACTS AND BIBLIOGRAPHY. 1950. Vol. 1, pp. 175–205. (The most important papers listed therein appear to be: C-121, C-122, C-129, C-131, C-140, C-147, C-148, C-149, C-150, C-161, C-165, C-171, C-172, C-173, C-176, C-183, C-189, C-190, C-196, and C-204.)
2. SCHAEFER, V. J. 1946. The production of ice crystals in a cloud of super-cooled water droplets. Science, vol. 104, pp. 457–459, Nov. 15.
3. VONNEGUT, B. 1947. The nucleation of ice formation by silver iodide. Journ. Appl. Phys., vol. 18, pp. 593–595, July.
4. LANGMUIR, I. 1948. The production of rain by a chain reaction in cumulus clouds at temperatures above freezing. Journ. Meteorol., vol. 5, pp. 175–192, October.
5. VONNEGUT, B. 1950. Experiments with silver iodide smokes in the natural atmosphere. Bull. Amer. Meteorol. Soc., vol. 31, pp. 151–157, May.
6. SQUIRES, P., and SMITH, E. J. 1949. The artificial stimulation of precipitation by means of dry ice. Australian Journ. Sci. Res., A. Phys. Sci., vol. 2, pp. 232–245.
7. LANGMUIR, I. 1946. Memorandum on introduction of ice nuclei into clouds. General Electric Res. Lab., Schenectady, N. Y., Aug. 16.
8. FINDEISEN, W., and SCHULTZ, G. 1944. Experimentelle Untersuchungen über die atmosphärische Eisteilchenbildung I. Forsch. u. Erfarhrb. Reichs. Wetterd., Ser. A, No. 27, Berlin.

SUPPLEMENTARY NOTE

The preceding paper was written 15 years ago and a good many tons of cloud-seeding materials have flowed into the atmosphere in the interim. Much research has been carried out both in the laboratory and the atmosphere, which has led to significant advances in our knowledge of atmospheric precipitation processes. To bring the story up to date I will present some brief comments on the more recent developments as they amplify or amend my 1951 paper.

The more active phases of the controversy regarding the efficacy of cloud seeding have subsided but there is still disagreement. For the most part this is now between the scientists and the prospective water users rather than within the scientific community.

Only a few clear-cut results have emerged from the many seeding experiments that have been conducted. It has been demonstrated that supercooled stratiform clouds can be dissipated by seeding them from above and that areas of any desired size can be cleared if a sufficient quantity of dry ice can be distributed over the area from aircraft. Similar success has been achieved in clearing supercooled fog over airports and this is now on an operational basis at certain airports where supercooled fog is a significant operational problem.

Unfortunately no such definitive results have been forthcoming from experiments designed to increase precipitation or to decrease hail. In many cases these experiments have been carefully designed both meteorologically and statistically to be as sensitive as possible to changes in the precipitation. Their failure to yield convincing results does not show that the rainfall was not increased but only that any increase was below the resolution of the experiment. In a typical randomized cloud-seeding experiment some 20 storms may be seeded in a year out of a total of about twice this number. Thus it would take five years to obtain two sets of about 100 cases each of seeded and nonseeded storms for statistical analysis. The inherent variability of storms, secular trends, and the inaccuracy of areal rainfall measurements from rain gauges severely limit the sensitivity of such statistical evaluations.

Progress has been more notable in the understanding of natural precipitation processes. Much has been learned about the properties of ice-forming nuclei, both natural and artificial. Means have been devised for the measurement of the concentrations of natural and artificial nuclei. In a few hundred cases the presumed nuclei of individual snow crystals have been viewed in the electron microscope and identified by electron diffraction. The concentration of natural ice-forming nuclei is found to vary over several orders of magnitude in a rather irregular way. Rather high concentrations have been found in the stratosphere suggesting an extraterrestrial origin, whereas the electron microscope has indicated that the nuclei are clay minerals, thus implying a surface origin. These conclusions are open to certain objections, but there is no reason why they cannot both be correct. An extraterrestrial origin is more intriguing, and there have been two other findings that seem to point in this direction. First, Bowen[3] presented evidence that, on the average over many years, the heaviest rains fell about 30 days after the dates of prominent meteoric showers; he hypothesized that the micrometeoritic particles were acting as nuclei. Second, workers in the United States and Australia announced simultaneously that the rainfall over both hemispheres varied significantly with the phase of the moon. It was suggested that this could be due to some kind of a lunar modulation of the streams of micrometeoric particles. The indeterminate results from cloud seeding using nuclei much more active than micrometeoric material cast doubt on these suggestions. It seems much more likely that the lunar effect is related to tidal phenomena in the atmosphere, but there is room for much further speculation and analysis.

A better understanding of the dynamics and precipitation mechanisms of convective clouds has been gained through numerous studies in the atmosphere, in the laboratory and through the use of numerical models. This has led to the general impression that the dominant precipitation process in convective clouds is the coalescence of cloud particles in the gravitational field. This would seem to explain the general lack of success in increasing convective precipitation through seeding. The possibility still remains of suppressing hail by converting the bulk of the supercooled water to ice, but there is good reason to believe that this would require much more massive seeding than has been used so far. Further studies of the effects of the latent heat released by glaciating a supercooled convective cloud suggest that explosive growth and enhanced precipitation may ensue in a significant fraction of active tropical clouds. A few test seedings have lent support to this conclusion.

Much of the precipitation from typical midlatitude cyclonic storms is probably initiated by the ice-crystal process, although convective elements are frequently embedded in them. In spite of

---

[3] Since this note is not a review in the usual sense, no references to the literature or to the names of investigators are given. The single exception is E. G. Bowen of Australia, whose name is so inextricably attached to his meteoric dust hypothesis.

this and the highly variable concentration of natural ice-forming nuclei, there is no convincing evidence that seeding cyclonic storms leads to increased precipitation. This may be due, in part, to the failure of the nuclei from ground-based silver-iodide generators to penetrate to the appropriate levels. Of more fundamental importance is the fact that a cyclonic storm is a continuously operating machine that draws upon large currents of moist air which are lifted to cause condensation and precipitation. The water that can be stored in the clouds is a very small fraction of the total moisture flowing into the storm during its lifetime. A relatively very small part of the condensed water can be lost from the storm by outflow at high levels. Thus the major part of the condensed water vapor must be precipitated regardless of the details of the precipitation process, and the total precipitation will depend primarily on the inflow of moist air and on the extent and vigor of the lifting processes. According to this view, cloud seeding could increase the precipitation only if the latent heat of glaciation were to significantly enhance the vertical motion.

Current research is directed primarily to a further elucidation of the precipitation process, with greater emphasis on the interrelationships between the microphysics of cloud and precipitation particles and the dynamics of cloud-forming motions. In this context cloud seeding is used as an experimental tool rather than as a means for augmenting precipitation. It is becoming clear that a substantial increase in precipitation can result only from enhanced vertical motions. Cloud seeding may be one means to this end under certain circumstances. Another may be the recent proposals to favor convective activity by "black-topping" large areas or by artificial heating of the surface air. The high hopes that cloud seeding alone could greatly increase precipitation have faded. The research that this hope engendered has markedly accelerated the acquisition of knowledge of precipitation. Weather modification has not yet become a reality, but progress to this end now rests on a much sounder foundation.

W. F. G. SWANN

The Science of Yesterday, Today, and Tomorrow

[FROM THE SMITHSONIAN REPORT FOR 1960]

IN THIS article one of America's most distinguished scientists takes a philosophical look at what other members of his profession have been doing in the past and the present, and what in his opinion they may be up to in the future. The late Dr. W. F. G. Swann was until recently Director Emeritus, Bartol Research Foundation of the Franklin Institute, and a senior staff advisor for the Franklin Institute Laboratories for Research and Development. He delivered this lecture a few years ago at a meeting of the Institute at which he was honored for his 32 years as Director of the Bartol Research Foundation. No introduction to his article will be attempted, except to say that he makes clear the tremendous change in every phase of scientific endeavor brought about by the new understanding of the mysterious things that go on inside the atom. So if the present century is to be known in the future as the Age of the Flowering of Science, as suggested in the Introduction to this volume, its rootstock will surely be looked upon as the amazing corpus of discoveries concerning the tiny world of the atom.

INTRODUCTION

I<small>T</small> IS within a period of less than three-quarters of a century, a period less than the span of life which many of my audience have experienced, that one of the world's most eminent men of science volunteered the idea that the discovery of nature's laws was ended, that the brain of man had solved the riddle of the universe, and that science was dead.

It is true that there were a few unopened, or partially opened, boxes which had come to light, and which seemed to contain things of some interest, but it was generally supposed that these things were, in principle, much the same as the things to be found outside. The contents of the boxes seemed to be in a rather messy state. However, it was generally believed that if they were cleaned up and put in order, they would reveal nothing new. The job of cleaning them up seemed to invite little interest, so for the time being, they were left as they were.

And so, even as the great surgeon, having performed his major operation, leaves to a humble assistant the task of cleaning up and removing the stitches, so the man of science felt that his work was done, and that he might leave to lesser lights the task of polishing up the contents of those boxes and of finding out how they fitted together to useful ends.

But when the boxes were opened, it was found that many of them contained things of a nature quite unexpected. The things which were in the boxes did not behave according to the common sense of the day. They had to do with such phenomena as gases excited to emit light by electric discharge. By and large, they had to do with glowing things. If in those days there had been any radio tubes, they would undoubtedly have been found in the boxes, together with all the paraphernalia of modern electronics. Indeed, many of the materials necessary to bring to light this important realm were there, but they were constructed on a scale too small to be perceived by the eye of man, so they passed notice as useless debris. In this debris would have been found the substances out of which today we make transistors which supply your hearing aids. In the boxes would have been found things which, by proper assembly, would have produced X-rays. Some of them would have contained substances like radium and all the multitude of atoms which today we know as isotopes; or at least, they would have contained the wherewithal to produce these things which today play such an important part in medicine and industry. In one big box there would have been found the sun itself uttering complaints that the man of science had given him no guarantee that he would be able to go on emitting light practically forever, that the physicist had provided no security for the maintenance of his bank account of energy, and that without it he was in danger of degenerating into celestial bankruptcy.

In those boxes would have been found all the ingredients necessary to produce atomic bombs and provide for the release of atomic energy in general. In them would have been found, in a form too small for the eye to see, all the mechanisms necessary to provide for the doings of the greater universe, for the behavior of the stars and the great galaxies of space with all their mysteries, including the continuous production of cosmic rays, and the like.

Truly, those men of science of three-quarters of a century ago, who left those boxes to the care of underlings for the unraveling of their contents, as the surgeon leaves to his assistants the task of cleaning up the patient, truly these great men of science died with a huge, if unknown, responsibility upon their shoulders. They are almost fortunate in having died before they were suspected of having left so much unfinished while they had declared that all was, indeed, finished.

Since man attained the stage of mentality in which he felt the desire to think about himself in relation to his surroundings, he acquired the ambition to understand nature. The basis of such an understanding is an elusive thing. It is by no means obvious. To put the matter in a nutshell, we may perhaps say that, in the past, to understand has been, for man, the ability to see in new phenomena which he studies, nothing more than the operation of the same principles that he has already accepted in the things which he has previously studied.

THE SCIENCE OF YESTERDAY

And so, in the beginning, the things which man learned to accept were the behaviors of beings like himself. Thus, in order to understand how he and his surroundings could be controlled from the outside, he invented beings like himself who, indeed, had the power to control these things, even as he and his fellows had, on a smaller scale, power to control those who served them. Reversing the policy cited in Holy Writ, man invented these omnipotent beings in his own image, and with many of his own vices and shortcomings, as well as with his beneficent characteristics. The gods were angry, and they hurled thunderbolts. The gods were pleased, and they showered the earth with the blessings of spring. Anger and pleasure are such common attributes of mankind that they seem to call for no explanation in themselves. As regards a wider range of characteristics, the capriciousness of the gods, the uncertain temperament of the gods, and so forth, man, in seeking a basis for the acceptance of these things as normal, had to do no more than think of all the prima donnas of his age, and indeed of all the ladies of his own acquaintance. Alas, in those days there were no psychiatrists to analyze man's emotions as the outcome of more fundamental "causes"; and so mankind was content to "understand" in terms of the laws which governed his primitive feelings and experiences.

Early in his history, *Homo sapiens* became conscious of the efforts of his muscles, and the need for exertion in order that things should be accomplished. To bring stationary things into a state of motion, man found that he had to do something; and in the doing of it he became conscious of effort, so that there arose a vague concept of force. However, to push anything and to make it move, one had to come into contact with it. A man could not, by merely flexing his muscles, cause something at a distance to start moving. The force had to be transmitted from point to point in order to become effective. As a matter of fact, insofar as there is any difficulty in understanding motion at all, there is just as much difficulty in understanding it through the transmission of force from point to point in a medium as there is in understanding action at a distance. The late Sir Oliver Lodge once remarked that it is as yet an inexplicable fact that when one end of a rod is pushed, the other end moves, to which observation *Punch* replied that it is also an inexplicable fact that when one end of a man is trodden upon, the other end shouts. However, the layman readily accepted the philosophy that what the eye cannot see the mind need not trouble about. And so, the transmission of force through minute distances seemed to present much less of an obstacle than did its transmission over great distances.

THE AETHER, AND THE TRANSMISSION OF FORCE

The motions of the heavenly bodies became explained in the hands of Newton as motions which should be thought of as caused by "forces" whose origins were in the heavenly bodies themselves; and while Newton himself would probably have taken a more philosophic view of the meaning of this statement than would many of his followers, those who wished to "understand," and had faith in the meaning of such understanding, felt, for the reasons I have already stated, unhappy about the acceptance of such a philosophy. They demanded some kind of a medium permeating all space between the heavenly bodies, a medium which could transmit the desired force. Later, this medium was charged with the duties of every conceivable kind of phenomenon by which one body appeared to influence another body at a distance. It became charged, among other things, with transmitting the light and heat of the sun to earth, and later it was charged with the transmission of radio waves. It was natural to try and understand this medium as something like a solid or a liquid, or a gas of our common experience, but alas, the demands on it did not harmonize with any of these characterizations. And so this medium, this "aether," as it was called, remained as a mystery. As long as one did not inquire too much about the mechanisms of its activities, it served as a balm to the conscience of common sense in seeming to relieve us of the terrors of action at a distance. Many were the attempts to provide inner mechanisms by which man could understand, in terms of the common sense of the day, all that seemed to be happening; but the mechanisms for different activities were inconsistent and all that remained was the apparent potentiality of transmitting something from one place to another with a finite velocity, even though one did not know what the something was which was transmitted. It was with this dilemma in mind that, some years ago, I defined the aether as a "medium devised by man for the purpose of transmitting his misconceptions from one place to another." It was during the period of prohibition, and I added an observation to the effect that "of all subtle fluids invented for the stimulation of the imagination, it is the only one which, so far, has not been prohibited." Later, alas, it also became prohibited, when the theory of relativity came upon the scene, declaring that it had no substance in reality, was inconsistent in philosophy, and was a useless encumbrance to the brain which tried to use it.

And so, it came about that insofar as it was meaningful to speak of one body as "acting upon" another, one had to accept "action at a distance" as something which, while dubiously respectable, was not a thing to be talked about in polite scientific society. I think, however, that we must realize that with his banishing of the aether to the realms of nonsense, man took one of his first steps in removing his ideas from the realm of popular understanding in terms of the everyday experiences of the times.

THE PRINCIPLE OF PREDETERMINATION

In this evaporation of some of the elements which were part and parcel of the intuitive thinking of a hundred years ago, there yet remained one principle which man was loath to discard. This principle invoked the idea that, at any rate as regards the inanimate world, that which is happening now determines that which will happen just a little later. And that which happens a little later determines that which will happen still a little later, and so on, ad infinitum. It is the principle of predetermination. It had its most explicit exemplification when science, through the activities of Newton and his contemporaries, described the motions of the heavenly bodies in terms of the well-known laws of astronomy. The concentration was on what we call the laws of motion of the bodies. These took the form of what are called the differential equations of motion. However, it is sufficient to say that these laws were such that, if you specify what exists now, they tell you what will be found just now — at the next moment, that is — and so on, ad infinitum. If you asked what must be expressed now, the answer, in terms of Newton's laws, is to the effect that you must assign a position and velocity for each one of the bodies whose motion you wish to discuss. In terms of these positions and velocities, the future is determined completely in terms of the present. In order that you should not derive too much comfort from this statement, however, I must remark that if you should specify the positions and velocities of the bodies 1,000 years hence, those laws will equally well serve to determine where they are now. It is hardly polite to destroy your comfort in the belief that the present determines the future by asking you to accept a doctrine to the effect that the future also determines the present. I once worried myself about the problem of why, if I am to understand memory in terms of the present as determined by the past, I cannot also remember the future, if the laws work both ways.

The great success of the classical astronomy of Newton and the discovery of the atomic nature of matter and of the fact that the atoms themselves are composed of what we call particles, made it almost inevitable that man should try to understand atoms and their doings in a crude way by picturing them as models of the solar system itself on an enormously reduced scale; and so, some three-quarters of a century ago, there arose atomic theories based on this idea and carrying with them, therefore, in principle, the laws of predetermination. Perhaps I should pause for a moment to state what, in the last analysis, is indicated by the acceptance of such a principle. The matter is illustrated by the story of a man and his slave.

It appears that there was an ancient noble whose belief in predetermination was very firm. And the noble had a slave who stole some of his master's possessions. For this sin, the noble made preparations to chastise his slave. However, the slave, being of a wily and ingenious disposition, said: "My master, you must know that I am not responsible for this sin which I have committed; for according to the philosophy to which you subscribe, it was preordained that I should steal this, your possession." However, the master replied: "Yes, my slave, that is indeed true; but by the same token, it was also preordained that I should beat you for your offense." I commend this principle to those who have charge of the destiny of youthful delinquents.

Anyone who subscribes to the principle of predetermination, and who is confronted with a situation in which a system suddenly departs from the course predicted for it by the laws assumed, would have but two views of the matter open to him. He could deny the truth of the laws, or he could regard the occurrence as a miracle. This is, indeed, no more than a crystallization of the meaning of the word "miracle."

THE SCIENCE OF TODAY

THE MIRACLE OF ATOMIC SCIENCE

Now, in opening up the boxes of which I have spoken earlier, it was found that those things therein which were pertinent to the structures of atoms and molecules do not behave according to the principle of predetermination. They do not behave according to that smooth running of things which science had come to idealize. Every change which the atom experiences is a sudden one, with no clear-cut relation to the past, and no promise as to the future. Every change is a miracle in the sense in which I have sought to define that word. Moreover, it seemed, to most physicists, impossible to devise any laws consistent with the facts and according to which changes in atoms and in the realms immediately dominated by atoms occurred in any strictly predictable manner. The best that could be done was to invoke the concept of averages and to devise laws which told the chance that any particular occurrence would happen under certain assigned conditions. The laws were analogous to those which the insurance specialist uses when he predicts the fraction of all the people over, say, 50 years of age who will die in the next year. He cannot predict what will happen to any individual, but he can predict with considerable certainty what will happen to groups of individuals. In a sense, we may say that the whole quantum theory of today is a crystallization of the best laws which man has been able to devise for describing the nature of miraculous happenings. Of course, you may well say that if the insurance man should consult the physician of each individual and should order continual tests to be made of the state of health of each individual, then he could approximate with some certainty to accurate predictions as regards the individuals. You may say that there is really no miracle about the matter. His uncertainty as regards the individual is simply something founded upon his ignorance of the complete story and of the impracticability of supplementing his knowledge to the end of making detailed predictions. And so you might think that the same thing would apply to the atom, and that, if you would only work hard enough to invent a more complete set of laws to govern its actions, the complete life history of every atom would be known and there would be no need to invoke miracles. However, physicists have worked very hard in an endeavor to do something of this kind, but without success, and the nature of their thinking is such as to convince many of them that complete success could never be attained, and that, as regards the atomic realm, we shall always have to put up with miracles. And now we are confronted with a curious psychological paradox. The average man of science, secure in the conviction that, as regards matter in bulk, nothing miraculous ever happens, is perfectly content to accept such happenings in the atomic world. Miracles on the scale of size of anything which we can see would be an abomination to him, but happenings which he cannot see, which the mind can only think about, but which he believes to occur, are acceptable. However, he avoids clash with his conscience by refusing to give them a name. Perhaps a still more curious thing is that with the advance of experimental techniques, man can actually observe certain of the miracles of the individual atoms; but here he feels his activities so far removed from anything to do with mankind that again his philosophical conscience makes no protest.

I feel it quite safe to say that if I should describe to any intelligent layman who was unacquainted with mathematical physics the principles according to which our so-called laws of atomic and nuclear structure operate; and if I could get my message across in a very short time, so that the layman would not become inveigled step by step into this way of thinking without encountering at each stage more than his philosophic conscience could swallow, I think that if I could do this, the layman would have to admit that the occurrences permitted in nuclear physics are, in terms of his normal criteria of common sense, more abstract and bizarre than any occult phenomenon which had been said to have occurred and which, under that name, he would probably dismiss immediately as evidence of insanity in those who subscribe to it.

During the last three-quarters of a century, science has brought forth many marvelous things which seem commonplace today and which have not startled mankind unduly at any stage of their development because their development has come upon us gradually. If, 100 years ago, someone had awakened in the morning to find in evidence an apparatus which enabled him to hear the voice of a man speaking in Paris; if, as he listened, he saw an airplane overhead, and if, on going into the street, he found vehicles dashing about without the aid of horses, he would surely think that he had come upon an age of miracles as remarkable as any of which he had read in the past. However, these things are no longer miracles to him because the scientists have told him that they know how it all happens; but when he gets down to ultimate fundamentals, even the scientist himself has to base his understanding upon processes which, if he could suddenly convey their nature to the layman, would have to be regarded by that individual as miracles in terms of his natural criteria of common sense. It is the miracles of the atomic and subatomic world which determine the activities of things on a larger scale, where their activities come to the attention of all of us, as symbolized by that docile entity "the man in the street." This man hears of the atomic bomb, so like an enlarged version of one of the urns of the *Arabian Nights*, urns from which, as the result of proper incantations, terrifying beings emerged. He learns that two apparently inert pieces of uranium of the same kind, on being brought suddenly into close proximity, explode in a manner such as to emulate all the furies of hell, pouring forth all sorts of evil things in the form of poisonous radioactive radiations and the like. It is as though these two pieces of metal, on being brought together, became infuriated by each other's presence and, in their anger, revealed all the evil that was within them. Indeed, from the standpoint of over-all results, the performance of these two innocent pieces of uranium surpasses, in immeasurable degree, all the mysteries described in the immortal book of Arabian fairy tales. And our man in the street, on witnessing the atomic bomb, might well say "Here, at last, I find a real miracle — a miracle which can be repeated at will." But the men of science tell him that they know all about what has hap-

pened and that there is no miracle. In this they play some decep-
tion on that layman, for, if they could reveal to him the picture
of those more subtle atomic processes which are involved, he
would be likely to exclaim, "But these processes in terms of which
you explain the bomb are, to my way of thinking, miracles themselves." And the man of science, if honest with himself, will have
no choice but to reply, "Yes, my friend, that is indeed true to your
way of thinking; but to me, who has lived with these subatomic
phenomena so long, the phenomena have ceased to carry with
them the stigma of the word 'miracle.' And so," says the man of
science, "I ask you to be content in my statement that all is really
well in the philosophy of the matter. Then you will not be worried
unless you think too much. I shall be content on account of the
fundamentality of my knowledge and the broadness of my philosophy, while you shall seek refuge for contentment in the depths
of your ignorance."

And so, after a time, the man in the street learns to regard the
behavior of the atomic bomb as something not too much to be
marveled at, and he accepts it as he has accepted radio or as, at an
earlier time, he had accepted the ordinary phenomena of electricity, the running of streetcars as the result of something peculiar
happening in copper cables which, by some mysterious means, are
said to transmit electric power. He accepts these things as in a
still earlier epoch he accepted the motions of the heavenly bodies
as phenomena not to be denied, phenomena familiar in the experience of all, but phenomena which did not seem to weld together with the idea of action through contact, which the naive
intuition of the day seemed to regard as a natural haven of contentment in the understanding of all things.

Now, in spite of all I have said to persuade you that we live in
a world of miracles, you will perhaps be unhappy about my definition of that term. You may prefer to regard a miracle as a thing
of such unusual occurrence, that the fact of its having occurred at
all is open to doubt. You may then maintain that atomic phenomena are not miracles because they are always occurring, and their
continual occurrence provides, in its totality, for the phenomena
evident around us. If you say this, I fear that the Lord hath delivered you into mine hands; for in this sense, practically all the

phenomena of the atomic world would indeed be miracles to any supposed inhabitants of the atom.

Consider the emission of an X-ray from an atom. Even if, in imagination, you lived on one of the atoms which compose the part of the X-ray tube from which the X-rays come, so rare would be the emission of a ray from an individual atom that you would be put in an atomic lunatic asylum if, as a resident of such an atom, you maintained that any such phenomenon had ever occurred. Only because there are so many atoms does the physicist observe a strong emission of X-rays from the X-ray tube. And so, what is a miracle to the resident of the atom is no longer a miracle to him who observes a multitude of atoms. A similar remark applies to practically every phenomenon in atomic physics.

A cosmic ray, passing through this room, detaches an electron from an atom here and there, and by observing this phenomenon we investigate and measure the rays. Yet, to the individual atom, this theft of an electron by a cosmic ray is such a rare event that the chance of its happening to any particular atom in the period of, let us say a day, is no more than the chance that one of you would be murdered in that day if, with the earth at its present population, only one murder were committed in 300 years.

And so it is with all the happenings of atomic physics. And yet it is these miraculous happenings which, in their totality, produce all the interesting things which our coarse-grained senses observe. And to these coarse-grained senses there is no miracle; everything happens smoothly with apparent certainty of prediction.

HARMONIZATION OF DIFFERENT DOMAINS OF SCIENCE

So far I have concentrated on laws and phenomena associated with what is customarily called the realm of physics. Even here I have to admit that theoretical physics is at present in rather a messy state. When, however, we contemplate the wider realms of knowledge embracing biology and what we have recently learned in astronomy, there is much to be desired. Our knowledge of nature is like that of a world of little islands and countries, separated from each other, each being governed, apparently, by its own laws, with no very satisfactory relationship between the laws of

one country and those of another. In the affairs of men one can
tolerate a situation of this kind. One does not expect the laws of
all nations to agree, although one has a hope that in time they
may. In science, however, we have sufficient respect for the design
of the universe to believe that there is a unified scheme covering
all realms of phenomena, and indeed, in the last analysis, the affairs of mankind as a particular case. The idealistic philosopher
will not cease to search for such a scheme and it is right that he
should do so. If and when he succeeds, however, it may well be
that we shall find that the scheme which he has found is of very
little practical use.

As a matter of fact, a very general scheme covering as particular
cases a wide range of phenomena dare not, in the nature of things,
be very specific about any one of the phenomena. It can only be
specific about things which are common to all the phenomena;
and of these there may be very few. The very general theory will
be like a very evasive politician. As an active member of a group
devoted to economy in public affairs, you come to him and ask
what he has to say about expenditure on armaments, hoping perhaps to get a detailed budget, stating how much may be assigned
to this and to that, and how much may be saved from armaments
for peaceful projects. However, the reply you get is something like
this: "Our expenditures should be such as to maintain a stable and
safe economy which reflects security in all that pertains to our
lives." Well, you don't get very much out of that; and as you
leave, and as you pass through the door, there comes a man fa-
natically devoted to military preparedness who wishes to ask about
budgets designed to secure the most up-to-date equipment for all
that pertains to war; and on posing his question, the politician
again replies: "Our expenditures should be such as to maintain a
stable and safe economy which reflects security in all that pertains
to our lives."

Any statement which has to cover a wide range of circumstances
cannot, in the nature of things, say much which applies to all; and
indeed, when the range of circumstances is infinitely wide, the
safest thing is to say nothing. However, if you are expert in the
art of oratory, you will be able to say it with force and conviction.

Let us consider, as an example, a physicist who studies the science of electrodynamics and gravitation separately and later desires to mold them into a common theory. It will be unnecessary for us to think of gravitation in the light of the general theory of relativity. The old Newtonian concept will suffice.

Our physicist studies the laws of the heavens and finds that they conform very well to the Newtonian law of gravitation. I point out to him that some of the celestial bodies are magnets and that their attractions for one another will be modified in form and degree by this circumstance. The physicist replies quite correctly that the phenomenon is of very small numerical magnitude and that he proposes to neglect it. Next day, I find the physicist in his laboratory studying the attraction of magnets and of electrically charged bodies for one another. I point out that these bodies also attract gravitationally, and that he should take this into account. Again he replies, quite correctly, that in these experiments the gravitational effects are so small compared with the electromagnetic effects that he is justified in neglecting them. In other words, in one problem of the universe, our physicist neglects the phenomena which are the whole source of interest in another problem, in which other problem, moreover, the phenomena dominant in the first problem are now negligible.

Now neglect of the small gravitational effects in the electromagnetic experiments is justifiable so long as one maintains the principle that the gravitational effect is, in actuality, there. If the gravitational effect is omitted, even in the formulation of the general principles of the subject, on the basis of its being too small to detect in electromagnetic experiments, and if the laws of these experiments are, therefore, placed on the statute books without it, they will possess no power to recognize it in any other phenomena of nature where the circumstances may be different. They will, in fact, be in danger of actually denying its existence in any field whatever, and of rendering its subsequent discovery in the astronomical field a phenomenon puzzling to comprehend, and apparently antagonistic to the science of electrodynamics.

Now, if a general theory embracing electrodynamics and gravitation is provided, it may take care of problems in which gravitational forces and electrodynamical forces are equally important even though nature may present us with no such cases where they are of equal importance. Such a general theory is able to extrapolate itself to one end to a case where gravitation is unimportant and electrodynamics is all important and to extrapolate itself also to the other end to a case where the relative importance of these respective phenomena is reversed. The theory thus provides a bridge by means of which the two extreme cases are seen to be not inharmonious, whereas individual theories for each case, formulated on the basis of all that experiment can reveal, would appear at first sight mutually antagonistic.

However, the language of the bridge which spans electrodynamics and astronomy may not be very simple when asked to speak the story of either of these subjects separately. If I concentrate on the domain which is astronomy, I shall tend to paint pictures and make models characteristic of that end of the bridge, pictures which emphasize very strongly to my intuition the salient phenomena of astronomy, but pictures which would have to become more and more out of focus as I walked across the bridge to the realm of electrodynamics. And when I reached this realm, I would find them completely out of focus and unable to convey to me any meaning at all. On the other hand, if I start at the end of the bridge which is electrodynamics, and do the same kind of thing, I shall paint pictures and make models appropriate to the most important phenomena characteristic of that end. And these pictures will, in turn, become more and more hazy as I cross the bridge to the end concerned with astronomy. If I am a philosopher, and willing to realize the limitations of my pictures at both ends of the bridge, I shall not be disturbed by their becoming hazy as I cross from one end to the other. However, if I am a nonphilosophical astronomer, the pictures which I have painted, and the models which I have created to understand my subject will be very fundamental to me; and if I tamper with them my mind will protest that what I am doing produces nonsense. A similar thing will happen for the nonphilosophic student of electrodynamics at the other end of the bridge. He will create his pictures and the elements of his creation will be for him the basis of reasonable understanding. Thus while the philosopher will be able to cross the bridge in contentment in either direction, adjusting himself to the scenery on the way, the nonphilosophic astronomer and the nonphilosophic student of electrodynamics will feel that their realms are quite distinct and that the laws of one subject have no connection with those of the other. While the general formulation of the philosopher will extrapolate harmoniously, both ways, from one end of the bridge to the other, the more specific pictures and models appropriate to the two ends will not extrapolate, for the elements of these pictures and models which are prominent in the phenomena at one end may be of negligible importance to the phenomena at the other end.

And yet, at each end of the bridge, the philosophically imperfect pictures appropriate to that end may be more useful than the generalized picture painted by the philosopher. Thus, 300 years ago, many believed that light was composed of rays which traveled like arrows from source to image. Later came the wave picture of light, and later still the picture characteristic of the quantum theory. However, even today, the optician who insisted on making spectacles with philosophic regard to all the features of the quantum theory would soon go out of business. No; the optician makes his spectacles with no thoughts in mind other than those of his forerunners who thought entirely in terms of rays for all optical phenomena 300 years ago.

It becomes increasingly important that the physicist, who has attained success in much of his specialized field by invoking certain principles, should not fail to inquire as to the extent to which those principles may play a leading role in other domains in which, perhaps, as yet they have not been utilized.

THE ROLE OF PATTERN

The atomic physicist has been brought up to think in terms of particles with what he calls forces between them. He learned to do this in the early birth of astronomy and has clung to the procedure. In the beginning the procedure was to seek the laws of motion of the particles. Thus, if, in astronomy, one gave the positions and velocities of the heavenly bodies at some instant, the laws were such as to spell out step by step how each of them moved; and in terms of those positions and velocities originally assigned, tell the inevitable story of what happens subsequently.

In terms of positions and velocities taken as starting points, the system was one of predetermination. All motions calculable in this way, and consistent with some initially assigned sets of positions and velocities, were regarded as possible. Of course, different starting points resulted in very different developments. In some cases we should realize a body like a sun with other bodies traveling in circles or ellipses around it. In other cases, we should have bodies coming in from outer space, visiting the sun for a brief period, and returning to infinity by other paths. In still other cases, bodies would interweave their ways in complicated paths among their fellows. There were, in fact, innumerable patterns which could evolve from different starting points, and each of these patterns had its own peculiarity inherent in its own particular starting point. Thus, all sorts of different astronomical universes were possible insofar as the motions of the bodies which constituted them were concerned. However, the custom was not to concern oneself too much with the patterns as fundamental, but rather to regard them merely as the consequences of the particular positions and velocities which, by chance, had been originally specified.

When science came to regard atoms as groups of particles, the same kind of procedures was envisaged; although the laws of motion of the particles were spelled out in different fashions when other things like electromagnetic radiations became involved and claimed a place for the harmonization of such things as light, X-rays, wireless radiations, and so forth.

And as science advanced, particularly in the atomic realm, it became evident that the theoretical procedures born of astronomy were becoming increasingly unsuccessful in providing a description of all that happened. It became evident that the procedure which was likely to work was a procedure in which one concentrated more on inquiring as to the patterns which can exist in nature, patterns of motions of particles, in the first instance, and later, patterns of more abstract things which the physicist called "*psi* functions." The old laws of motion of particles formerly occupied the central stage of our interest. Any pattern to which they led could be regarded as permissible; and of the permissible patterns, there was an infinite variety. In the new era of atomic philosophy what remained of the old laws of motions of things was relegated to the service of limiting the patterns which could occur. The fundamental duty of these old laws, as dressed in their new garb, was to declare as meaningless all patterns but a limited set, the set which could be evolved out of them. The fundamental bricks of nature's structure were patterns which, born of these laws, dictated the things which could occur as distinct from those which could not occur.

The bricks of nature — the atoms, the molecules — were, in principle, more like a set of oriental rugs than minute astronomical systems. These rugs, indeed, were only symbolic and with them there went a scheme of interpretation of their significance. There is a faint analogy between these rugs and the oriental rugs which adorn your houses, for I believe it is a fact that the various patterns and subpatterns in these rugs are created with interpretable meanings.

And so, in science, what had formerly been laws of motions of particles were transformed to laws which determined what patterns could exist in nature, and with this scheme of things there went a key for the interpretation of the patterns. It was, indeed, a far cry from one who thought to understand these laws of patterns in the sense in which, perhaps, he may have thought he understood the laws of astronomy. If you ask a maker of oriental rugs in what sense he understands the meaning of the rugs, he may rightly reply: "I do not have the problem of understanding why these rugs exist. I and my forerunners created the designs ourselves, but we have endeavored to weave into them a symbolic meaning which reflects the relationships of things in the world around us. Why these things should be and why that which happens does happen, we know not. Our function is that of systematic cataloguers of events, and our rugs are the symbolic catalogues."

Now, I do not mean to say that the citizens of Arabia who make rugs would say everything that I have put into their mouths if I started with them a discussion on the matter. All I maintain is that they might have said it; and if, in the saying of it, they had sought to develop a systematic scheme symbolizing the ways of the atomic world, instead of the limited domain of living things and the immediate elements of their experiences, hope, love, fear, and so forth, they might have been on the way to doing something rather similar to what the atomic physicist is doing today. Of course, the atomic physicist has at his disposal that great logical scheme of mathematics which he can use freely in his designs, and he is not limited to the utilization of simple elements of geometry.

I have spoken of the patterns of atomic structure as being abstract things distinct from pictures of particles and other material things which may be around. However, the patterns appropriate to groups of atoms which constitute the things we see, come, in some of their manifestations, to assume actual shapes of things in the elementary meaning of that word. And so, today, we see patterns, born in the understanding of atoms, extending themselves into combinations of atoms — to molecules. Here the pattern is as yet unobservable to the eye, and its abstract form must be inferred from chemical behavior. But from molecules, pattern extends itself into large structures, into crystals where form is evident in that which can be perceived by the eye. And in this domain of crystals, pattern provides a rich harvest of phenomena which, in the role known as that of semiconductors, has, within the last two decades, revolutionized the world of electronics, and here man found that his colossal achievement in inventing the radio tube and all that goes with it, was already anticipated and beaten by nature in providing what we now call transistors, which reduce in size and increase in compactness all such electronic devices.

Pattern has always been evident on a large scale in biological structures, but now we find it playing a fundamental role, not only in things which can readily be seen, but in the seeds of life itself, in the chromosomes of the cells whose behavior is so vital in cell division, and in the transmission of hereditary characteristics. And through such processes, we may, in time, learn to comprehend that crowning achievement of pattern to be found in man himself, an achievement in which a single germ cell contains in itself a pattern which insures that the being to which it grows shall duplicate, not only the general form, but many of the characteristics of his ancestors. The substance of the individual dies several times during what we call the span of his life, but pattern goes on from generation to generation; and even an abnormality in the being, a crooked finger, or a prominent jaw formation, can survive in its pattern for a thousand years. One thing about man, even as he is evident to those around him, goes far toward being immortal. It is pattern.

RELATION BETWEEN THE SCIENCES OF YESTERDAY AND TODAY

To return to the title of this address, the science of yesterday was largely the evolution of blind discovery of phenomena, the discovery of fire, the discovery of the potentialities of the wheel, the ingenious combinations of circumstances and principles, which were ever before us, to the use of man. There was another crude but nevertheless practical and extremely ingenious ordering of the things of nature in the systems of laws formulated by Newton and Galileo, and later by the giants of science of the 19th century, culminating in a sensing of the potentialities of the newly discovered phenomena of electricity. These developments led to the formulation of the general principles of electrical engineering, the realization of the dynamo, the electric motor, and later wireless telegraphy, and so forth. Then, starting toward the end of the 19th century, came an era of new interests. Experimental researches resulted in the discovery of phenomena not continually evident to the eye of man, phenomena which could only be brought into existence by the efforts of his researchers. The behavior of the planets, the general phenomena which govern mechanical machines, were always displayed before mankind and awaited only the exercise of man's ingenuity to harmonize them, and use them to his service when possible. The phenomena of electrical engineering of three-quarters of a century ago were not things evident to the eye until researchers ferreted them out and organized them into purposeful activity. The later developments beginning toward the end of the 19th century concerned the contents of the boxes of which I have spoken earlier. They concerned the discovery of the electron, the proton, X-rays, and allied phenomena of atomic behavior. These things were completely unevident to the eye of man until research forced them out of hiding and caused them to reveal their activities in newly created devices which would not have existed except for man's activity. Having become released from their bondage of obscurity, it became clear that these strange new things had, all along, been playing a part in phenomena which had been available to man's viewing from time immemorial. Up to this time, the laws of chemistry were largely empirical as were the laws of biology. The laws of what we call physical astronomy, as distinct from those of celestial mechanics, were in a very scrappy state as regards consistency of understanding, and the things of greatest interest had not forced themselves spontaneously upon man's notice. However, the development of the great telescopes and allied equipment presented an entirely new challenge for the understanding of things and behaviors vastly different in both scale and nature from those which, up to that time, had been the only things displayed for man's curiosity. And it came to pass that the new discoveries in connection with atomic laws went far toward providing for these things an understanding which would have been impossible without them. These same discoveries of the atomic realm did much to provide a more complete picture of what was going on in chemistry, and even in biology.

THE SCIENCE OF TOMORROW

And here we stand today. We have a consciousness of vast accomplishment in the interplay of what we call fundamental experimental research and fundamental theoretical research. Much harmony has been brought into things which would otherwise be obscure; and yet, the returns of the harvest of discovery have tended to reveal so much more to be fitted into the scheme and have given evidence of so much more yet to be discovered, that the expected labors of the future may well outweigh all those of the past. And what direction may these labors be expected to take in this era of the future — in this science of tomorrow?

While there is much yet to be done in correlating and enriching all that is known about what we call the material world, I feel that before long, we shall have to face the problem of the nature of life and of all that goes with it, if real progress is to be made. We cannot forever keep the laws of dead matter separated from those of living things; for after all, everything that happens as the result of our efforts in the utilization of what we have already learned must be initiated by the mind of man. I can imagine the heavens to go on their courses without any attention from mankind. I can be happy in the thought of a continual process of activity which, in its gross aspects at any rate, follows the kind of deterministic behavior which, a hundred years ago, might have been thought to be the "way of life" of all nature. But if, today, I make an atomic bomb which does drastic things, it is I who formed the decision to make it; and in so doing, I interfere with what would have happened had I not made this decision. At this point, the mind of man seizes upon the otherwise smooth running of things, and, in some way, that which is in my mind interlocks with inanimate nature to direct its course.

THE ROLE OF NEW ENTITIES

And in facing the necessity of bringing harmony into realms which today stand apart, what has the experience of the past taught us? We have a clue in what has happened in the domain of atomic structure itself. There was a time when all we had to work with were atoms regarded as indivisible things, without any properties other than were provided by empiricism as demanded by the laws of chemistry. No progress was being made in understanding the laws of spectroscopy or the laws which related the elements to one another. Even the periodic table was an unfathomable mystery. Then came the discovery of the electron and the proton, two entities whose existence had not before been recognized, and at least a promise of further understanding was achieved. It was a faith in this promise which caused many to believe that the end of discovery was near. However, a barrier to further progress was soon reached. Many had wished to invoke the possibility of another kind of particle — a neutral particle — but conservative science, having with reluctance accepted two new things, the electron and the proton, smaller than the atom, looked with great distaste upon any upstart who wanted more atomic bricks to play with; and it was not until, through experiment, a neutral particle, the neutron, was proved to exist that progress went ahead with leaps and bounds.

We can readily understand the hesitancy of science to accept a neutral particle. One had almost come to regard as self-evident the principle that all atomic forces were electrical, and how could a neutral particle exert a force on anything or, indeed, how could it be influenced by anything? In the spirit of the times it had to be regarded as a completely dead entity. Perhaps the greatest clash with convention was the recognition of the fact that this entity, dead in the sense of all understandable happenings, could indeed play a part in its own way, a way so foreign to anything which was in the conventional picture. It was not so much by the fact that the neutron represented a new particle that science became disturbed, but rather that it represented a new set of relationships between things, a relationship which was not in the picture before. One had to admit what are called nuclear forces as distinct from electromagnetic forces — a new world of law and order. And what was more astonishing, one had to provide for interlocking relationships between this new domain of phenomena and the old domain which was so unlike it, and which, up to this time, had claimed authority over all nature.

HARMONIZATION OF THE SCIENCE OF TODAY AND THAT OF TOMORROW

And so, in contemplating the harmonization of life with what we call the laws of inanimate matter, I expect to find a new set of laws, laws which do not deny anything we had before except in the denial of the claim of those laws to finality. And I expect to find these new laws interweaving with the old knowledge in such a manner as to produce a more comprehensive whole, a whole in which all sense of barriers has become dissolved in an all-embracing harmony. For many purposes it may be convenient to keep the new domain separate from the old, as the maker of spectacles keeps his science of geometrical optics separated from the quantum theory of light; but there will be bridges connecting all parts of the new territory with the old domains in such fashion that he who travels across these bridges will have no sense of sudden change; and even as one who travels from tropical regions to the poles can accommodate himself to his satisfaction at each stage of the journey, so the philosopher, in traveling over this wider domain which I envisage, will find himself content wherever he may be.

In developing the foregoing thoughts I have called attention to the rapid advance which took place in physics itself once one was willing to accept a new particle, the neutron, and furnish it with the wherewithal to operate. Now I do not expect it to be necessary to find a new particle which will cement the old materialistic realm with the realm of life and all that goes with it, but I may expect to find the formal recognition of some kind of a new entity differing from those which we have encountered in physics. I do not necessarily expect that this entity will be something which can be described in terms of space and time, although I shall expect it to be accompanied by well-defined laws of operation which provide, not only for the activities peculiar to its own purposes, but for the possibility of cementing it logically with the knowledge of the past. We must not be too astonished at the invocation of an entity which does not call for expression in terms of space and time. After all, I may speak of such things as good and evil without accompanying them with coordinates x, y, z, t, to express where they are and when they were there. For the sophisticated physicist, I may recall that even the coordinates which represent Fourier amplitudes in the analysis of radiation in an ideal box are not coordinates of a material point in ordinary space, but, as coordinates in an abstract, multidimensional space, they perform a useful service in physics. In the last analysis, much that is spoken of in the quantum theory of physics involves concepts having little to do with the old conventional notion associated with the expression of all relevant concepts in terms of some thing or things having positions at certain times. I shall not be surprised to find the new entity playing a part in the survival of pattern, so dominant in living things. I hesitate to limit its potentialities by giving it a name already appropriated and endowed with properties of vagueness too foggy to be permitted in a scientific discussion, and so I will not call it by the name "soul." If it is to be of service, it must not shrink away from its duties and take refuge as part of high-sounding sentences. Its functions and modes of operation must be well defined and it is only natural that in conventional science it will have to go through the process of skeptic criticism which has fallen to the lot of all its predecessors in the materialistic realm. I should expect to find it play a role in those phenomena which for long have lain in the borderland between what is accepted by all and what is accepted only by few, even though representatives of the few may be found in all periods of man's history. I refer to such things as extrasensory perception, the significance of the immortality of man, clairvoyance, and allied phenomena, and the significance of the fact that our universe exhibits what we may call a planned design, whether or not we are willing to admit the hazy notion of a planner, or say what we mean by that postulate.

PREDETERMINATION AND A PLANNED UNIVERSE

Perhaps the existence of the universe as an entity with strongly planned features provides the greatest argument against use of the undeniable fact that if we are willing to work hard enough and involve ourselves in a sufficient complexity in mathematical expression, we can possibly regard any universe as operating on a principle of predetermination. In general, the principle invoked in such an arbitrary manner may rule out many notions which seem so important in the life of mankind by regarding everything as inevitable, even as in the parable of the slave and his master at the beginning of this lecture the theft by the slave was inevitable and the beating received for it was also inevitable. If the universe were a chaotic affair without any of the properties which I have associated with the word "planned," there might be some sense in falling back on predetermination, but to invoke such a principle with things as they are is something like asserting that a cathedral of great beauty, which I had not seen before, was formed by the accumulation of dust in an accidental manner through the ages.

NEW DOMAINS FOR SCIENTIFIC INVESTIGATION

In discussing such matters as I am now venturing near, I think it is essential to avoid all theological doctrine as a starting point. I would rather see a theological doctrine emerge spontaneously as part of the over-all scheme of nature, than I would see the workings of nature forced into a frame provided by a preconceived theological doctrine as a starting point.

In the past it has been a tradition of mankind to divide phenomena into two classes, those which may be investigated, and those concerning which we should not inquire. Between these two sets of phenomena there has been a barrier, and to cross that barrier was a sin against dogma, or, in less solemn vein, a violation of sound principles of research only to be undertaken by those who are a little queer. As times progressed, this barrier has shifted, so that all astronomy now lies on the respectable side of it, in spite of the fact that 300 years ago much of it lay in the forbidden region, where also much of the embryo science of chemistry was to be found. Today, chemistry is thoroughly established in the unrestricted region.

Even as many radicals become conservatives when they rise to power, so the science of the materialistic age, much of which lay on the dark side of the barrier in the past, on becoming promoted to the free side, started to fortify still further the barrier which it had passed, so that things which did not readily find a place in its philosophy were held in the forbidden region. Yet behind this fortification of division which materialistic science itself has strengthened, stand the shadows of bygone days: the philosophies, the practices, the beliefs, and religions of ancient times, so vulnerable in many of the dogmas with which history had endowed them, that they oft fell an easy prey to the shafts of the newborn science of our era. The weaknesses in their armor bred a kind of conviction that all the wisdom of the ancient past was afflicted with the disease of superstition, a disease eating like a cancer into its whole system. Thus, many things which had been accepted for thousands of years were cast into the category of witchcraft. In the totality of these things there were, however, certain realms which, by virtue of the power which had supported them through the ages and because of their moral influence on mankind, stood with some security against the attacks of modern philosophy. These were, for the most part, the standard religions of mankind. There was a sort of truce between the two camps, a truce in which the realm of religion ruled on Sundays, while the materialistic philosophy governed the rest of the week. Some things, well accepted in the past, but apparently at variance with materialism, found themselves without the powerful support accorded to the great religions and so they were left to the ridicule of the new age. Some of these things which had been part of the doctrine of the churches of the bygone era found themselves disdained by the faiths which had nurtured them, and the guardians of the faiths became anxious to avoid contamination with practices which might be attacked with some apparent success by the warriors of the new age. Thus, healing by the laying on of hands, belief in the existence of spirit entities in our midst, even such were cast out by the religions which had originally fostered them, or if admitted at all, were retained as machinations of the devil, a being so beloved by the faiths that have created him that he has succeeded in holding his own in religion in the face of science itself. Naturally, at times he became very convenient as an agent to whom one could attribute all the shortcomings and inconsistencies in the faiths and dogmas which sought to rule, as well as his own shortcomings. In contemplating his identity, one is reminded of the little girl who, on being asked by her younger sister the question: "Is there really a devil?," replied: "No, of course not, it's just like Santa Claus; it's Daddy."

And now what we call orthodox science has itself grown a type of philosophy so different from the old science born of materialism that if it were forced to pause long enough to confess what, years ago, it would have called its philosophic sins, it would find those sins no more free from materialistic criticism than much of the sins of philosophy which it has held behind the barrier.

THE ULTIMATE HARMONIZATION OF SCIENCE

Perhaps some day, not too far distant, orthodox science will find the urge to extend its domain of inquiry into regions formerly forbidden, and in the hope that all the phenomena of nature may find a place in one larger scheme of harmonization. I would hope that in this more comprehensive philosophy no man would have occasion to forsake any of the ideals which in the past he had fostered. When this condition arrives, I envisage a sage charged with the duty of answering the questions of all who would make inquiry. The musician will say: "Where is my art in this scheme?" and the sage will reply: "See, it is here, complete in itself, but joined by this bridge, in perfect logical continuity with yon domain which is the domain of abstract mathematics." And the priest will ask: "Where are the essentials of my faith in which I have lived and which has been my anchor of security?" And the sage will answer: "Cast your vision upon yon territory. There you will find it. It is joined by a bridge of great beauty to the domain of your archenemy, the domain which was formerly that of materialistic science."

And in this picture those things for which the mind and soul long shall no longer appear veiled in nebulous shrouds of uncertainty, but shall stand out as jewels adorning the greater universe in all its richness and splendor. And if some doubtful inquisitor should ask of the sage: "Where, in all this, shall I find the devil who has meant so much to me in my life?" he will receive the reply: "The devil — oh, the devil! He is in hell. You will find hell behind the old barrier, and the devil is the only occupant."

INDEX

A

I

J

K

L

T

U

V

W